The Value of Birds

Edited by

A. W. DIAMOND and F. L. FILION

Based on the Proceedings of a Symposium and Workshop
held at the XIX World Conference of the International
Council for Bird Preservation, June 1986,
Queens University, Kingston, Ontario, Canada

ICBP Technical Publication No. 6

British Library Cataloguing in Publication Data

The value of birds: proceedings of a workshop held during the 19th World Conference of the I.C.B.P. in June 1986 at Queen's University, Kingston, Ontario.—(ICBP technical publications; no. 6).
1. Birds, Protection of
I. Diamond, A. W.   II. Filion, F.
III. International Council for Bird Preservation. *World Conference (19th: 1986: Queen's University, Kingston, Ont.).*   IV. Series
639.9'78   QL676.5
ISBN 0-946888-10-8

Prepared for publication by Anagram Editorial Service, Guildford, Surrey, England.
Typeset by Paston Press, Loddon, Norfolk, England.
Printed and bound by Page Bros. (Norwich) Ltd, Norfolk, England.

INTERNATIONAL COUNCIL FOR BIRD PRESERVATION

ICBP is the longest-established worldwide conservation organization. It is devoted entirely to the protection of wild birds and their habitats. Founded in 1922, it is a federation of 330 member organizations in 100 countries. These organizations represent a total of over ten million members all over the world.

Central to the successful execution of ICBP's mission is its global network of scientists and conservationists specializing in bird protection. Its ability to gather and disseminate information, identify and enact priority projects, and promote and implement conservation measures is unparalleled. Today, ICBP's Conservation Programme includes some 100 projects throughout the world.

Birds are important indicators of a country's environmental health. ICBP provides expert advice to governments on bird conservation matters, management of nature reserves, and such issues as the control of trade in endangered species. Through interventions to governments on behalf of conservation issues ICBP can mobilize and bring to bear the force of international scientific opinion at the highest levels. Conferences and symposia by its specialist groups also attract worldwide attention to the plight of endangered birds.

Publications include the international *Bird Red Data Books*. ICBP maintains a comprehensive databank concerning the status of all the world's threatened birds and their habitats, and from this the *Red Data Books* are prepared. The most recent edition, *Threatened Birds of Africa*, was published in 1985. A series of Technical Publications (of which the present volume is the sixth) gives up-to-date and in-depth treatment to major bird conservation issues.

ICBP, 219c Huntingdon Road, Cambridge CB3 0DL, UK.

UK Charity No. 286211

CONTENTS

PART II: BIRDS AS BIO-INDICATORS OF
ENVIRONMENTAL CONDITIONS

FOREWORD

by Christoph Imboden, Director,
International Council for Bird Preservation

The Value of Birds: This might seem a somewhat unusual title for inclusion in our series of Technical Publications on bird conservation. However, the value of birds to human society is now widely recognized and can be extensively traced beyond their immediate products. In recent years, the 'cash value' of wildlife has featured increasingly in the arguments for conservation. Wildlife tourism, ranching and sustainable utilization of natural resources are promoted as sources of foreign exchange for developing countries. In many industrialized countries, the revenue from birdwatching and related 'industries' can be counted in millions. Birds continue to provide vital data as the complex mechanisms of atmospheric pollution and the effects of pesticide residues are slowly unravelled.

The case studies in this volume provide up-to-date examples of the value of birds as socio-economic resources and bio-indicators. As much as I think it is important to bring such aspects into the conservation discussion, I must say that the economic usefulness of wildlife, birds included, can *never* be the *most* important rationale behind its conservation. Too many species are likely to lose out as being apparently without economic worth. We do not know how their contribution to our quality of life may one day be measured, and most economists are shy of such mysteries. Above all, conservationists must defend their arguments from positions of ethical strength. That is why we chose to call this book *The Value of Birds*. We must learn to appreciate value as well as price.

I am most grateful to the Canadian Wildlife Service for allowing the editors, Anthony Diamond and Fern Filion, to produce this outstanding volume and to organize, on behalf of ICBP, most stimulating discussions at our World Conference in Kingston.

EDITORS' PREFACE

by A. W. Diamond and F. L. Filion

Modern society is strongly motivated by economic and social forces which shape the attitudes of decision-makers all over the world. This inevitably gives rise to debate on the possible justification for particular proposals for bird conservation. The Symposium on Birds as Socio-economic Resources, on which the first part of this book is based, was intended to place the uses and values that people attach to birds in an economic and sociological framework. It is clear that one of the most important current and future uses of birds is as indicators of environmental conditions, and part two of this book, based on a Workshop on Birds as Bio-indicators, addresses this issue specifically.

The book as a whole will complement two other recent symposia; one held in South Africa in 1983 on 'Birds and Man' (Bunning 1985) and the other, held in Finland and predominantly European in coverage, on 'Birds as environmental indicators' (Solonen 1985).

PART I
BIRDS AS SOCIO-ECONOMIC RESOURCES

BIRDS AS SOCIO-ECONOMIC RESOURCES

CONVENORS' INTRODUCTION

A. W. DIAMOND & F. L. FILION

Canadian Wildlife Service, Ottawa, Ontario K1A 0H3, Canada

Bird conservation has traditionally been approached as an essentially biological issue. The concept that we put forward in the Symposium on Birds as Socio-economic Resources is that conservation problems arise out of interactions between birds and people, and that effective solutions must therefore incorporate sociological and economic considerations as well as biological ones. We hope also to demonstrate that the values that human societies place on birds are far greater than is generally realized, and amply justify increased allocations of resources to conservation; and that socio-economic studies and approaches offer new tools and opportunities to increase the effectiveness of our conservation efforts.

The papers presented at the Symposium introduce economic and sociological approaches to conservation and management problems, and show how they complement one another (Filion). They include detailed analyses of bird data in recent statistical surveys of the economics of wildlife use (Jacquemot & Filion) and of societal attitudes towards wildlife (Schulz); case-studies from widely different parts of the world, contrasting some of the uses to which local bird populations are put (Scott, Skira, Haynes, Dekker, Isack); and a wide-ranging review of human uses of birds (Diamond). Clark's paper is an example—by a professional economist—of the use of economic arguments in a case where the use of a site for bird conservation was in direct conflict with development proposals. It will probably be particularly useful to others faced with such conflicts.

In organizing this Symposium, and listening to the discussions it provoked, we were conscious of the distance that currently separates 'traditional', biologically-oriented conservationists from professional sociologists and economists. While there is a growing field of study in the socio-economics of wildlife use—particularly in the United States—this approach seems not to have been adopted widely elsewhere. It seems also to meet some resistance within the bird-conservation community. This is reflected, for example, by a discordance between the rationale of ICBP's Action Plan (Anon. 1986), which frequently refers to the socio-economic importance of wild birds, and the limited extent of follow-up within the Plan itself.

We suspect that the compilers of the Action Plan, and others in the bird-conservation community, may be nervous of socio-economic arguments, and that their reservations arise from a misunderstanding of the nature of these arguments. Too often, socio-economic values are perceived as narrowly 'commercial' ones (i.e., cash exchanged in the market-place); but as several papers in this volume demonstrate, modern socio-economic studies include considerable information on peoples' attitudes, motivation and knowledge about wildlife and conservation.

The fact that peoples' attitudes and motivations can be expressed in monetary terms does not mean that the 'dollar value' is the only one of importance; dollars are used here as units of measurement, and are useful because the same unit of measurement is usually used in opposing arguments. In particular, we would argue that it is inaccurate to *contrast* economic values with ethical ones (as, for example, in Section 2.4 of ICBP's Action Plan). A code of ethics, like money, is one form of social value, and a society's ethical view of a topic (such as conservation) can be compared explicitly to other values only if they are expressed in a common denominator, of which the monetary equivalent is the most widely used.

Sociological investigations offer great opportunities to conservationists to quantify the considerable support that exists for conservation among the general public, and so enable us to influence decision-makers much more effectively. Political decisions in particular are even more likely to be influenced by evidence that 80 to 90 percent of the general public are willing to pay more for a clean environment and more abundant wildlife, and rank them among their highest political priorities (as, for example, in the US and Canada), than they are by evidence of the large amounts of money and economic impact generated by the public demand for wildlife-related activity. Such studies offer real and important opportunities for conservation, which we believe can serve as stepping-stones to a more effective integration of conservation into political and development programmes in general.

Socio-economic information would make a powerful contribution to a number of the Objectives identified in ICBP's Action Plan, notably in education and training (particularly in educating senior decision-makers on the value of conservation); in providing new arguments for international co-operation; in conservation counselling; in evaluating projects; and in fund-raising. Armed with suitable socio-economic data, conservationists would be in a strong position to evaluate not only 'environmental threats' but also the 'numerous socio-economic benefits which could be sustained in perpetuity'—and which are at risk if bird populations are allowed to decline or vanish. Quantifying public support for conservation initiatives would also be useful in strengthening ICBP's interventions to governments and other decision-making bodies. The concept of management (the Action Plan's 6th Objective) needs to be refined in such a way that the notion of 'sustaining unique bird-related benefits to people' becomes a valid objective of conservation. After all, if conservationists are successful in sustaining these benefits to people, they must also be successful in maintaining species and habitat.

The subject of this Symposium is an inter-disciplinary one which does not yet have clear boundaries or participants. A major purpose of the meeting and of this publication is to encourage the development of a coherent body of work in this field. We hope that Part I of this book will not only reassure our colleagues in conservation that the socio-economic approach embodies all our existing concerns, but will also convince them that it offers a new perspective with enormous potential for increasing the success of our endeavours. The papers offered here will, we hope, serve both to increase awareness of existing expertise and suggest directions for future work to follow.

REFERENCES

ANON. 1986. Action plan 1986–1990. Cambridge: I.C.B.P.
BUNNING, J. L. (ED.). 1985. Proceedings of the Birds and Man symposium. Johannesburg: Witwatersrand Bird Club. 361 pp.
SOLONEN, T. (ED.). 1985. Proceedings of the symposium on birds as environmental indicators. *Ornis Fenn.* **62**, 34–105.

BIRDS AS SOCIO-ECONOMIC RESOURCES

CHAIRMAN'S INTRODUCTION

JACK H. BERRYMAN

International Association of Fish and Wildlife Agencies, 1412 16th Street NW, Washington DC 20036, USA

Society as a whole—the world over—has been aware of the cultural, religious and symbolic importance of birds from man's earliest times. The role of birds in their ecosystems, and their biology, have been the subject of increasing studies resulting in an ever-increasing body of knowledge. The economic importance of game-birds, at least in North America, is generally well understood, as are expenditures for the enjoyment of the non-game forms. Economic losses caused by bird damage are well documented. Management of the birds, as well as their habitats, has been a responsibility of the fish and wildlife managing agencies, at least in North America, especially for the game forms and generally for the non-game birds. The bulk of the funds for management have come from hunter expenditures and, to a lesser extent, from various kinds of volunteer contributions for the non-game birds.

Looked at in this perspective, society's appreciation of birds has been and remains fragmentary. I am not aware of an overall public awareness, a public sense of responsibility, or a public willingness to expend funds, commensurate with the total value of birds to society. Therefore, this symposium is extremely important in attempting to bring information together and view the overall value—the sociological, ecological and economic values—of birds to society and the need for society's understanding and support.

Consider that most of the 50 United States have a state bird, and reflect for a moment on the Bald Eagle which is our national symbol. Eagles are magnificent birds which have inspired man throughout the ages. In Rome the eagle was the symbol of Jupiter, the supreme god, the symbol of victory, the standard under which the legions marched. It represented supreme authority. It later became the symbol of Germany and with the rise of Christianity became the symbol of ascension. Napoleon's troops marched under the symbol of the eagle, and in 1782 the Bald Eagle became the symbol of the United States. It is on our coinage, the emblems of the President and most branches of the armed forces, and it was chosen as the name for the lunar module which was to make history.

The California Gull is Utah's state bird because it saved the early Mormon pioneers from the ravages of crickets; the dress and dances of the Plains Indians are patterned after the Prairie Grouse; the dove is the bird of peace the world over; the migrations of birds have captured man's fancy since earliest times and have led to many legends to explain this natural phenomenon; the turkey is our bird of Thanksgiving.

These examples are cited only to emphasize the point I wish to make—that birds are now, and always have been, extremely important in our cultural heritage. Other contributors mention further specific examples. One could prepare a very lengthy essay on the role that birds have played in the history, culture, and religion of the many peoples of the world. No other group of animals has played such a prominent role. This importance is quite separate from the ecological roles and the known economic significance of birds. It is therefore ironic that it is extremely difficult to obtain funds and public support for the benefit of birds, especially the non-game forms, and their habitats.

The threats to bird life are also well known: habitat destruction or degradation; chemical contaminants; and unregulated use. But, too often, these too seem to be accepted.

Legislative bodies in free nations generally reflect the will of the people—as that will is expressed. Despite the almost phenomenal cultural and social importance of birds, and the threats to their well-being, direct appropriations for their welfare have been modest indeed, and the most notable exceptions have been made only after some forms have become endangered. In the United States, our efforts to save the Bald Eagle, our national symbol, the Whooping Crane and the California Condor have been outstanding examples and have enjoyed political and public support.

There have been a number of pieces of legislation aimed at protecting the integrity of the environment or halting its degradation. These, of course, have included benefits to bird life along with other life forms. There are also numerous obvious and very successful private efforts. The National Audubon Society, the World Wildlife Fund, the educational work of the National Geographic Society and others are notable examples of successful private efforts on behalf of birds. But despite these successes a common focus is lacking: there seems to be no real public consciousness. Too often the appreciation and the well-being of the birds have been relegated to the bird watchers. Their enjoyment is categorized as a non-essential form of recreation, a kind of hobby interest, something of a luxury in a modern industrialized society. Public support, morally and financially, has simply not matched the importance of birds which has, I believe, been taken for granted.

While progress must be acknowledged, we are far short of the mark and this will remain the case until the public, the legislators, policy makers and administrators overcome the attitude that birds are really in the province of the bird watchers or 'the little old ladies in tennis shoes'. There needs to be a recognition that all birds are part of our natural resource treasure; that their well-being is a responsibility of the people and the governments of all nations; that their well-being is not dependent entirely upon fish and wildlife and other natural resource agencies but is a responsibility of all agencies that have responsibilities or activities that impact upon birds and their habitats; and that the well-being of birds needs to be considered in all legislation and regulations which can impinge upon their habitats.

I think this will be one of the positive benefits of this symposium. The International Council for Bird Preservation, with its global network of scientists and conservationists in 270 member organizations and over a million members in 86 countries, provides a splendid forum. It will focus attention. The thinking expressed here and the ideas generated will be as the ripple in the pond moving outward toward other shores.

BIRDS AS A SOCIO-ECONOMIC RESOURCE: A STRATEGIC CONCEPT IN PROMOTING CONSERVATION

F. L. FILION

Canadian Wildlife Service, Ottawa, Ontario, K1A 0H3, Canada

INTRODUCTION

In a recent address to the World Congress on National Parks, Kenton Miller presented an action plan for the future of protected areas. He referred to the plan as 'a revolutionary advance' because it broke with management's traditional 'insular approach' and linked conservation initiatives with social and economic needs. Among the numerous actions proposed was the notion of developing 'new economic tools' for supporting conservation. His argument went as follows: 'By focusing on the ability of a protected area to contribute to human needs in a variety of tangible and quantifiable ways, the resource manager demonstrates that the area is a fundamental link in local, national and international economies. By so doing, the manager increases his ability to obtain the freedom and the resources to maintain the protected area in a manner that both preserves the integrity of the ecosystem and satisfies the needs of the human population' (Miller 1984: 760). This key element in the Bali Action Plan for protected areas advances a concept closely related to the subject of this Symposium and the focus of my paper.

The notion that birds are a socio-economic resource implies that birds are beneficial to mankind. This paper explores the concept of managing birds as a socio-economic resource by advancing five interrelated hypotheses which examine the linkages among people, birds and management. My objectives are two-fold: (1) to persuade preservationists that gauging the nature and extent of these benefits can provide powerful incentives for conservation initiatives and convincing justification for existing management programmes, and (2) to provide a global framework for other symposium papers which touch a diverse range of complex socio-economic issues.

HYPOTHESIS 1

Birds are valuable to people because they contribute to a wide variety of human needs

Economics could be described as the study of mankind's activities in satisfying its wants and needs. If we choose to consider birds and other forms of wildlife as socio-economic resources we must ask ourselves what needs and wants, if any, could possibly be met by these resources. To assist in answering the question I will refer to a theory of human needs proposed by Abraham H. Maslow (Maslow 1970) which is one of the most frequently cited explanations of human motivation.

Maslow argued that all humans share certain needs which can be arranged in a hierarchy of five levels, from the most fundamental physiological needs to the needs of intellectual and spiritual fulfilment. These needs are enumerated in *Table 1*. First in the hierarchy are 'physiological needs' for necessities such as food and clothing. These are followed by 'safety needs' for security, protection, stability and order. At the third level are 'belongingness and love needs' which allow individuals to become part of something larger than themselves. These are followed by 'esteem needs' for self-confidence, achievement, knowledge, recognition and status. Finally Maslow identified a fifth 'need for self-actualization' which allows one to grow, to develop and to realize one's potential as a human being. It is at this final stage, Maslow argued, that strong emotional 'peak experiences' are encountered and that 'aesthetic needs' are met.

Table 1:   Maslow's hierarchy of human needs.

1. Physiological needs
2. Safety needs
3. Belongingness and love needs
4. Esteem needs
5. Need for self-actualization

My purpose is not to defend Maslow's theory but rather to suggest that it is useful in helping us appreciate more fully why birds are important to humanity for a multitude of different reasons. Are any or all of the above need levels met by the existence of birds and the interactions humans have with this living resource? Let us consider a few examples. For centuries birds have contributed to man's physiological needs for protein and clothing and they continue to do so today in many parts of the world. Birds contribute towards mankind's safety needs by consuming incredible amounts of insects which would otherwise destroy crops and by serving as valuable bio-indicators which warn us of the changing quality of the natural environment upon which human life depends. An indication that 'belongingness and love needs' are satisfied by birds is reflected in the fact that many humans spend considerable amounts of time and money providing food and shelter for birds. In many cultures birds are revered and even attributed religious sanctity (Diamond, this vol.). 'Esteem needs' are met when a successful hunt confirms the skill of the hunter or when a committed birdwatcher adds yet another species to an enviable life list. The 'need for self-actualization' is gratified in many ways. Among them are the inspiration birds provide for art or through the peak experience provided when the awesome power and overwhelming beauty of a rising flock fills the skies with sublime pandemonium.

These examples illustrate but a few of the numerous ways in which birds contribute towards all levels of Maslow's hierarchy of human needs. In fact, it is difficult to imagine another resource capable of contributing as fully and as completely to mankind's diverse needs. In my opinion, this makes birds and other wildlife forms an exceptionally precious socio-economic resource—a fact that bird conservationists of the world may already recognize but may not frequently exploit to defend and promote their vital work. Cognizance of the value of birds brings us to the second hypothesis which is at the heart of this symposium.

HYPOTHESIS 2

Conservation issues related to people warrant a share of the attention traditionally confined to bird population and habitat issues

Those responsible for bird conservation and wildlife management devote a considerable amount of time and resources to studying bird populations and habitats. This is understandable given the professional training of ornithologists, wildlife biologists and ecologists, and the beauty and complexity of a subject close to their hearts. What this means is that bird conservation has traditionally been approached as an essentially biological question. The central theme of this Symposium is that conservation programmes and bird management benefits and problems arise out of interactions between birds and people. Promotion of bird management programmes and effective solutions to management problems must take full account of socio-cultural and socio-economic factors as well as biological ones.

This is illustrated by a model, *Figure 1*, which shows the dynamic interactions

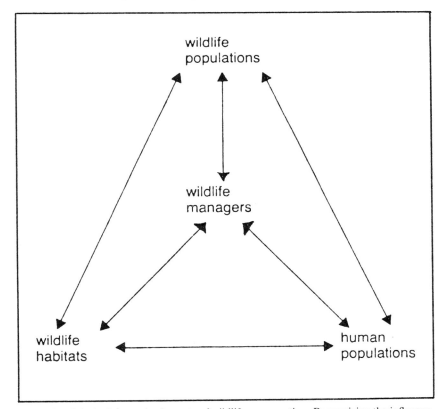

Figure 1: Principal dynamic elements of wildlife conservation. Recognizing the influence of human populations on bird management and devising strategies to grasp the opportunities this knowledge provides can contribute to the success of new conservation initiatives. (From Filion & Parker 1984)

among the four main components of wildlife management. Central to the model is the assumption that wildlife managers play a pivotal role in maintaining an equilibrium in the interactions among bird populations, bird habitats and human populations. The key influence that socio-economic and political demands may have in either hindering conservation efforts or enhancing them is acknowledged by the presence of the 'human populations' component. About one-third of critical wildlife management issues are assumed to be directly related to human populations. Of course, this may be considerably higher depending on cultural differences and the proximity of habitats to major human settlements. The bi-directional arrows point out that humans not only have a critical influence on the management model but are also recipients of bird-related benefits and other management effects. This gives rise to a number of unorthodox questions which influence the success of conservation initiatives; for example, how much do conservationists know about the demands that humans place on bird populations and habitats? How much do they know about how these demands are presently met, and how they may be shifting over time? How much do we know about the socio-economic benefits that result from birds and bird habitats? How much do we know about the lifestyles, attitudes and behaviour of the many different publics which influence bird management models, and how effective are we in communicating with these publics?

Devoting more human and fiscal resources to the socio-economic component of the wildlife management model can be beneficial in several strategic ways. Here are some of them:

- Senior decision-makers who control the resources on which bird conservation programmes depend are sensitive to public sentiment. Documenting public interest in birds is an important asset.
- In times of fiscal constraint, bird conservation programmes are likely to come under scrutiny. It is wise to be ready to demonstrate the socio-economic benefits these programmes provide if the probability of cut-backs is to be minimized.
- The publics that benefit directly from bird populations are usually prepared to pay for the benefits they receive. These payments could be an important source of funding for projects that seek to enhance bird populations and habitats.
- When bird poulations are threatened, there is almost certainly a group of people somewhere who will suffer from the anticipated decline. Quantifying the magnitude of those losses in socio-economic terms, and seeking compensation from the source of the threat, may prove effective.

Managers interested in strengthening the socio-economic component of the wildlife management model may not always know where to begin. This is the subject of the next hypothesis.

HYPOTHESIS 3

Gauging the rich diversity of interactions between birds and people is an effective means of demonstrating the benefits birds provide

It is virtually impossible to quantify the value of any bird in the wild. However, it is feasible to evaluate bird-related products or experiences that are enjoyed by humans. This can be done by examining the interactions that occur between birds and people and assessing in socio-economic terms the wants and needs that are fulfilled in the process. I will not attempt to list every possible kind of bird-related product or interaction. My preference is to advance a general classification of wildlife-people interactions. Ideally the final classification should be capable of covering the full range of human needs identified earlier under Hypothesis 1.

Table 2:   Potential interactions between people and wildlife. The beneficial interactions that occur between humans and birds are diverse and complex. A better understanding of these interactions provides convincing evidence of the magnitude of the socio-economic significance of birds to mankind. (From Filion 1984).

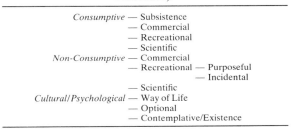

```
        Consumptive — Subsistence
                    — Commercial
                    — Recreational
                    — Scientific
    Non-Consumptive — Commercial
                    — Recreational — Purposeful
                                   — Incidental
                    — Scientific
Cultural/Psychological — Way of Life
                    — Optional
                    — Contemplative/Existence
```

Table 2 proposes a potential list of 11 types of interactions between people and wildlife. They are grouped under three main headings—consumptive, non-consumptive and cultural-psychological. Many of these potential interactions will be covered in the papers that follow. For lack of a better word the term 'consumptive' refers to activities like hunting, in which birds are extracted from the population, in contrast to 'non-consumptive' activities in which they are not. Both consumptive and non-consumptive activities involve direct sensory contact with wildlife whereas cultural/psychological interactions refer to a state of mind or a social heritage that is influenced by wildlife. Examples of consumptive interactions with birds are provided in the papers by Scott, Dekker, Skira, Diamond and Jacquemot (this vol.). Examples of non-consumptive commercial and recreational interactions with birds are provided in papers by Clark, Diamond, Dekker and Jacquemot. Examples of the cultural/psychological interactions have already been provided by our chairman, Jack Berryman, and further examples will be given by Schultz, Isack, Scott, Dekker and Diamond (this vol.).

Several bird-related activities are not covered adequately in this section of the book. Among them are the scientific consumptive and non-consumptive interactions. This includes the socio-economic importance of bird-related activities such as medical research, museum specimens, films, domestication and the educational value of animals, to name just a few. Another major omission regards the socio-economic significance of optional and contemplative interactions with birds. Optional interactions may be described as the right or the ability of people to benefit from consumptive or non-consumptive bird-related activities in the future. Contemplative/existence interactions are mental states in which people derive satisfaction from knowing that birds exist or perhaps from the fact that a threatened species is being saved. I believe that optional and existence interactions have considerable socio-economic value to mankind, yet very little quantitative work has been done on this very complex subject.

No pretence is made that the classification is currently complete. I offer it as a starting point to mobilize conservationists to think about evaluating the multitude of socio-economic benefits that stem from wild bird populations of the world in a comprehensive rather than a fragmented manner. The classification could be helpful in laying a foundation upon which international socio-economic indicators could be developed to gauge and monitor the importance of birds and the merits of conservation initiatives and management programmes. The next hypothesis offers general suggestions on how the indicators might be used effectively.

HYPOTHESIS 4

The multiple benefits that birds provide to mankind can be sustained in perpetuity

One of the outstanding characteristics of birds as a resource is the fact that they are renewable. Given adequate protection and management, the multiple benefits that birds provide can be sustained in perpetuity. Similarly it is possible to increase and sustain the potential benefits that a small or threatened bird population can provide. That is a vital strategic aspect to emphasize when bird populations and habitats are threatened by competing proposals for development which promise merely short-term gains.

The context is appropriate to introduce a definition of wildlife management which encompasses many of the ideas mentioned above. The definition is inspired by Giles (1971).

> *"Wildlife management is the science and art of studying and influencing the nature and interaction of habitats, wildlife populations and human populations in order to achieve specific goals or benefits by means of the wildlife resource."*

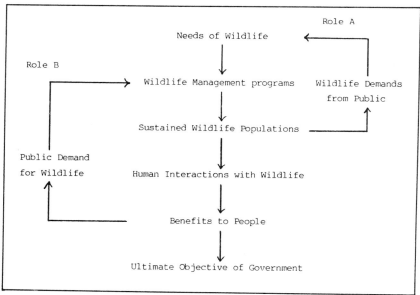

Figure 2: Wildlife management contributes to the ultimate objective of government. Monitoring the level of benefits (Role B) that bird management programmes (Role A) attempt to sustain can provide strategic evidence on whether or not sufficient resources are being deployed to successfully maintain the ecosystem and genetic diversity of birds.

The definition is consistent with the concepts that have been introduced so far and is applicable to bird management and conservation. The strength of the definition lies in the fact that it invites scientists to look beyond their immediate research concerns and to embrace goals that are essentially in the political arena.

This leads us to the conclusion that wildlife management contributes to the ultimate objective of government which is to maintain or enhance the 'well-being' of people. Examples of needs that are included in the term 'well-being' were provided under Hypotheses 1 and 3. The result is illustrated in *Figure 2*. The figure suggests that bird management has two main roles. Role A is traditionally concerned primarily with the stewardship of bird populations and habitat at public expense. It could be perceived by some as a substantial burden on taxpayers. Role B is concerned with the benefits that well-managed bird populations and habitats provide to people. Role B is the strongest 'marketing' tool that bird conservation organizations have with which to defend, maintain or enhance Role A. In the past, Role B has generally received little or no attention from conservationists. This socio-economic role casts an appealing light on bird conservation initiatives by demonstrating how they contribute towards the ultimate objective of governments, the most significant sponsors of conservation programmes. Role B also provides essential public feedback to enhance conservation programmes and resulting benefits. Roles A and B are both complementary and necessary. However, some experts feel that conservationists should not be content to stop at this point, as explained in Hypothesis 5.

HYPOTHESIS 5

Long-term conservation strategies that seek to enhance socio-economic benefits will be more successful than strategies restricted to merely sustaining benefits

Had I delivered this paper several weeks ago I would have ended at the previous hypothesis thinking that I had adequately covered the range of relevant points on the contributions of the socio-economic perspective to bird conservation. However, I recently had the privilege of listening to Dr P. H. Pearse (1987), a well-known Canadian economist, who made a rather convincing argument that conservationists must consider going even further. The essence of his argument is summarized in Hypothesis 5 above, and is remarkably simple. He suggests that conservation objectives that tend to be defensive and are content with merely sustaining benefits provided by wildlife programmes will gradually be eroded. He states: 'I am absolutely convinced that, notwithstanding occasional successes, our wild fish and game will continue to lose in the face of pressure from other resource users driven by economic incentives. That is, unless we change our policies'. He invites government and non-government wildlife agencies to consider more assertive policies for managing wildlife and developing the values people derive from it in three ways:
  – By experimenting with means to accommodate a greater diversity in wildlife uses.
  – By enabling the fullest possible value of wildlife in both marketable and non-marketable benefits to be realized.
  – By developing institutional management to allow non-government groups to manage and enhance wildlife.

CONCLUSION

The proposed socio-economic hypotheses may seem novel and perhaps even provocative to some bird conservationists. However, I believe that the nature of the arguments that they infuse have the potential to produce stronger conservation policies and more effective programmes than may have been possible in the past. For example, policies and programmes that are enhanced by socio-economic perspectives will have greater strategic appeal to politicians and the public because they acknowledge birds as an important renewable resource, they are affirmative rather than defensive, and they extol the real benefits that birds provide to the people who bear the costs of conservation.

The concept of birds as a socio-economic resource casts a new light on the perceived products of bird conservation programmes. Monitoring the diverse beneficial interactions that occur between birds and people provides valuable information which pertains to the third objective of the World Conservation Strategy on 'sustainable utilization'. From a political point of view, 'sustained utilization' is an influential socio-economic concept, not only because it may be more meaningful to senior decision makers than many ecological indicators but also because it can be perceived to encompass the other two World Conservation Strategy objectives. In other words, information about a strong stream of benefits resulting from 'sustained utilization' of birds provides evidence of the relative success of conservation programmes in 'maintaining ecosystems' and 'preserving genetic diversity' (IUCN 1980). This observation is strategically important in two ways:

– Widely known information on the stream of socio-economic benefits attributable to bird populations and habitats decreases the likelihood of cuts in conservation programme funding for fear of jeopardizing recognized benefits.
– Measured declines in the stream of socio-economic benefits provide an effective means of justifying funding increases for programmes dealing with bird populations and habitats. Conversely, estimated increases in the stream of socio-economic benefits resulting from projected bird population and habitat enhancements provide convincing political arguments favouring new conservation proposals.

In light of their imminent contributions toward effective bird conservation initiatives I recommend that valid and reliable socio-economic indicators be developed by a group of international socio-economic experts to gauge and monitor the multiple contributions of birds to the well-being of mankind.

REFERENCES

FILION, F. L. 1984. Toward a national conservation strategy: observations on the role of wildlife utilization in Zaire. MS report to IUCN (Project No. 9049).

FILION, F. L. & PARKER, S. A. D. 1984. Human dimensions of migratory game-bird hunting in Canada. *Can. Wildl. Serv. Occ. Pap. No. 51*. Ottawa.

GILES, R. H. 1971. The Approach. *In:* Giles, R. H. (ed.) *Wildlife Management Techniques*. The Wildlife Soc., Washington, D.C.

IUCN 1980. *World Conservation Strategy*, Gland.

MASLOW, A. H. 1970. *Motivation and Personality*. Harper and Row, N.Y.

MILLER, K. R. 1984. The Bali Action Plan: A Framework for the Future of Protected Areas. *In:* McNeely, J. A. & Miller, K. R. (eds.) *National Parks, Conservation and Development. The Role of Protected Areas in Sustaining Society*. The Smithsonian Institution Press, Washington, D.C.

PEARSE, P. H. 1987. *Wildlife Policy in Canada: Perceptions, Policies and Prospects*. Proc. Colloquium on Wildlife Conservation in Canada. Can. Wildl. Serv., Ottawa, pp. 7–22.

THE ECONOMIC SIGNIFICANCE OF BIRDS IN CANADA

A. Jacquemot & F. L. Filion

Canadian Wildlife Service, Ottawa, Ontario, K1A 0H3, Canada

ABSTRACT

Wildlife resources are highly valuable to Canadians. More than 15 million residents (84 per cent of the population) participate in wildlife-related recreational activities during the year. Waterfowl and other wild birds are a major source of benefits. They are enjoyed by people who watch films and television programmes, and by those who read books and magazines about birds. The majority of Canadians feed and study birds around their homes. Many make excursions with the primary purpose of observing and photographing birds, while even greater numbers enjoy birds during trips taken for business purposes. Game-birds also attract a number of hunters who enjoy their succulent meat.

The millions of participants in bird-related recreational activities receive direct benefits that they personally estimate to be worth $347 million annually. Assuming that these direct benefits can be sustained in perpetuity, it is concluded that they have a capitalized economic value of $6.9 billion at a discount rate of five per cent. The expenditures that Canadians make on bird-related recreational activities amount to almost $2 billion. These expenditures provide a significant annual stimulus to Canada's economy in terms of Gross Business Production ($4.1 billion) and Gross Domestic Product ($2.4 billion). The impacts which are expressed in 1981 dollars support 86,000 jobs during the year and provide Federal and Provincial Governments across Canada with tax revenues worth nearly $870 million. These effects are based on a comprehensive survey of 100,000 Canadians and on analyses conducted by Statistics Canada.

The findings are conservative because they exclude, among others, the commercial and subsistence value of birds and their recreational use by non-residents of Canada.

INTRODUCTION

Canada has a wide diversity of natural habitats including grasslands, wetlands, forest and tundra which support hundreds of millions of birds distributed amongst 578 species. More specifically, waterfowl such as ducks and geese have a joint breeding population of over 50 million (Anon. 1986). These birds play an important role in Canadian society by providing eggs and meat to thousands of natives and by supporting numerous bird-related recreational activities for millions of Canadians.

The purpose of this paper is to show the popularity and economic importance of these bird populations in Canada by evaluating the economic benefits derived from the *recreational* activities they support. The data used were collected by Statistics Canada, a Federal Government agency, which surveyed a national sample of about 100,000 persons randomly selected from the 18,473,091 Canadians over 14 in 1981 (Filion *et al.* 1983). Although the focus of this paper is primarily on birds, some results are also given for other wildlife in order to illustrate the relative importance of birds in Canada. The paper is organized into three sections. Section 1 indicates the popularity of birds in Canada. Section 2 explains the concept of direct economic benefits that participants receive from birds. Section 3 presents the expenditures incurred by participants in bird-related activities and the indirect benefits that accrue to Canada's economy as a result of those expenditures.

1. PARTICIPATION IN RECREATIONAL BIRD-RELATED ACTIVITIES

Canadian wildlife resources allow a majority of Canadians to participate in a multitude of wildlife-related activities ranging from enjoying TV programmes on wildlife to hunting game. In all these recreational activities, wild birds play a major role.

According to the National Survey results, in 1981 some 700,000 Canadians (*Table 1*) hunted waterfowl such as ducks and geese, while one million Canadians hunted other game-birds such as grouse, partridge and pheasant. Special trips or outings whose main purpose was to observe, photograph or study waterfowl attracted 2.2 million Canadians, while 2.4 million Canadians reported watching or studying other birds (pigeons, hawks, owls, etc.) on similar trips or outings. Over 25 percent of the Canadian population encountered waterfowl incidentally while on outings or trips taken for business or pleasure. Incidental encounters with other birds were even more popular among Canadians who said that the unplanned encounters contributed considerable enjoyment to their trips (Filion *et al.* 1983).

Table 1: Popularity of wildlife and bird-related recreational activities in Canada, 1981. (*Source:* National Survey carried out by Statistics Canada in 1981.)

Type of activity	Participants[1] in millions	Percentage[1] of Canadians participating[2]
A. ALL WILDLIFE		
Recreational hunting	1.8	9.8
Primary non-consumptive trips	3.6	19.4
Incidental wildlife encounters	8.1	43.9
Residential wildlife activities	12.3	66.8
Indirect wildlife activities	15.5	83.8
B. WATERFOWL AND OTHER BIRDS		
Recreational hunting		
Waterfowl	0.7	3.6
Other birds	1.0	5.3
Primary non-consumptive trips		
Waterfowl	2.2	11.7
Other birds	2.4	13.1
Incidental wildlife encounters		
Waterfowl	4.7	25.4
Other birds	5.1	27.8

Notes: 1. Since most participants are involved in more than one activity, the figures are not additive.
2. Based on 18,473,091 Canadians above 14 years old.

Survey results for residential and indirect wildlife-related activities are not detailed by animal species. However, we can assume that the importance of birds in these activities is *at least* equivalent to, if not more important than, the role played by them in the three other types of activities in Section B of *Table 1* because of their high visibility in all parts of Canada. Residential wildlife activities include feeding, watching, studying, and photographing wildlife, as well as maintaining shrubs or plants for wildlife around one's home. In 1981 these activities attracted more than 66 percent of Canadians. Indirect wildlife activities allow the participant to experience wildlife outside its natural setting through a variety of modes such as reading, watching films or TV, purchasing art or crafts, and visiting institutions dealing with wildlife such as zoos, game farms, aquariums or museums of natural history. It is estimated that these activities attract about 84 percent of Canadians annually.

The popularity of wildlife-related activities generates two types of economic benefit; (1) direct economic benefits, which are received by those who participate in such activities, and (2) indirect benefits resulting from the impacts of the participants' expenditures on the Canadian economy. The magnitude of these benefits is examined below.

2. DIRECT ECONOMIC BENEFITS

Direct economic benefits are concerned with the enjoyment or satisfaction received directly by participants in bird-related activities. In *Figure 1* the left column represents the total amount of enjoyment received by participants from a given bird experience. In order to benefit from this enjoyment it is assumed that participants are prepared to sacrifice a sum of money that could be used to purchase benefits provided by alternative activities such as golfing, dancing etc.

The manner in which this willingness to pay, represented by the middle column, may be quantified is shown on the right of *Figure 1*. The actual costs incurred by participants usually represent only a portion of the total enjoyment they obtain, and tend to underestimate the gross economic value of bird-related activities. The net economic value of the enjoyment provided by birds, illustrated in the upper part of the third column, is correctly expressed by the difference between expenditures actually incurred by participants and the total amount of money they *would be willing to pay* to participate in the bird-related activities. According to *Figure 1* the gross value of the enjoyment provided by bird-related recreational activities to Canadians in 1981 was about $2.3 billion. This accounts for almost half of the gross value provided from recreational use of all birds and all mammals combined. The expenditures of participants in bird-related activities amounted to $1.9 billion while the net economic benefit participants received was worth $347 million.

To evaluate these direct benefits and expenditures respondents to the Survey were questioned on their actual participation costs and then asked what additional amount of money they would have been prepared to pay before giving up bird-related recreational activities because they were more costly than they were worth. *Table 2* shows the direct economic benefits received by participants in all wildlife (column A) and in bird-related recreational activities (column B). Direct economic benefits received by those involved in bird hunting ($180 million) and non-hunting activities ($167 million) appear more or less equally distributed among hunters and non-hunters. However, the large preponderance of participants in non-hunting bird-related recreational activities as indicated in *Table 1* means that bird hunters receive greater direct benefits than non-hunters. The

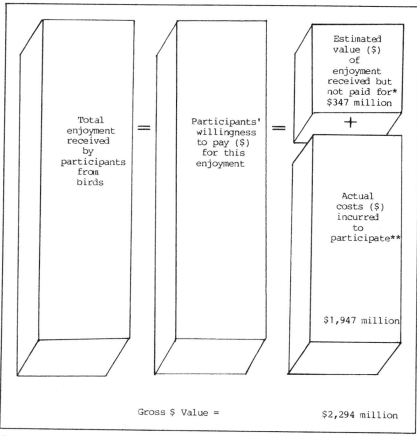

Figure 1:   The enjoyment received by participants in bird-related recreational activities, expressed in economic terms. (* This value represents the amount of 'direct economic benefit' received by participants in bird-related activities. ** These expenditures are used to compute 'indirect benefits' or impacts on the economy in *Table 4.*)

same seems to be true for participants in all wildlife-related activities. These direct benefits for bird and wildlife-related activities are conservative because they do not include figures for residential, indirect, and incidental participation.

The last two columns of *Table 2* present the capitalized values of the annual direct economic benefits received. If we assume that effective wildlife management results in the perpetuation of wildlife populations and a sustained yield of direct economic benefits we may 'capitalize' the benefits observed for 1981. In other words we may compute[1] the capital needed to yield an annual dollar value in perpetuity equivalent to the amount of direct economic benefits provided by wildlife. In our calculation we used an interest rate (discount rate) of five percent net of inflation and we expressed the results in constant 1981 dollars. The results show a *capitalized* value of $6.9 billion for direct economic benefits derived from

Table 2: Direct economic benefits in millions of dollars to participants from two bird-related recreational activities. Canada, 1981.

Type of activity	Net annual value			Capitalized value[1]	
	A All wildlife	B Waterfowl and other birds	B/A	A[1] All wildlife	B[1] Waterfowl and other birds
Recreational hunting	$418M	$180M	43%	$8,360M	$3,593M
Primary non-consumptive trips	$361M	$167M	46%	$7,219M	$3,339M
TOTAL	$779M	$347M	45%	$15,579M	$6,932M

Note: 1. Assuming a discount rate of 5% net of inflation in perpetuity.

bird-related recreational activities. The capitalized value provides a conservative estimate of the magnitude of direct economic benefits that would be lost to current and future generations of Canadians if bird-related recreational activities were allowed to disappear (Filion *et al.* 1985).

3. INDIRECT BENEFITS

Indirect benefits consist of impacts on the economy that occur as a result of the money spent on bird-related activities by participants. These impacts are reflected in economic indicators that show indirect benefits in terms of increased business production, personal income, employment, etc. The questionnaire used in the national survey was designed so that annual expenditures on wildlife-related activities would be registered only if they were incurred *primarily* for wildlife and bird-related recreational activities. The expenditure-related questions covered seven kinds of costs: expenditures on accommodation, transportation, food, equipment and other items; maintenance and improvement of natural areas for wildlife; and memberships in, and donations to, wildlife-related organizations.

Table 3 shows a breakdown of the expenditures according to four types of activity. Hunting and non-consumptive trips account for the majority of expenses. Almost half of the total expenses on wildlife may be attributed to birds. With 43 percent, birds account for a lower proportion of wildlife-related expenditures on hunting than any other one activity.

Table 3: Expenditures in millions of dollars by participants on wildlife and bird-related recreational activities. Canada, 1981.

Type of activity	A All wildlife	B Waterfowl and other birds	B/A
Recreational hunting	$1,186M	$513M	43%
Primary non-consumptive trips	$2,085M	$964M	46%
Incidental wildlife encounters	$85M	$52M	61%
Residential and indirect wildlife activities	$834M	$418M	50%
TOTAL	$4,190M	$1,947M	46%

Table 4: Indirect benefits in millions of dollars to the Canadian economy generated by the expenditures of participants on wildlife and bird-related recreational activities. Canada, 1981.

Economic indicators	A	B
	All wildlife[1]	Waterfowl and other birds[2]
Gross Business Production	$8,758M	$4,071M
Gross Domestic Product (GDP)	$5,184M	$2,410M
Personal income	$3,009M	$1,399M
Government revenue from taxes	$1,867M	$868M
Number of jobs	184,860	85,928

Notes: 1. Economic impacts are generated by participants' expenditures amounting to $4,190 million.
2. Economic impacts are generated by participants' expenditures amounting to $1,947 million from *Figure 1.*

The indirect benefits reported in *Table 4* include all the economic effects generated by the $1.9 billion spent on bird-related activities. These effects were computed by Statistics Canada using their national Input-Output econometric model. The results of this economic analysis are shown for five economic indicators.

Bird-related expenditures contributed more than $4 billion to Canada's Gross Business Production. The Gross Business Production represents both final and intermediate industrial production generated in the business sector by the bird-related spending.

Gross Domestic Product (GDP at market price) amounted to some $2,410 million as a result of bird-related spending. GDP is generally regarded as a good indicator of the performance of the economy because it excludes duplication from the value of production of goods and services at intermediate levels.

The economic impacts reflected in the above Gross Business Production and GDP generated almost $1.4 billion in personal income. This includes the wages and salaries of almost 86,000 jobs which were supported by bird-related recreational activities in the country.

The expenditures made on bird-related activities and the subsequent economic stimulus are responsible for substantial tax revenues to Federal and Provincial Governments treasuries. In 1981 alone this amounted to $868 million in revenues from direct and indirect taxes net of the government subsidies given to the business sector. Economic impacts attributable to bird-related expenditures account for 46 percent of all impacts stemming from all wildlife-related activities in 1981 (Jacquemot *et al.* 1986).

CONCLUSION

This paper has demonstrated the economic importance of birds in Canada by evaluating the popular recreational activities that healthy bird populations and habitats support. Two categories of economic values have been conservatively estimated: direct benefits which are received by the participants in wildlife-related activities, and indirect benefits which contribute to the health of the country's general economy. It is important to consider that these benefits can be sustained in perpetuity and the formula used here to compute 'capitalized' values reflects this (see below). The economic benefits are made possible because of continuing management programmes which seek to maintain abundant bird populations throughout Canada. The values are influential in pointing out the magnitude of economic benefits that would be at risk if Federal and Provincial Government and private bird management programmes were allowed to disappear.

FOOTNOTE

1. The formula for computing bond yield with constant annuities compounded once a year may be applied:

$$V = \frac{R}{i} \text{ where } V = \text{capitalized value}$$

$$R = \text{return or yield}$$
$$i = \text{discount rate}$$

REFERENCES

ANON. 1986. North American Waterfowl Management Plan. A Strategy for Cooperation. Canadian Wildlife Service. Environment Canada. Ottawa.

FILION, F. L., JAMES, S. W., DUCHARME, J.-L., PEPPER, W., REID, R., BOXALL, P. & TEILLET, D. 1983. The Importance of Wildlife to Canadians. Highlights of the 1981 National Survey. Canadian Wildlife Service. Environment Canada. Ottawa.

FILION, F. L., JACQUEMOT, A. & REID, R. 1985. The Importance of Wildlife to Canadians, An Executive Overview of the Recreational Economic Significance of Wildlife. Canadian Wildlife Service. Environment Canada. Ottawa.

JACQUEMOT, A., REID, R. & FILION, F. L. 1986. The Importance of Wildlife to Canadians. The Recreational Economic Significance of Wildlife. Canadian Wildlife Service. Environment Canada. Ottawa.

ATTITUDES TOWARDS BIRDS AND OTHER WILDLIFE IN WEST GERMANY AND AMERICA

WOLFGANG SCHULZ

*Wildbiologische Gesellschaft München, Postfach 170,
D-8103 Oberammergau, West Germany*

ABSTRACT

To measure attitudes towards wildlife in West Germany we used Kellert's questionnaire, developed in America. The questionnaire was translated into German, and in parts modified to suit German conditions. In this way it was possible to compare American and German attitudes towards wildlife. These measured attitudes also included public attitudes towards birds.

Kellert defined eight different attitudes and attitude scales, his categories being moralistic, naturalistic, humanistic, ecologistic, negativistic, scientistic, utilitarian and dominionistic.

In Germany the following hierarchy of attitudes was found: moralistic, humanistic, naturalistic, ecologistic, negativistic, scientistic, utilitarian and dominionistic. The American results showed a different distribution: the most widespread attitude was the humanistic one, followed by moralistic, negativistic, utilitarian, naturalistic, ecologistic, dominionistic and scientistic. The strength of the attitudes also differed between the two countries, especially for the moralistic attitude test: in Germany there was a scale score of 0.632 and in America 0.275.

Respondents were asked to record their different uses of wildlife, and we were therefore able to compare the attitudes of diverse wildlife users in West Germany and America. For example, birdwatchers have very high scale scores for naturalistic, ecologistic and scientistic attitudes in both Germany and America. Overall, the results in Germany as well as in America indicate that birds as a group of animals are very popular. Only domestic animals are more highly favoured.

INTRODUCTION

Before exploring this subject it is important to consider the following questions. Why are we interested in measuring attitudes towards wildlife? What is the object of this measurement? Does it help us in seeking solutions to conservation problems?

Campbell (1979) notes that, 'Humans are the dominant species in every national park. As a result of our social evolution we have expanded into one niche after another. Further, we are a highly generalized animal, capable of an immense range of behaviors . . . In short, to understand the natural systems of the park [you] must understand the park's most dominant species.'

In general, this statement applies everywhere; not just in national parks. One part of any natural system is its wildlife, and therefore we must take account of the human dimension in wildlife management, policy formulation and planning. Kellert & Brown (1985) have written, 'The wildlife management profession has recognized for some time that a key to its ability to manage wildlife effectively is an understanding of the public's relation to this resource'. A first step, then, must be to identify, measure and assess public attitudes towards wildlife. These criteria will indicate the interests, needs, perceptions and demands of the public—and thus provide a basis for better management and conservation policies.

There are many examples in America of the usefulness of attitude studies in wildlife management and nature conservation (Langenau 1984; Kellert & Brown 1985). One example in Germany involves the conflict between ski mountaineers and Capercaillies (*Tetrao urogallus*). Ski mountaineers go skiing in the Alps looking for rest and untouched nature, well away from the managed skiing areas. They climb the mountains and then ski down through the forests, and this special kind of skiing is a problem in nature conservation because the ski mountaineers often disturb Capercaillies. Therefore the Wildbiologische Gesellschaft München tried to identify the interests, perceptions, needs and demands of these ski mountaineers. On this project, in areas where there were Capercaillie, we signposted tracks for the skiers to use when climbing up and going down, so that the Capercaillies would not be disturbed. Most of the ski mountaineers accepted these tracks and thus we were able to reduce the level of disturbance inflicted on the Capercaillies.

DEFINITIONS AND METHODS

Kellert (1980b) proposed a range of attitude scales—eight in all—and for each attitude provided a definition and a description of the associated behaviour patterns and perceived values and benefits. It is assumed that because birds are a major component of wildlife in general, the attitudes displayed are equally valid for birds as they are for wildlife in the broader sense.

There are countless definitions of, and theories about, 'attitude': in this paper I take attitude as the disposition of a person to perceive, value and deal with objects in their environment in a particular manner (Brandstätter 1983). One of the most widespread theories is the so-called 'three component model' developed by Sherif & Cantril (1945), the three components (*Figure 1*) being the cognitive, the behavioural and the affective.

The humanistic attitude implies a 'primary interest in, and strong affection for, individual animals, principally pets. Regarding wildlife, the focus is on large attractive animals with strong anthropomorphic associations' (Kellert 1980b). Common behavioural expressions are pet ownership, wildlife tourism and casual zoo visitation. The most related values or benefits are companionship and affection.

Another attitude type is the moralistic. For these people the primary concern is, 'for the right and wrong treatment of animals, with strong opposition to exploitation of and cruelty toward animals' (Kellert 1980b). They support animal welfare, and are members of animal welfare organizations. Their concern for animals is ethical and existential.

'Primary interest and affection for wildlife and the outdoors' (Kellert 1980b) are characteristic of the naturalistic attitude. Here the common behavioural expressions are outdoor wildlife-related recreation, back-country use, birding and hunting. The only benefit is outdoor recreation.

The fourth attitude type—the ecologistic—is defined as 'primary concern for the environment as a system, for interrelationships between wildlife species and

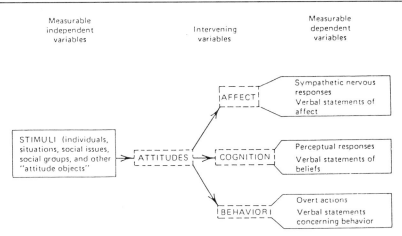

Measurable
independent
variables

Intervening
variables

Measurable
dependent
variables

AFFECT — Sympathetic nervous responses / Verbal statements of affect

STIMULI (individuals, situations, social issues, social groups, and other "attitude objects") → ATTITUDES → COGNITION

COGNITION — Perceptual responses / Verbal statements of beliefs

BEHAVIOR — Overt actions / Verbal statements concerning behavior

Figure 1:   The three-component view of attitude. (*From:* Rosenberg & Howland 1960.)

natural habitats' (Kellert 1980b). People with the ecologistic attitude support conservation, are members of conservation organizations, and pursue ecological studies. There are ecological values and benefits.

In the scientistic attitude the primary interest is in 'the physical attributes and the biological functioning of animals' (Kellert 1980b). This attitude is combined with scientific studies and collecting. There is a scientific value.

The negativistic attitude is an expression for 'an active avoidance of animals due to fear or dislike' (Kellert 1980b). Common behavioural expressions are cruelty and overt fear behaviour. There are few or negative values.

'Primary concern for the practical and material value of animals' (Kellert 1980b) comprises a utilitarian attitude. Expressions of behaviour are consumption of furs, raising meat, bounties and hunting. There are consumptive and utilitarian benefits.

The last attitude is the dominionistic, characterized by 'primary satisfactions derived from mastery and control over animals, typically in sporting situations' (Kellert 1980b) like animal spectator sports and trophy hunting.

To measure these attitudes Kellert developed a questionnaire with 69 attitude questions. For the construction of the attitude scale Kellert (1980a) used the so-called Likert method. Out of more than 1000 attitude questions or statements he determined with statistical methods the final attitude scale items. The respondents had to respond to these statements on a scale from, 'Strongly agree' to 'Strongly disagree'. Every attitude type was measured by a set of statements. The answers to all statements of one attitude type were added together to give the values for each attitude scale. To demonstrate the kind of statements used, I give one example of a negativistic scale question. Respondents are asked to decide if they 'Strongly agree', 'Agree', 'Slightly agree', 'Slightly disagree', 'Disagree', or 'Strongly disagree' with the following statement: 'I dislike most beetles and spiders'.

In the USA, in 1980, Kellert conducted a nationwide survey based on a representative sample of about 3000 Americans. In 1983/4 we questioned 1500 pupils from every part of West Germany studying at adult colleges. Adult colleges are called in Germany 'Volkshochschule' and they offer courses for the general

Table 1:   Demographic profiles of college survey samples and census data for West Germany. (*From:* Schulz 1986.)

	1983–84 College survey sample	1982 Census data
SEX		
Male	35.0%	47.8%
Female	65.0%	54.2%
AGE		
−24	33.6%	20.1%
25–34	23.7%	16.9%
35–44	21.4%	17.0%
45–54	11.0%	15.4%
55–64	5.6%	15.5%
65+	4.7%	18.1%
EDUCATION		
Primary School	15.2%	72.7%
Six-form High School	38.5%	16.8%
Secondary School	47.3%	10.5%

public. The courses cover many disciplines like languages, type-writing, cooking etc. With our sample we were able to reach all demographical groups, as shown in *Table 1*. In this sample, there were more females, younger people, and higher levels of education than in the general population according to 1982 census data. A comparison of census data between West Germany and the USA shows that the populations had similar profiles for age and sex.

RESULTS

The first comparison between West Germany and America is of the hierarchy of attitudes and scale scores of the total sample (*Figure 2*). In West Germany as well as in America, the predominant attitudes are emotional ones: the moralistic and the humanistic. But in Germany the moralistic attitude scale score is more than twice as high as in America.

The utilitarian and the dominionistic attitudes have higher ranks in America, which means that the naturalistic and the ecologistic attitudes are less widespread. Also the negativistic attitude is higher in America.

The results indicate that there is a strong affection for animals, and for birds as well, in West Germany as in America. But there are differences in the ranks of the other attitudes. In America the next two attitude types are the negativistic and the utilitarian. Kellert (1980a) interpreted the first four common attitudes in America as follows: 'The greater prevalence of these four attitudes in the national sample provided some understanding of the conflicts existing among Americans today in their perceptions and relationships to animals. This was especially evident when one compared the basic perspectives of the moralistic and utilitarian attitudes, where a fundamental difference centers around the perceived right of humans to exploit animals'.

Whereas there are conflicting attitudes in America, in West Germany one finds a different situation. The third and the fourth most prevalent attitudes are the naturalistic and the ecologistic. These attitudes do not compete with the first two—the moralistic and the humanistic; rather they regard nature as a whole, not just as individual animals. But this situation leads to another conflict in West Germany. It is a conflict between animal welfare groups and nature conservation groups. The latter accuse the former of seeing only the rights of animals, and maintain that this is not enough to protect nature.

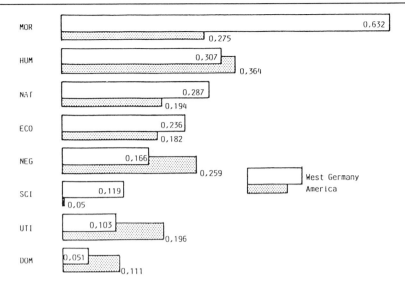

Figure 2: Attitude scale scores in West Germany and the USA compared. (*From:* Schulz 1985 and Kellert 1980b.)

There is a particularly interesting aspect of attitudes toward birds in the two surveys based on the three-component model of attitudes. The affective component turned out to be a very important part of the attitude toward birds. One question in the questionnaire was: 'Please indicate whether you like, dislike or have no opinion about, the following animals', followed by a list of 33 animals. We divided the 33 animals into five groups: domestic animals, mammals, birds, amphibians-reptiles-fish, and invertebrates. Birds are the second most popular group in both countries; the first one is the domestic animals (*Table 2*).

This result indicates that one of Kellert's hypothetical factors (Kellert, 1980a) may be open to debate. This factor states that the phylogenetic relatedness to human beings is important for the popularity of an animal. The results show, however, that birds are more popular than mammals, although mammals are more familiar, and phylogenetically closer, to human beings than birds are. There might be some other factors contributing to the popularity of birds. First of all, birds are very common; people can see them everywhere in their gardens, or in parks, and it is very easy to watch birds. Secondly, most birds are not dangerous to people; and third, there is a great symbolic value of birds derived from their flight as a symbol of freedom and independence.

Table 2: Animal group preference scale for West Germany and the USA.

West Germany		America (USA)	
Rank	**x̄**	**Rank**	**x̄**
1. Domestic animals	2.01	1. Domestic animals	2.08
2. Birds	2.71	2. Birds	2.98
3. Mammals	3.06	3. Mammals	3.40
4. Amphibians, reptiles, fish	3.35	4. Amphibians, reptiles, fish	3.55
5. Invertebrates	4.14	5. Invertebrates	4.64

Table 3:   Animal preference scale for West Germany and America.

West Germany Rank	x̄	America (USA) Rank	x̄
1. Robin	1.70	1. Dog	1.70
2. Dog	1.80	2. Horse	1.79
3. Butterfly	1.81	3. Swan	1.97
4. Horse	1.89	4. Robin	1.99
5. Ladybug	1.91	5. Butterfly	2.04
6. Swan	2.02	6. Trout	2.12
7. Eagle	2.28	7. Salmon	2.26
8. Owl	2.30	8. Eagle	2.29
9. Elephant	2.31	9. Elephant	2.63
10. Cat	2.33	10. Owl	2.66

This popularity of birds can also be seen by looking at individual species. Four of the ten most popular species are birds. In West Germany as well as in America, the robin, the swan, the eagle and the owl are among the most popular animals; and in Germany the robin is the most popular of all 33 animals (*Table 3*). In short, birds are the most popular group of wildlife in West Germany and in America.

In both countries, the attitudes towards wildlife differed within special activity groups. One of these activity groups consists of the birdwatchers. In West Germany, 15 percent of the national sample reported birdwatching during the previous two years. For America, Kellert (1985) records 25 percent. But more interesting is the distribution of the attitude types of the birdwatchers in comparison to the general population (*Figure 3*).

In West Germany, birdwatchers have higher moralistic, naturalistic, and scientistic scale scores than the general population, and they have lower scale scores on the humanistic, negativistic, utilitarian, and dominionistic attitudes. It is similar in America, except that the American birders do not differ from the general population on the moralistic attitude, and they have a higher mean score on the dominionistic attitude.

One can summarize that birdwatchers have a more scientific interest in nature and they are very interested in nature as a whole and in nature conservation. They have little interest in exploiting nature or animals.

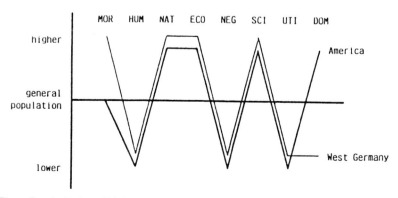

Figure 3:   Attitudes of birdwatchers in West Germany and the USA, in comparison with the attitudes of the general population.

CONCLUSION

Since people have a special affection for birds, birds can help in environmental education by leading people to nature and promoting a better understanding of nature. Thus birds are important representatives of nature as a whole. And the more people understand nature, the easier it is to develop greater awareness and support for nature conservation.

The popularity of birds should be capitalized upon to disseminate the ideas of nature conservation among the general public and to demonstrate the increasing destruction of nature. In schools one should use birdwatching more extensively, and use birds as a channel for explaining general principles of ecology. Pupils reach a better understanding of ecology and nature from birdwatching than from textbooks.

Likewise, birds could serve as symbols for campaigns against the destruction of nature. If you explain to the general public that, for example, seabirds are threatened by the pollution of the sea, it is easier for them to understand this than general statements about the threat to marine systems. Most people understand ecological and environmental problems more easily if the problems are explained by the example of birds. One should therefore use the popularity of birds embodied in the general public to call on them to struggle against the destruction of nature.

REFERENCES

BRANDSTÄTTER, H. 1983. Sozialpsychologie. Kohlhammer; Stuttgart – Berlin – Köln – Mainz.

CAMPBELL, F. L. 1979. The edge effect: Life in the ecotone. Presented by Second Conference on Scientific Research in the National Parks. San Francisco.

KELLERT, S. R. 1980a. *Knowledge, Affection and Basic Attitudes Toward Animals in American Society.* Fish and Wildl. Service, Washington D.C.

KELLERT, S. R. 1980b. Contemporary Values of Wildlife in American Society. *In:* Shaw, William W. & Zube, Erwin H. (ed.): *Wildlife Values.* Center for Assessment of Noncommodity Natural Resource Values. Institutional Series Report No. 1, Arizona.

KELLERT, S. R. 1985. Birdwatching in American Society. *Leisure Sciences,* **Vol. 7, No. 3,** 343–60.

KELLERT, S. R. & BROWN, P. J. 1985. Human Dimensions Information in Wildlife Management, Policy and Planning. *Leisure Sciences,* **Vol. 7, No. 3,** 269–80.

LANGENAU, E. E. 1984. Utility of Socio-Economic Research in Wildlife Management. *Trans. N. Amer. Wildl. and Nature. Resourc. Conf.* **43,** 43–53.

ROSENBERG, M. J. & HOWLAND, M. J. (ed.) 1960. *Attitude organisation and change.* Yale Univ. Press, New Haven, Conn.

SCHULZ, W. 1985. Einstellung zur Natur—eine empirische Untersuchung. Dissertation, University of Munich.

SCHULZ, W. 1986. Attitudes toward wildlife in West Germany. *Human Dimensions in Wildlife Newsletter* 5(3). 1–13.

SHERIF, M. & CANTRIL, H. 1945. The psychology of attitudes: I. *Psychological Revues,* **52,** 295–319.

ICBP Technical Publication No. 6, 1987

ECONOMICS AND MARKETING OF 'CANADA'S CAPISTRANO'

WILLIAM R. CLARK

206 Alfred St., Pembroke, Ontario, Canada K8A 3A3

ABSTRACT

The practical significance of economic concepts and methods to bird conservation is demonstrated using the Pembroke, Ontario, swallow roost as a case study. This mass flocking spectacle of over 100,000 birds has attracted national attention and draws up to 10,000 visitors each year.

A detailed benefit-cost analysis is given of the decision to create a sanctuary to protect the roosting habitat, featuring the Travel Cost Method for quantifying so-called 'intangible' social benefits. Two advantages of the techniques employed are the ready availability of most of the data required, and the relative simplicity of the methodology. The present net social worth of the site is conservatively estimated at $520,000; benefits outweigh costs by nearly four to one.

The overnight celebrity of this once-unknown avian wonder, and its subsequent evolution into a precious socio-economic asset and educational venue, are the direct result of an aggressive marketing campaign begun in 1983 to save the habitat from imminent destruction. A brief overview of this economics-based conservation strategy and the apparent reasons for its success are presented.

INTRODUCTION

The general aim of this paper is to demonstrate the relevance and practical importance of economics and marketing to bird conservation. A Canadian case study is employed: (a) to show how economics and marketing have been used strategically to achieve conservation goals; (b) to exhibit how marketing techniques have helped to generate economic demand (and hence value) for a bird resource where before there was no evidence of value; (c) to demonstrate the methodology of benefit-cost analysis for measuring the contribution of a project to social welfare; and, in the process, (d) to illustrate the Travel Cost Method for valuing unpriced benefits.

Conservation is fundamentally an economic concept because it concerns the allocation of scarce natural resources among competing human demands. Public resource allocation decisions, like all decisions, involve a choice among alternative courses of action or outcomes; the best option is normally that which maximizes public welfare based on the values of the resource inputs (i.e. costs) relative to outputs (i.e. benefits). Since all decisions imply that a relative valuation is made, the only question is whether: (a) the valuation is done as explicitly, systematically, quantitatively (and thus defensibly) as possible, or (b) whether the

Figure 1:   A wave of swallows leaves the Pembroke roost (right) at about 6 a.m.

decision-maker relies (and is allowed to rely) solely on his own judgement to weigh alternatives. The case study in Pembroke, presented below, exemplifies the former approach to conservation decision-making.

Pembroke, Ontario (Lat. 45.8°N, Long. 77.1°W; population 14,000) is located on the Ottawa River 150km northwest of Ottawa, the capital of Canada. For about four weeks each summer, starting in late July, enormous numbers of swallows gather to roost in a relatively tiny (0.23ha) grove of predominantly Crack Willow (*Salix fragilis*) covering Swallow Island on the downtown water-front. The highest reliable count to date is 150,000 birds in August 1984. In addition, the birds perform spectacular aerial displays at dawn and dusk as they enter and exit their dormitory *en masse* (*Figure 1*). Using the perceived but untested tourism potential of this spectacle as a chief justification, a proposal was made in 1983 to rescue the site from looming commercial development. In the comparatively short time since then, driven by intensive marketing efforts, the attendance has grown to nearly 10,000 people per year.

Rare and endangered species tend to dominate the agenda of wildlife conser-vationists; swallows, by contrast, are among the world's most abundant and wide-ranging birds. Why, then, the attention on the Pembroke swallow roost? Scientifically, this pre-migratory roost is notable for its large population, mixed species composition (see Appendix A), annual site fidelity, and long period of occupation, but perhaps more for the potential it has to add to our scant knowledge of communal roosting in swallows and our understanding of bird coloniality generally. Of greater immediate importance, however, is its educational value. How better to school large numbers of the general public in the need for conservation than by using this prominent natural spectacle of commonplace birds as an example. How better to strengthen the teachings than to *prove* the value of conservation to society—thus the present challenge.

The paper describes the applicable concepts and methods of benefit-cost analysis in logical sequence, in a practical context, and often in considerable detail. Nevertheless, the reader will doubtless have to consult the literature cited or to engage the help of an economist to actually apply the methods. Footnotes are used so as not to derail the reader in providing fine explanatory points. Thus exposed to the 'dismal science', the reader will perhaps come to appreciate not only the scope and general utility of economics as it pertains to wildlife conservation, but to realize that the perceived 'net value to society' is *always* the criterion by which conservation policies are ultimately judged.

THE CONSERVATION CAMPAIGN

The Pembroke swallow roost was known only to a few naturalists until 1983 when the true size and significance of the phenomenon was first established. The timing was fortunate because plans for a $50-million development in the same area suddenly emerged. To counter this threat, a detailed presentation was made to the City's Economic Development Committee on 2 August 1983 (Clark 1983). This proposal offered fame for the Pembroke swallows and socio-economic gain and prestige for the City—like that of San Juan Capistrano, California[1]—if the roost were promoted as a tourist attraction. A separate section explicitly addressed the expected costs and benefits. This was the first expression of an evolving strategy shaped by economic principles to win long-term protection and scientific management for the site.

Both the City and the mass media seized on the idea. The swallows achieved celebrity status locally overnight; national acclaim soon followed. Local business and education groups were targeted early for their formal support, in keeping with the emphasis on direct socio-economic benefits. Numerous conservation and other groups were likewise petitioned successfully.

Broadening support from the community as a whole, and the media, followed naturally. The City adopted the swallow as its unofficial logo, to appear on promotional literature. Local businessmen enticed travellers to 'Follow the Swallow' downtown year-round by erecting bright yellow highway signs. Organized tours for naturalists were led. A new bird club was fledged, and in 1984 began hosting an annual festival. Meanwhile a stream of technical and popular articles began to appear, helping to give the attraction added exposure and credibility. Further details are found in Clark (1984, 1986).

METHOD

Benefit-cost analysis
A benefit-cost analysis (BCA), according to Sassone & Schaffer (1978, p. 3) is 'an estimation and evaluation of net benefits associated with alternatives for achieving defined public goals'. A complete analysis, they expand (p. 132), should include '*all* costs and *all* benefits' of a public undertaking. In practice, however, arbitrary distinctions are commonly made among (a) *economic impacts* (i.e. '. . .

effects on the "national economic development" objective'), (b) *social impacts* (i.e. '. . . effects on the distribution of income as well as on the psychological, social, and physical well-being of individuals affected . . .'), and (c) *environmental impacts* (i.e. effects on '. . . our physical and biological surroundings as they are perceived to effect [*sic*] the quality of life'). 'In the end . . . the economic or environmental consequences of a [government undertaking] are ultimately interpreted by their effects on social well-being. The term *social cost-benefit analysis*, . . . abbreviated to *cost-benefit analysis,* properly focuses our interests.'

In essence BCA involves little more than adding up all the benefits expected from an undertaking, adding up all the costs, and finding the difference. This process is repeated for each option. (In the present example only one option is analysed.) The need to express all data values at a single point in time for the sake of comparison (normally the present) complicates the arithmetic but does not alter the basic idea. The option having the maximum net benefits is theoretically the best, other things being equal. In these respects BCA is identical to *present net worth* analysis used to evaluate private business investments. The main difference is the broader scope of a public investment analysis, which must necessarily go far beyond just the monetary costs and revenues that enter internal corporate accounts.

The benefits of public undertakings such as conservation projects often tend to be 'intangible', with unreliable prices or, more commonly, no price at all. For this reason BCA is fraught with practical problems relating to the definition, and especially the measurement, of benefits. Costs frequently pose a problem, too. Consequently a broad variety of indirect methods for calculating a monetary equivalent have been devised. The Travel Cost Method, employed here, is a method for estimating benefits.

The following paragraphs give context to the present benefit-cost analysis. Swallow Island is the property of the Crown and thus the people of Ontario. Custody and management are delegated to the elected Minister of Natural Resources. The decision-maker, for purposes of this paper, is both the Minister (or *his* delegate) and the Council for the City of Pembroke (since it must decide the appropriate land use). The proposition is whether to manage this property as a natural area and promote it as a tourist attraction, or to sell it to a developer for commercial use. We shall assume that the decision is being made today and that, for mathematical simplicity, the project has an infinite life span. **The criterion on which the decision rests is to maximize the present value of net social benefits, which equals the net benefit to consumers (i.e. the consumers' surplus) minus the costs of providing the site.**

In general, the future value-data enter the analysis expressed in constant 1986$, then are discounted at an annual inflation-free rate of five percent[2] to obtain their relative worth today (i.e. *present value*)[3]. The following assumptions are also made. On the benefit side, no transition period for attendance is provided for during the first three years, as actually happened. Instead, attendance is held constant from the start at 7000 visits per year, which is 16 percent below the third-year (1985) level of 8333. On the cost side, the amount of resources used is based on the experience during the first three years and is assumed to remain constant over time. Prices are mainly from the literature and are inflated to 1986$ if necessary using the Consumer Price Index (Statistics Canada 1986a).

All data are from secondary sources, collected by the author after-the-fact. Supporting assumptions are based either on information applicable elsewhere if available, or on the author's personal experience (as a professional economist as well as a conservationist). Despite these unavoidable shortcomings, the estimates presented herein are adequate for demonstrating the methods and are thought to portray accurately the orders of magnitude. The final estimate of the total net social benefits is probably conservative.

Benefits
Travel cost method. The Travel Cost Method (TCM) (Sinden & Worrell 1979, p. 364) is a technique for evaluating unpriced social *benefits*. It is based on the premise that the willingness of visitors to pay for the experience (here, of seeing the Pembroke swallows) may be inferred from their evident willingness to incur trip-related expenses. A summary of the key steps in applying the method is presented in *Table 1*. Some important theoretical points, prerequisite for the following discussion, are treated in Appendix B.

The TCM begins with the grouping of attendance data into geographic zones of origin of successively increasing distance from the attraction. The number of visits by zone is then expressed per 1000 inhabitants to eliminate the distortion caused by unequal zonal populations. (The visit, rather than the visitor, is the unit of analysis because people often visit repeatedly.)

For each zone the average travel cost is calculated. Eligible costs may include anything that is expressly for the purpose of the trip whether for travel *per se* or not. In the case of multi-destination trips some rational means of apportioning the expenses must be used. Equally important, only that fraction which is extra or *marginal* to everyday living expenses, and which therefore governs the decision to travel, is eligible (Sinden & Worrell 1979, p. 368).

Knowing the implicit price (i.e. the average cost per visit) and the corresponding quantity of visits gives us one point on the demand curve for each zone. Plotting the zone-average points on the same axes defines the *composite* demand curve.

To calculate net benefits we may first decompose this curve into its zonal constituents, then calculate the consumers' surplus separately for each zone in the same way described for the conceptual model in Appendix B (i.e. as the area below the demand curve and above the horizontal price line). The demand curve for each zone is assumed to be identical to the composite curve determined above (a property peculiar to the Travel Cost Method). To restore the true scale we

Table 1:   Key steps in applying the Travel Cost Method.

1. Collect data on the number of visits, by place of origin.
2. Group these visitor data into convenient zones (e.g. counties, metropolitan areas) of progressively increasing distance from the site.
3. Collect data on the population of each zone. To eliminate the effect of different zone populations, express the number of visits (1) per 1000 population.
4. For each zone, calculate the average cost of a visit to the site, including only those costs that are (a) above and beyond any costs that would have been incurred anyway (i.e. the marginal or additional costs), and (b) that are solely associated with the trip to the site itself and not some secondary destination too (in which case an adjustment is needed). Vehicle-related expenses, and the costs of travel time, accommodation, food, and site entry are examples of eligible expenses.
5. For each zone, on the same axes, plot the number of visits per 1000 population (3) against the average cost per visit (4), then fit a curve to these points.
6. For each zone, using the above curve (5) interpolate the total attendance that would result for each of a series of progressively higher hypothetical entrance fees. For each new extra fee (e.g. $5, $10, $15, etc.), sum the predicted total attendance from all zones. The result is a series of x/y coordinates, where y is the extra fee and x is the total predicted attendance resulting from that hypothetical price increase.
7. Plot this set of points (6), fit a curve, and calculate the total area under this (demand) curve. The result is the total net benefit of the site to visitors (i.e. the consumers' surplus), or the gross benefits of the site to society.
8. The *cost* to society of providing the site must be determined by separate methods and then subtracted from (7) to provide the desired final estimate of net social benefits.

multiply the resulting estimate of zonal surplus by the population for that zone expressed in thousands. The total net benefit to consumers of the Pembroke swallow roost is the sum of these zonal surpluses.

Alternatively, as is done here, we take the analysis one step further. For each of a series of progressively higher hypothetical entrance fees, we interpolate from the composite demand curve the corresponding attendance in each zone. This process continues until any higher fee will produce zero visits from any zone. The result is a schedule revealing the quantity of visits corresponding to these extra costs (i.e. admission fees) to which a 'second stage demand curve' (Dwyer *et al.* 1977) is fitted. This time the *total* area under the curve represents, as above, the consumers' surplus or the total net benefits to consumers. (The entire area equals the consumers' surplus because the hypothetical fees, by definition, are in addition to what visitors already pay.)

This new estimate is theoretically identical to the amount calculated using the composite curve (Rosenthal *et al.* 1984, p. 2). In practice it is somewhat higher, as noted by Sinden & Worrell (1979, p. 370). The advantages of generating a second demand curve are twofold. First, the curve itself is more readily interpreted because zones are no longer distinguished. Second, the impact of proposed admission fees can be directly observed by site planners.

The Travel Cost Method is site-specific and thus well suited for use with the Pembroke swallow roost. In addition, this unique sanctuary tends to be the main destination of visitors. This fact minimizes the problem of allocating costs among the different destinations in the case of multi-purpose trips, which is always a somewhat arbitrary procedure.

For further detail and criticism of the TCM the reader is referred to Clawson (1959); Clawson & Knetsch (1966, Chapters 4–5); Coomber & Biswas (1973, pp. 12–18, 23–26); Langford & Cocheba (1978, pp. 14–16); Sinden & Worrell (1979, pp. 364–74) and Rosenthal *et al.* (1984). A succinct description of recent developments is contained in Sinden & Worrell (pp. 372–4). Rosenthal *et al.* (1986) have developed software to solve a Travel Cost model automatically.

Travel cost data.   The total travel costs are a function of attendance. Estimates of total attendance in 1985 and the breakdown by zone of origin for a sample of these visitors were obtained from the City of Pembroke. These data were collected and summarized by the Pembroke and Area Bird Club, who maintained a guest book for visitors to sign voluntarily. The resulting non-random samples amounted to 19 percent (1583) of the total attendance count of 8333. For present purposes the unregistered visitors were distributed among seven zones of origin; three-quarters are assumed to have been local (i.e. zones 1 and 2). Zones 5, 6 and 7 were then dropped, leaving the reduced estimate of 7000 total visits for projections in this analysis[4]. To adjust the number of visits from these zones of unequal population to a common base (i.e. visits per 1000 population), census data from Statistics Canada (1985, 1986b) were used.

Estimating the average round-trip distances from each zone required road maps and local experience to decide probable routes. The average driving time was calculated by using an assumed speed. The total time requirement is the sum of driving time and time spent on-site (1.0h).

These data enable the following four categories of trip-related expenses to be estimated: (1) vehicle, (2) time, (3) accommodation, and (4) food. The total cost per vehicle is equal to the distance travelled times the average cost per kilometre for gas, oil and wear-and-tear. The conversion factor, $0.09/km, is the rate at which the Canadian Government reimburses employees in Ontario who elect to use their own car for business travelling. The product is distributed equally among all members of the party to yield the vehicle cost per visit. The party size of 1.71 used for this purpose is from a 1982 study of Ontario visitors to eastern Ontario—an average of overnight (1.75) and day (1.67) visitors (OMTR 1985b). 'Time is money', Benjamin Franklin once astutely observed. The cost of time spent travelling is equal to its value in the next most desirable activity, that is, its *opportunity cost*. How to establish what that activity might be, and its value, is, however, a subject of considerable and unresolved academic debate (e.g. Chase 1968, pp. 9–14). The method used here is suggested by the US Water Resources Council (1979, p. 72958) for evaluating water project recreation benefits, and is based on observed trade-offs between leisure time and money. According to this authority, leisure time should be valued at one-third the average wage rate in the zone of origin for adults and one-twelfth for children. Here 75 percent of the visits are assumed to have been made by adults, the rest by children; the wage rate used is an average for all employees in the Province of Ontario, obtained from Statistics Canada. The weighted average value of leisure time (undistinguished by zone) is therefore estimated at $3.00 per hour. (For comparison, Cable *et al.* (1984) used values of nil and $5.00 per hour for travel time in their study of visitors to a nearby forest interpretive facility.) The total cost of time for each zone is the product of the above rate and the number of hours devoted to the average visit.

The cost of accommodation obviously applies only to overnight stays, so in this case only the more distant zones are affected. Of visitors originating from zones 3 and 4, it is assumed that only 25 percent pay for accommodation while in Pembroke. The total cost is the product of this reduced number of visitors and the weighted-average, high-season price of a two-person motel room in Pembroke, $53.38, or $26.69 per person (OMTR 1985a). The two-person rate was used because it is closest to the average party size of 1.71.

Food costs were included only for visitors from outside Pembroke (i.e. zones 2, 3 and 4). All meals are assumed to be eaten at restaurants and to cost $20 per person per day. Assuming three meals per day and deducting the assumed average *per diem* cost of home-cooked meals of $10, the extra cost of food is therefore $3.33 per meal. The number of meals eaten is in direct proportion to the time spent travelling, which differs by zone. The total cost of food is again price times quantity.

Costs

The decision by City Council to spare the roost area from development involved no outlay of cash initially. Nevertheless, alternative land use opportunities *were* sacrificed and soon even some capital was required to cope with the swallows' soaring popularity.

The components of this investment in conservation, as in any other, fall into three broad categories—land, capital and labour—corresponding to the physical resources required to produce a commodity or service. In each case the applicable cost is that which is incurred by not employing these resources in their next best use (i.e. the *opportunity cost*).

Two kinds of land costs are germane, both related to income foregone by not selling the property to commercial interests and both, therefore, related to the value of the property. One is the sale revenue foregone; the other, property tax foregone. Swallow Island is unattractive as a building site because it is inundated for prolonged periods during the annual spring freshet. On the other hand, it could hardly be more centrally located. The Island is also new land, formed since 1950 at the Muskrat River mouth, so there are no past transactions to serve as a guide to value. The approach used here to estimate the property value was to extrapolate the value of a bare-land waterfront property located about 1km to the

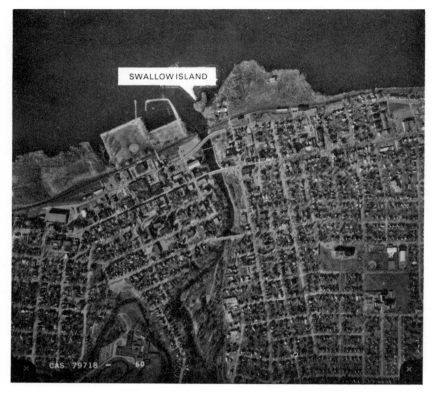

Figure 2:   Location of the Pembroke swallow roost. (Date 31.10.79).

west that was assessed for the City in 1985. A 50-percent downward adjustment for development constraints was recommended by the Renfrew County Assessment Office. The market value of Swallow Island, thus calculated, is $7400.

The property tax foregone is a function of the value of the land as assessed for commercial purposes. In Pembroke, this tax is applied at the rate of $320 per $1000 of assessed commercial value, which in turn is 10 percent of the above market value.

Although plans to upgrade the waterfront generally were already afoot, the discovery of a new attraction was opportune, for it added impetus to this process. Capital improvements, including paving of the large parking area, new lighting, washrooms, sewers, fencing, and landscaping, were undertaken in the immediate vicinity of the viewing area (the marina breakwater, *Figure 2*). For present purposes one-tenth of the $234,000 cost of contracts (1986$) was attributed to the swallows, based partly on the assumed contribution of swallow-watchers to the approximate overall attendance in the area, and partly on the seeming importance of the attraction. The annual cost of this capital investment is the equivalent monetary benefit lost by not using that money for some other public purpose, here set at five percent annually after inflation.

By far the major investment has been and probably will continue to be in the

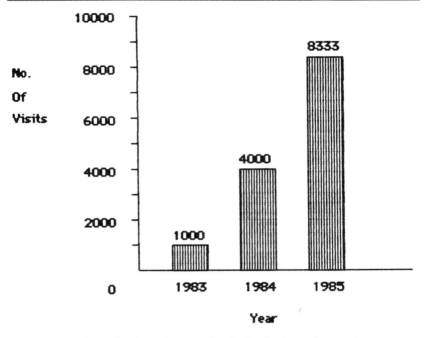

Figure 3:   Attendance trend at the Pembroke swallow roost.

form of volunteer labour for research, planning, management, marketing and associated tasks. The equivalent cost of this time is the value of leisure opportunities foregone. The valuation method is identical to that used for visitors' travel time, except that this opportunity cost is based on the adult rate only, \$3.67/hr. The annual labour requirement is assumed to be one person-year, a blended average of the heavy start-up workload and the anticipated long-term requirement.

RESULTS

The conservation campaign
On 16 August 1983, just two weeks after the proposal was made to them, Pembroke City Council unanimously moved to take steps to protect the site. In May 1984 Swallow Island and the adjacent shoreline buffer area were re-zoned from 'Development' to 'Park and Open Space'. In April 1986, the Swallow Roost Advisory Committee[5] formally recommended that a national Migratory Bird Sanctuary be established. That recommendation, which enjoys the support both of the concerned politicians and of senior officers of the Canadian Wildlife Service (who bear ultimate responsibility for making the official designation), only requires the approval of the Province, which owns the site.

Attendance rose sharply between 1983, when the initial excitement attracted about 1000 people, and 1985, when 8333 visitors were counted (*Figure 3*). Preliminary 1986 results indicate that attendance would be high again.

Table 2: Number of visits to the Pembroke swallow roost by zone of origin, 1985.

Zone	Place of origin	Base population in 1985[a]	Visits			Average round-trip distance	Estimated total travel and on-site time[d]
			Estimated total[c]	Per 1,000 population			
		No.	No.	No.		km	hr.
1	Pembroke, Ontario	14,026[b]	2,800	200		10	1.3[e]
2	Other Renfrew Co., Ontario	76,874	2,700	35		100	2.2[f]
3	Ottawa, Ontario	592,200	600	1		300	4.8[f]
4	Other Ontario	8,383,100	900	0.1		600	8.5[f]
	TOTAL	9,066,200	7,000				

Notes: (a) Source: Statistics Canada. 1986b.
(b) Source: Statistics Canada. 1985.
(c) Basis: Unpublished guest registry data (Pembroke and Area Bird Club; City of Pembroke). Unregistered visitors (81% of total) allocated as follows: approximately 75% split between zones 1 and 2; approximately 25% evenly split among zones 3 to 7 (zones 5, 6 and 7 are not shown).
(d) Includes 1 hour on-site.
(e) Assumes average speed of 30km/hr.
(f) Assumes average speed of 80km/hr.

Benefit-cost analysis

The following paragraphs relate directly to the steps summarized in *Table 1*.
Steps 1 to 3. *Table 2* shows the breakdown of 1985 attendance by zone of visitor origin. The usable fraction of total attendance is 84 percent, or an estimated 7000 visits. This is distributed among four zones: Pembroke itself, 40 percent; Other Renfrew County, 39 percent; Ottawa, 9 percent; and Other Ontario, 13 percent. Also shown for each zone is the population, the average round-trip distance, and the estimated time requirement.

Step 4. *Table 3* documents the itemized travel costs for two separate models for each zone. **Model A** assumes that the swallow roost is the main destination of every visitor, and that therefore all eligible costs may be used as an indication of willingness to pay. A more realistic scenario is **Model B** which is used throughout the analysis hereafter. This model recognizes that the farthest travellers (i.e. zones 3 and 4) will often have other destinations in addition to the swallow roost. Half of the travel costs from these two zones have been disallowed for this reason. Other Renfrew County (zone 2) and Other Ontario (zone 4) visitors account for nearly three-quarters of these expenditures. Vehicle costs account for 38 percent, time for 48 percent, accommodation for 5 percent, and food for 8 percent.

Table 3: Estimated expenditures by visitors to the Pembroke swallow roost in 1985, by expense category and zone.

Zone	Vehicle[a]	Time[b]	Accom.[c]	Food[d]	Total cost per visit	Total visitor expend.[e]
			—1986$[f]—			
(A) Main-destination basis (**Model A**):						
1	0.53	3.90	—	—	4.43	12,404
2	5.26	6.60	—	1.67$8^1$	13.53	36,531
3	15.79	14.40	6.67	3.33$8^2$	40.19	24,114
4	31.58	25.50	6.67	5.00$8^3$	68.75	61,875
TOTAL						134,924
(B) Multiple-destination basis (**Model B**):[h]						
1	0.53	3.90	—	—	4.43	12,404
2	5.26	6.60	—	1.67$8^1$	13.53	36,531
3	7.90	7.20	3.34	1.66$8^2$	20.10	12,060
4	15.79	12.75	3.34	2.50$8^3$	34.38	30.942
TOTAL						91,937

Notes: (a) Assumes average party size of *1.71* [after OMTR 1985b: 5,7] and average mileage cost of *$0.09/km* [Government of Canada reimbursement rate].

(b) The value of leisure time used here is approximately one-third the average wage rate in the case of adults, and one-twelfth for children (US Water Resources Council 1979, p. 72958). Here the weighted mean estimate of *$3.00/hr.* (assuming 75% adults, 25% children) is based on average earnings for Ontario workers of $440/wk. (Statistics Canada, unpublished data, adjusted for inflation) and an assumed 40-hr. work week.

(c) Assumes motel accommodation based on a weighted, average, two-people-per-room price of $26.69/person/night [after OMTR 1985a: 115], for assumed 25% of visits from zones 3 and 4 only, averaging *$6.67/visit*.

(d) Assumes restaurant meals @ $20/day/person compared to $10/day for meals at home, for an extra daily cost of $10, or *$3.33/meal*; but only for assumed 50% of visits from zones 2, 3 and 4 only, averaging *$1.67/meal/visit*.

(e) Equals total cost per visit × total no. of visits (from *Table 2*).

(f) Basis for adjustment to current dollars is the Consumer Price Index [Statistics Canada. 1986a].

(g) The total number of meals eaten per visit is: $g^1 = 1$, $g^2 = 2$, $g^3 = 3$.

(h) For zones 3 and 4, 50% of all eligible costs are allocated to other purpose(s) (e.g. visiting relatives).

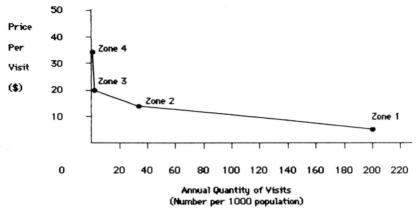

Figure 4:   Composite demand curve for the Pembroke swallow roost (basis: Model B).

Steps 5 and 6.   *Figure 4* is the composite demand curve for the Pembroke swallow roost (fitted as a series of straight lines for simplicity), illustrating the response of visitors (*Table 2*) to different prices (*Table 3*). From this behavioural model we can test the response to hypothetical entrance fees and thereby obtain a more direct estimate of the value of the attraction. The results of this test are found in *Table 4.*

Step 7.   *Figure 5,* the second stage demand curve, shows the relationship between the hypothetical extra costs and the predicted attendance based on *Table 4.* The curve conforms to expectations: at low price levels the number of visits changes greatly with a relatively small change in price; more importantly, at high price levels the number of visits drops off very slowly, showing that the roost is capable of drawing people from long distances. The net benefit to consumers (i.e. the *gross* social benefit) is the area under this demand curve, here determined graphically, and equals $35,400 per year, or $5.06 per visit.

The main result of effective advertising is to shift the demand curve for a commodity or service to the right, which increases the area beneath it and therefore the total benefits. Here the heavy promotion has not only moved the demand curve for visits to the right—it has created demand where none previously existed.

Table 4:   Predicted annual attendance at the Pembroke swallow roost resulting from hypothetical price increases, by zone of origin[a,b].

Zone	$0	$5	$10	$15	$30
1	2,800	1,540	420	70	0
2	2,700	769	62	31	
3	600	415	178	0	
4	900	0			
TOTAL	7,000	2,724	660	101	0

Notes: (a) Basis: Model B.
    (b) By interpolation of *Figure 4,* expanded by the population for each zone.

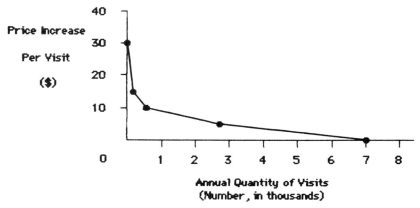

Figure 5:   Second-stage demand curve for the Pembroke swallow roost (basis: Model B).

Figure 5 also allows us to predict easily how much cash revenue could be raised by actually imposing an admission fee, and how many visits would be sacrificed. For example, a heavy $5.00 fee would cut attendance to approximately 2700 annually but would yield $24,300 in revenue. This income is equivalent to a one-time income of almost $500,000. (Coincidentally, estimated costs as high as six figures are being cited for a possible dike to protect Swallow Island from serious erosion and ice damage.)

Step 8.   The *costs* of providing the attraction are summarized in *Table 5*.

Table 5:   Estimated annual costs of providing the Pembroke swallows attraction.

Category	Total cost[a,b]	Cost per visit[c]
		—1986$—
Land[d]	600	0.08
Sale revenue foregone[e]	370	0.05
Property tax revenue foregone[f]	240	0.03
Capital improvements[g]	1,200	0.17
Labour[h]	7,600	1.09
TOTAL	$9,400	$1.34

Notes: (a) Figures may not add due to rounding.
    (b) Annualization of lump sums uses a discount rate after inflation of 5 percent.
    (c) Annual attendance is assumed to be constant at 7000 visits/yr.
    (d) Assumes market value of $7400 for the 0.23-ha site, based on a recent waterfront-area assessment (County of Renfrew Assessment Office; City of Pembroke Clerk's Office).
    (e) Annual equivalent of the land value.
    (f) Assumes municipal property tax @ $320 per $1000 of assessed land value (i.e. commercial mill rate). The assessed land value, in turn, is about 10 percent of the market value (note d), or $740 (County of Renfrew Assessment Office).
    (g) Based on a 10-percent share of recent adjacent waterfront improvements, or $23,400 (City of Pembroke Community Services Department).
    (h) Cost of foregone leisure opportunities for adult volunteer labourers @ $3.67/hr. (*Table 3*, note b).

Table 6:   Net social benefit of the Pembroke swallows attraction.

Criterion	Total monetary equivalent	Monetary equivalent per visit
	—1986$—	
A. *Annual* net benefits to visitors[a]	35,400	5.06
B. *Annual* costs to society of providing the attraction[b]	9,400	1.34
C. **Annual net social benefit** (A–B)	**26,000**	**3.72**
D. **Net social benefit expressed as a lump sum**[c] (C/0.05)	**520,000**	**74.50**
E. **Benefit-Cost Ratio** (A/B)	**3.8:1**	**3.8:1**

Notes: (a) The amount which visitors are implicitly willing to pay above and beyond that needed to cover travel expenses, as evidenced by a Travel Cost model of demand. This amount is the consumers' surplus benefit. Estimated from *Figure 5*.

      (b) Comprised of land, labour and capital costs (*Table 5*). The opportunity cost of volunteer labour accounts for more than three-quarters.

      (c) This criterion is equivalent to Present Net Worth that is used in the private sector. A discount rate after inflation of 5 percent is assumed.

Volunteer labour accounts for $1.09 of the total annual cost of $1.34 per visit, or 81 percent. Capital improvements account for $0.17, and the cost of land for only $0.08. The total investment is $9400 per year.

In summary, the yearly net social benefit of the Pembroke swallow roost is approximately $26,000 or $3.72 per visit (*Table 6*). The value of this annual stream of net benefits expressed as a lump sum today is $520,000. Benefits outweigh costs by a margin of 3.8 to 1.

DISCUSSION

The economics-based strategy adopted to win protection for the swallows seems to have worked well, judging by the benefit-cost results and other indicators. To understand why, and therefore where the approach might be applied successfully again, we must place the matter in context.

In 1983 there was little outward evidence to suggest that an appeal simply to save 'mere swallows' would succeed. Wildlife conservation issues were seldom high on the public agenda except for activities undertaken in support of hunting and fishing, the predominant outdoor pastimes. Neither were there any prominent naturalist organizations based within 150km. On the other hand the Pembroke City fathers were always alert for opportunities—like a new attraction, for instance—to improve the general welfare of their constituents and to enhance the stature of this important but somewhat remote regional centre.

The swallow roost, it appeared, would make an excellent tourist attraction. It is a very unusual natural phenomenon, truly spectacular when beheld close-up, which has since proved its appeal for people of all ages and backgrounds. The immense size alone is impressive. Fortunately the show is also dependable and never exactly the same from day to day. There are even some other fascinating natural features of the site too, such as Merlins (*Falco columbarius*) hunting swallows, and Great Blue Herons (*Ardea herodias*) fishing in an adjacent marsh.

The timing and location of the attraction, by good fortune, are also nearly ideal.

Not only does the spectacle occur through much of the prime tourist season, but the fact that it happens late in the day means that many non-local visitors would have to stay over in commercial establishments. On a hot summer evening, with the sun setting over the Laurentian Highlands in Québec and the prevailing Westerlies blowing gently in across the Ottawa River, there are few more relaxing places in the area. The viewing location is central, easy to get to, and close to the birds—but not too close, for the Muskrat River forms a moat that protects the roost from undue disturbance.

In retrospect it is not hard to imagine why the promise of 'Canada's Capistrano' must have seemed so seductive. Though the ensuing publicity quickly aroused a passion for birds within the general populace, the birds themselves have sustained that attention.

SUMMARY AND CONCLUSIONS

1. The decision in 1983 to protect the Pembroke swallow roost was clearly in the best interests of society, with the direct benefits shared by up to 10,000 people annually. The present net worth in recreational use of this social asset, based on consumers' surplus and expressed as a monetary equivalent, is $520,000. The benefit-cost ratio is 3.8 to 1.

2. The economics-based conservation strategy employed here may be applied elsewhere provided: (a) the candidate habitat has distinctive and enduring qualities and is not overly sensitive to disturbance, (b) the necessary resources, especially labour, are available to invest, and (c) the decision-maker is rational.

3. Benefit-cost analysis provides a logical, coherent structure within which environmental, economic and social objectives can be explicitly integrated into the decision process. Measurement problems, especially of benefits, will always present a challenge.

4. The Travel Cost Method is a relatively simple and effective way to estimate demand for, and evaluate the benefits of, bird conservation in particular site-specific situations.

5. Decisions about the allocation of public resources to various candidate uses are ultimately based on the relative net value of each use. Socio-economic considerations should therefore be a main and explicit focus of attention in bird conservation work, both from a conceptual and a strategic standpoint.

ACKNOWLEDGEMENTS

The photographs were taken by the author (*Figure 1*) and the Ontario Ministry of Natural Resources (*Figure 2*).

The author thanks Dr A. W. Diamond and F. L. Filion of the Canadian Wildlife Service for convening this prescient symposium; F. L. Filion and A. Jacquemot (also of the CWS), for their thorough review; S. L. Gray for proof-reading and comments; Caryl A. Clark for word processing, comments, and general support; and the people of Pembroke, Mayor A. Campbell, former Alderman S. Donaldson, the Federation of Ontario Naturalists and the many others who have contributed to the success of 'Canada's Capistrano'.

FOOTNOTES

1. Approximately 1500 Cliff Swallows nest at Mission San Juan Capistrano in Orange County, California, which was established by the Spanish in 1776. To celebrate the return of the swallows from Argentina each year—*always* on St. Joseph's Day, 19 March, according to legend but not in fact—the City of San Juan Capistrano (pop. 22,000) holds a week-long 'Fiesta de Las Golondrinas' (or Festival of Swallows). This event attracts about 5000 people each year, while in total the historic Catholic Mission hosts over 300,000 visitors. Fame has come to the swallows since 1910 with the writing of Father St John O'Sullivan, later with the national promotion of Monsignor A. J. Hutchinson, and finally in 1939 with the popular song 'When the swallows come back to Capistrano' by Leon René. Swallows, their nests and eggs are protected in the City under Federal, State and Municipal law. (*Source:* P. H. Gibson, City of San Juan Capistrano; R. F. Landy, Mission San Juan Capistrano).
2. The discount rate acts as a weighting factor, the amount depending on the rate used (here, five percent) and when the values arise. For example, a benefit of $1000 received today has a weight of 100 percent. The same benefit expected in 30 years' time is discounted, in this case to only about 23 percent of its nominal value, or $230. In short, society is not indifferent as to *when* benefits and costs occur, therefore *some* positive discount rate always applies. The five-percent rate used also compensates for the unrealistic infinite time horizon assumed here by giving little weight, as shown above, to the benefits and costs in the unpredictable distant future.
3. The general formula for 'capitalizing' a perpetual annual series of equal amounts is $Y = a/i$, where Y is the present value, a is the annual amount, and i is the rate of discount, expressed as a decimal. The annual equivalent of Y is found by rearranging the formula and solving for a. Here many of the value data are expressed as an annual amount, both as a total and on a per-visit basis.
4. The roost is presumed to be an incidental stop for visitors from the three large, distant zones, though we cannot be sure without data. Rather than risk distorting the benefits by a totally arbitrary attribution of travel expenses, therefore, these visits are ignored. The downward bias this imparts is probably minor because these zones account for only an estimated 16 percent of all visitors and, as implied above, only a small fraction of the benefits of any given trip are probably involved.
5. The SRAC was set up by the City in 1983 on the advice of the Canadian Wildlife Service to resolve issues and make recommendations related to the swallow roost. The Federal, Provincial and Municipal Governments are represented, along with a local college, two naturalist groups, a developer, and the author.

APPENDIX A

Colloquial and scientific names of swallow species (*Hirundinidae*) found at the Pembroke swallow roost.

Colloquial name	Scientific name
Purple Martin	*Progne subis*
Tree Swallow	*Tachycineta bicolor*
Northern Rough-winged Swallow	*Stelgidopteryx serripennis*
Bank Swallow (Sand Martin)	*Riparia riparia*
Cliff Swallow	*Hirundo pyrrhonota*
Barn Swallow (Common Swallow)	*Hirundo rustica*

Source: AOU (1983).

APPENDIX B

Relationship of 'consumers' surplus' and 'willingness to pay'

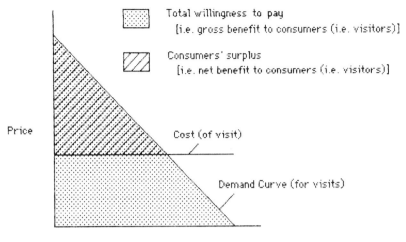

For present purposes the value of something is the amount that people are willing to exchange for it. This **willingness to pay** has two components: (1) the price actually paid, and (2) the *extra* amount one is prepared to pay. This latter amount is in effect the net benefit to the consumer, the **consumer's surplus,** and provides an indication of psychological and other unpriced personal benefits. It is also the conceptual basis for the valuation of social benefits used in this analysis.

The *monetary equivalent* of consumers' surplus can be calculated from the **demand curve** for a given commodity or service. A demand curve expresses the relationship between the price of something (y-axis) and the total quantity consumed/produced (x-axis) and is always downward sloping to the right. The total willingness to pay (i.e. the *gross* benefit to consumers) equals the total area under the demand curve; the consumers' surplus (i.e. the *net* benefit to consumers) is represented by that portion which lies above the price paid). For a broader discussion of economic demand, demand curves, and consumers' surplus, refer to Mansfield [1979, Chapters 2, 3, 4 (especially pp. 93–97), and 5 (especially pp. 129–133)].

REFERENCES

AMERICAN ORNITHOLOGISTS' UNION. 1983. *Check-list of North American birds* (6 ed.). AOU, Washington, D.C., USA. 811 pp.

CABLE, T. T., KNUDSON, D. M. & STEWART, D. J. 1984. The economic benefits to visitors of an interpretive facility. *Journal of Environmental Education* **15**, 32–7.

CHASE, S. B. 1968. Introduction and summary. Pp. 1–32 *In:* Chase, S. B. (ed.). Problems in public expenditure analysis. Proceedings of a Conference, 15–16 September 1966. Brookings Institution, Washington, D.C., USA. 270 pp.

CLARK, W. R. 1983. Pembroke, Ontario: Canada's Capistrano—Tourism and recreation possibilities for the annual summer swallow roost at the confluence of the Ottawa and Muskrat Rivers. Unpub. rep. prep. for City of Pembroke, Economic Development Committee (2 Aug.), 21 pp. + maps, append.

CLARK, W. R. 1984. Canada's Capistrano. *Nature Canada* **13**, 14–15.

CLARK, W. R. 1986. Conserving the Pembroke swallow roost. Unpub. paper presented at Annual General Meeting of the Ontario Field Ornithologists, Toronto, Canada, 26 October 1985. (Revised 26 Feb. 1986). 12 pp.

CLAWSON, M. 1959. Methods of measuring the demand for and value of outdoor recreation. Resources for the Future Inc., Washington, D.C., USA. Repr. No. 10. 36 pp.

CLAWSON, M. & KNETSCH, J. L. 1966. *Economics of outdoor recreation*. Pub. for Resources for the Future Inc. by Johns Hopkins Press, Baltimore, USA. 328 pp.

COOMBER, N. H. & BISWAS, A. K. 1973. *Evaluation of environmental intangibles*. Genera Press, Bronxville, New York, USA. 77 pp.

DWYER, J. F., KELLY, J. R. & BOWES, M. D. 1977. Improved procedures for valuation of the contribution of recreation to national economic development. Univ. of Illinois Water Resources Centre, Urbana, Ill., USA. Water Resources Center Research Rep. No. 128. 218 pp. *cited in* Rosenthal *et al.* (1984, p. 2).

LANGFORD, W. A. & COCHEBA, D. J. 1978. The wildlife valuation problem: a critical review of economic approaches. Fish. & Environ. Can., Can. Wildl. Serv., Occ. Pap. No. 37. 37 pp.

MANSFIELD, E. 1979. *Microeconomics: theory and applications* (3 ed.). W. W. Norton & Co., New York. 548 pp.

ONTARIO MINISTRY OF TOURISM AND RECREATION. 1985a. Ontario/Canada accommodations: 1985. 176 pp.

ONTARIO MINISTRY OF TOURISM AND RECREATION. 1985b. Ontario travel survey: 1982/Visitor Profile: Ontario East. Tourism Research Sect. Canada. 65 pp.

ROSENTHAL, D. H., LOOMIS, J. B. & PETERSON, G. L. 1984. The travel cost model: concepts and applications. U.S. Dep. Agric., Forest Serv., Gen. Tech. Rep. RM-109. 10 pp.

ROSENTHAL, D. H., DONNELLY, D. M., SCHIFFHAUER, M. B. & BRINK, G. E. 1986. User's guide to RMTCM: software for travel cost analysis. U.S. Dep. Agric., Forest Serv., Gen. Tech. Rep. RM-132. 32 pp.

SASSONE, P. G. & SCHAFFER, W. A. 1978. *Cost-benefit analysis: a handbook*. Academic Press, New York, USA. 182 pp.

SINDEN, J. A. & WORRELL, A. C. 1979. *Unpriced values: decisions without market prices*. John Wiley & Sons, Toronto, Canada. 511 pp.

STATISTICS CANADA. 1985. Census divisions and subdivisions: population, occupied private dwellings, private households, census families in private households—Ontario. Cat. 98–906.

STATISTICS CANADA. 1986a. Consumer price index. Cat. 62–001 (13 June).

STATISTICS CANADA. 1986b. Postcensal annual estimates of population for census divisions and census metropolitan areas: June 1, 1985. Cat. 91–211.

UNITED STATES WATER RESOURCES COUNCIL. 1979. [Procedures for evaluation of national economic development (NED) benefits and costs in water resources planning]. *Federal Register* **44**, 72950–65.

THE SOCIO-ECONOMIC SIGNIFICANCE OF WATERFOWL AMONG CANADA'S ABORIGINAL CREE: NATIVE USE AND LOCAL MANAGEMENT

COLIN H. SCOTT

Dept. of Anthropology, Leacock Building, McGill University, 850 Sherbrooke St. W., Montreal, Quebec, H3A 2T7, Canada

ABSTRACT

This paper examines the crucial role of waterfowl harvesting in the subsistence economy of the Cree of James Bay and Hudson Bay in northern Canada. Canada Geese (*Branta canadensis*) and Snow Geese (*Chen caerulescens*) account for a high percentage of the total subsistence product of Cree hunters. These and other subsistence harvests are essential to the welfare of northern native communities. But the importance of goose hunting for the Cree goes beyond the strictly economic. The migrations are seasons of intensive communal ritual and renewal. To foster a resource which is precious in their view, the Cree have evolved an effective system of local waterfowl management which aims at minimizing stress on migrating populations while obtaining optimum harvests over the long term. It is proposed that their participation in wildlife planning and management in the region is crucial to the well-being of both human society and waterfowl resources.

INTRODUCTION

Migratory waterfowl—geese, ducks and loons—are extremely important to northern Cree society, as the present examination of their subsistence economy will show. Subsistence, however, is just one dimension of the value that waterfowl and other wildlife represent to Cree. The harvest and sharing of food animals is fundamental to the maintenance of Cree social relations and symbolic life. Recognizing the importance of waterfowl to their way of life, the Cree are active stewards of this resource. Their stewardship involves sophisticated knowledge, communal management practices, and ritual reinforcement of these practices. These aspects will be discussed in later sections of the paper.

The following discussion is based primarily on anthropological field research in James Bay coastal villages, and on regional statistics from the James Bay and Northern Quebec Native Harvesting Research Committee (JBNQNHR Committee). The Committee's research arose from the aboriginal land claims agreement of the Quebec Cree and Inuit in 1975 (Anon. 1975). Its purpose was to determine current levels of subsistence harvesting by native hunters, so that guaranteed future harvests could be monitored and enforced. The JBNQNHR Committee's (1976, 1978, 1979, 1980, 1982) published results form what is probably the most detailed and comprehensive study of regional wildlife use by a native population in North America.

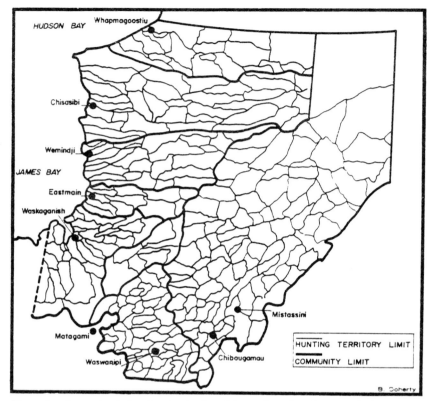

Figure 1: Approximate hunting territories of James Bay Cree hunters. (Adapted with permission from H. A. Feit 1986, 'Hunting and the Quest for Power'. In: *Native Peoples: The Canadian Experience,* R. B. Morrison & C. R. Wilson (eds.), McClelland & Stewart, Toronto.)

Eight Quebec Cree communities were surveyed, with a mean population of about 6,600 people during the 1974/5 to 1978/9 period of the study. Five of the communities are located on the east coast of James Bay and Hudson Bay, and three are at inland locations up to 400 kilometers from the coast (*Figure 1*).

THE ECONOMIC CONTRIBUTION OF WATERFOWL

Because the coastlines of James Bay and Hudson Bay are especially rich corridors for migrating geese (Thomas 1982), the five coastal communities represent some of the heaviest subsistence reliance on waterfowl on the continent. The three inland communities, whose reliance on waterfowl is not as great, though still very important, are perhaps more typical of the wider North American subarctic. Annual harvests for various species or species groups are summarized in *Table 1.*

The eight communities together harvest on average 800,000 kilograms, or 1.8 million pounds, of animal food annually.[1] Of this total, waterfowl contributes

Table 1:   Mean annual numbers of waterfowl species harvested by Quebec Cree
            communities, 1974/5 to 1978/9.

	Canada Geese	Lesser Snow Geese	Brant	Ducks	Loons
Coastal communities					
Great Whale	5,040	2,668	80	3,356	426
Fort George	29,906	5,683	4,175	13,632	1,430
Paint Hills	9,069	1,262	1,892	4,390	742
Eastmain	6,154	1,034	17	1,900	81
Rupert House	7,509	9,734	126	3,322	25
Inland communities					
Nemaska	428	152	24	768	31
Mistassini	4,458	102	25	17,250	743
Waswanipi	572	4	85	3,098	99
Total, all communities	63,136	20,639	6,424	47,716	3,577

Source: JBNQNHRC, 1982: xi.

200,000 kilograms, or nearly half a million pounds, representing about 25 percent of total wild animal food (*Tables 2* and *3*).[2] At the time of the aboriginal claims agreement, about 50 percent of Quebec Cree income consisted of bush food (in terms of the dollar equivalent of replacing it with store-bought meat, fowl and fish). The benefits of the James Bay Agreement in the late 1970's included higher cash incomes for most households, but bush food continues to account for an estimated 35 to 40 percent of total income. If one takes into account the fact that much of the new cash income is in the form of income support for hunters, over half of total income is still directly attributable to hunting, fishing and trapping activities (Scott 1984).

Per capita consumption of bush meat, fowl and fish averaged 121 kilograms or 266 pounds per year in the region (*Table 3*). For a typical household of six, the replacement value of this food would be about $6000 in 1986 dollars. The contribution of waterfowl to total consumption ranged from 29 to 44 percent in coastal communities, and from 4 to 10 percent in inland communities (*Table 4*). Especially for the coastal communities, then, the waterfowl resource is absolutely fundamental to household incomes and to community welfare.

Not only do migratory waterfowl make large contributions to the regional larder, but compared with most other game they are also very efficient to harvest in terms of yield per man-day of hunting, hunters' caloric expenditure per caloric return of food, and cash expenses involved. In the region as a whole, while spring and fall waterfowl harvesting occupied only 18 percent of annual harvesting days, the product from these activities amounted to about 25 percent of total harvested foodweight (JBNQNHR Committee 1979: 165, 1980: 120, 233; and *Table 4*).

Canada Geese (*Branta canadensis*) and Snow Geese (*Chen caerulescens*), hunted more or less concurrently during the spring and fall migrations, are highly esteemed species in coastal communities. They comprise about 30 percent of total subsistence harvests (*Table 4*). Canada Geese alone account for about 25 percent of coastal community harvests, though at the south end and on the west coast of James Bay, harvests of Snow Geese usually exceed those of Canada Geese.

Table 2: Mean annual available food from Quebec Cree harvests, 1974/5 to 1978/9
            by species and community, nearest ten pounds

	Canada Geese	Lesser Snow Geese	Brant	Ducks	Loons	All Waterfowl
Coastal communities						
Great Whale	24,630	8,000	90	5,660	1,040	39,420
Fort George	135,880	15,500	5,390	23,150	3,530	183,450
Paint Hills	31,110	3,190	1,400	7,440	1,830	45,470
Eastmain	28,320	3,400	30	3,220	170	35,140
Rupert House	35,580	41,730	100	5,630	60	83,100
Inland communities						
Nemaska	2,200	590	30	1,270	70	4,160
Mistassini	18,800	160	40	29,570	1,840	50,410
Waswanipi	2,160	10	50	5,240	220	7,680
Total, all communities	278,680	72,580	7,130	81,180	8,760	448,830

Note: Since absolute figures and percentages in this and associated tables have been rounded off on the
basis of foodweight figures expressed in pounds, the accuracy and internal consistency of the tables
are best served by leaving foodweight figures in pounds, as they appear in the JBNQNHR
Committee's published reports.
Source: JBNQNHRC, 1982: 227.

Table 3: Mean annual per capita foodweight available from waterfowl, and from all food
            animal species, by community, 1974/5 to 1978/9, nearest pound

	Mean community population	Per capita foodweight	
		All waterfowl	All food animals
Great Whale	373	106	338
Fort George	1,603	114	262
Paint Hills	665	68	237
Eastmain	319	110	298
Rupert House	999	83	213
All coastal communities	3,959	98	256
Nemaska	174	24	381
Mistassini	1,755	29	290
Waswanipi	760	10	235
All inland communities	2,689	23	280
All communities	6,648	68	266

Source: JBNQNHRC, 1982: 69, 230–232.

Table 4:   Mean annual available food from harvests of each species of waterfowl, as a percentage of total available from all food animal species, by community, 1974/5 to 1978/9

	Canada Geese	Lesser Snow Geese	Brant	Ducks	Loons	All Waterfowl
Coastal communities						
Great Whale	20	6	0	5	1	31%*
Fort George	32	4	1	5	1	44
Paint Hills	20	2	1	5	1	29
Eastmain	30	4	1	3	0	37
Rupert House	17	20	0	3	0	39
Inland communities						
Nemaska	3	1	0	2	0	6
Mistassini	4	0	0	6	0	10
Waswanipi	1	0	0	3	0	4
Total, all communities	16	4	1	5	1	25

Note: * Because of rounding-off, the addition of percentages given for individual species does not always exactly equal the total for all waterfowl.
Source: JBNQNHRC, 1982: 230.

Other waterfowl species make smaller but still significant contributions. In both coastal and inland communities, ducks are hunted throughout spring and fall, to some extent concurrently with geese, and they account for about five percent of total foodweight yields (slightly more than the contribution of large geese at inland communities). Brants (*Branta bernicla*) and loons (*Gaviidae*), hunted mainly in the aftermath of the migrations of the large geese, each contribute about one percent to harvests at coastal communities, and less at inland communities.

While it is revealing in a limited way to speak of hypothetical cash replacement values, in practice waterfowl and other subsistence resources are irreplaceable for the Cree, even in material terms. Most Cree people rank store-purchased items as inferior to bush food. In any case, store-purchased meat, fowl and fish substitutes are narrow in choice and very expensive in remote northern communities. The consumption of bush foods high in protein and other nutrients is fundamental to sustaining Cree community health (Feit 1978; Berkes & Farkas 1978).[3] When northern native people must incorporate more store-purchased food into their diets, starchy, canned and 'junk-food' items are the cheaper and more accessible substitutes. Community medical personnel have commented that the health problems of Cree on the land, where there is a higher proportion of bush food in diets, are significantly fewer than in settlements.[4]

THE SOCIAL ECOLOGICAL SIGNIFICANCE OF WATERFOWL

Bush food has high social value to the Cree. The killing, preparation, sharing and consumption of game is central to the seasonal renewal of social relations in Cree villages, and of a relationship to the land which is both secular and sacred in importance.

In the remainder of this paper I outline the social ecological ramifications of coastal Crees' extraordinary involvement with geese, in its various aspects. First, the development of sophisticated local knowledge about managing migratory goose populations—a body of knowledge and practice buttressed by an elaborate ritual and symbolic system which reinforces communal values and the psychology of stewardship. Second, the implications of potential competition from hunters who do not share in this system of knowledge and practice, or competition from other sources. And third, the benefits that accrue to conservation efforts when national governments recognize the interests and rights of indigenous hunters, and accommodate their local knowledge and management systems within broader strategies of wildlife preservation.

Here, I can introduce only some of the general features of communal waterfowl harvesting practice: more detailed accounts of Cree goose hunting strategies and their management implications are available elsewhere (Berkes 1977b, 1982; Scott 1983: 31–98). Extended ethnographic study of native hunting practices is required to learn the management models, systems of social control, and cultural codifications that operate in any given instance. Increasing attention is being directed to this work by both anthropologists and biologists, and evidence is accumulating that sophisticated systems of knowledge and resource management are widespread among the world's hunting societies (Nietschmann 1972; Feit 1973, 1978; Reichel-Dolmatoff 1976; Johannes 1978; Berkes 1977a, 1977b, 1982; Lewis 1982, 1985; Freeman 1985; Nakashima 1986; Norrevang 1986).

With certain sedentary species whose populations are more localized to Cree hunting territories, Cree hunting is the major variable by which population trends can be regulated. Experienced hunters are well aware of the effects of human use of wildlife resources, as well as other variables affecting population trends, and adjust their decisions about the location, mix and intensity of harvests accordingly. The eastern Cree management system for moose and beaver has been well-documented by Feit (1973, 1978) and for fish by Berkes (1977b).

In the case of waterfowl management, the regulation of populations is largely beyond the control of Cree hunters, since Cree harvests are less significant than many other variables in the population dynamics of these species. Cree are aware, via public media and discussions with biologists, that habitat erosion in more southerly areas, or harsh conditions on overwintering grounds, have adversely affected certain migratory populations along James Bay. Cree and Inuit hunters say that inclement weather at northerly nesting and rearing grounds also affects goose populations negatively—a finding supported by biologists (Boyd *et al.* 1982)—and that upswings in the fox population can contribute to low numbers of juveniles observed during fall migrations in certain years.

Kills elsewhere on the flyways are major variables influencing goose and duck populations, including mainly the harvests of US and Canadian sport hunters, but also those of other subsistence hunting native people. Of the main goose stocks present at James and Hudson Bay, Quebec Cree hunters have been estimated by Boyd (1977) to account for about 10.4 and 5.2 percent of Canada and Snow Goose kills respectively; Quebec Inuit 2.5 and 1.2 percent; other native subsistence hunters 2.4 and 8.5 percent; and sport hunters 84.7 and 85.1 percent. Other estimates (Reed 1984; Reed & Drolet 1985) indicate marginally higher utilization by northern Quebec natives of geese, with Quebec Cree accounting for 13.8 and 4.2 percent of Canada goose (mid-Atlantic stock) and Snow Goose kills respectively; Quebec Inuit 6.4 and 2.0 percent; and all other users 79.8 and 93.8 percent. The latter authors estimate that Quebec Cree and Inuit account for 21.6 and 3.3

percent of Atlantic Brant (*B.b. bernicla*) harvests respectively, while Quebec Cree and Inuit duck harvests combined are only about 3 percent, when added to sport hunting of these stocks in Canada and the US. Even for those stocks harvested relatively heavily by Cree, then, Cree kills (or indeed those of all native subsistence hunters combined) are less important to population dynamics than other factors.

But Cree hunters do make comprehensive efforts to foster the well-being of goose poulations locally, by keeping stress from human predation to a minimum, by making provision for the refuge of geese through the rotation of hunting sites, and by respecting local nesting areas. The ability of geese to learn human predation patterns and to respond socially to that learning, coupled with their inherent mobility, is a key resource management issue from the Cree hunter's standpoint. Virtually every aspect of hunting strategy is influenced in some way by the requirement to minimize the geese's awareness of human presence, and to limit disturbance caused by the act of harvesting geese *per se*.

This involves elaborate control and camouflage of human activity around sensitive goose staging areas. Ideally, only those flocks actually exposed to hunting parties' shots should have any clue of the presence of hunters. Of course, even careful hunting leads to disturbance to a significant number of fowl. It is in controlling the extent and consequences of this disturbance that proper co-ordination of hunting, in the right times at the right places, is crucial.

Of all Cree subsistence activities, goose hunting is the most communal in nature, owing to the particular management characteristics of geese, which demand co-ordination of hunters' efforts for best results. The coastline from north to south is divided into a few dozen goose hunting territories, each belonging to a few core households. On each territory, the group is led by one or two experienced hunters, *paaschichaau uuchimaauch* ('shooting bosses').[5] These leaders exercise important decision-making authority over the use of their respective groups' territories. The leader is a steward, on behalf of the group, of ecologically sensitive resources. He decides on the times, places, and methods for taking certain animals, so that good hunting will be available on a perennial basis. He is expected to be a model of responsible hunting practice, able to guide other hunters in efficient hunting, but also capable of initiating appropriate measures of hunting restraint, to ensure that attempts to maximize kills on a short-term basis will not undermine the group's longer-term access to geese. Of course, other experienced members of the hunting group are also aware of these considerations, and engage in discussion with stewards about when and where to hunt, and what strategy to employ (Craik 1975).

Shooting on calm days is avoided, because the sound of shooting carries a considerable distance without a wind to muffle and disperse it, disturbing geese over a broad area. Not uncommonly, hunters will wait two or three days in camp for a good wind, before going on a hunt. After a particularly productive hunt, which inevitably means that a high proportion of geese in the area have been exposed to hunters' shots, harvesting may be called off for a day or two to 'rest' the geese. Shooting after dusk or before dawn is always taboo. The flare from shotguns fired in darkness is said to be highly visible and extremely frightening to geese.

Of particular importance is the rotation and 'resting' of hunting sites. Each territory includes one or more coastal bays where migrating geese gather for two or three weeks to rest and feed, as well as peripheral islands, ponds, creeks, lakes, and ridges to which geese fly from the bays for diurnal feeding. At any given stage in a seasonal migration, a territory must have at least two or three hunting sites in rotational use, so that no site is visited two days in succession. All hunters who use a territory on a given day are expected to accompany the hunting group leader to a single site, allowing all other sites to rest. In this way, the geese that sojourn on the territory will have refuge at most sites on any given day, and furthermore will not learn to expect hunters in a particular place.

The coastal bays where geese concentrate require the most careful handling. To hunt these concentrations too early in the migration discourages the build-up of a large population on the territory. It takes long experience to discern at just what point in the season the optimum local population has been reached, and what circumstances of wind and tide are appropriate for a hunt in a given location. As the season progresses, hunting geese in the bays with an adverse wind can cause them to continue on their migration prematurely. Geese roused from a bay late in the spring migration when there is a south wind, for example, might take advantage of easy flight to points north, rather than return at the end of the day.

If management considerations of the kind I have discussed are ignored, a number of negative consequences ensue. Geese on the territory become increasingly anxious about the presence of hunters, and adjust their behaviour accordingly. They avoid spots where they have been badly frightened, or where they have been over-hunted. They begin to fly higher between feeding grounds, keeping out of shotgun range. They fly increasingly after dusk, when hunters have stopped shooting. By day, they fly in greater numbers to inferior inland feeding spots, which are widely scattered and more difficult of human access. They continue onward in their migration earlier than they otherwise would. Or they shift altogether onto inland migration routes. Because geese transmit these behaviours socially, it can take a long time—some hunters say years—for damage done by careless or uncoordinated hunting to mend. Correct hunting, on the other hand, minimizes stress on the migrating population while enhancing the long-term harvests available to the Cree.

Cree hunters typically accumulate many man-years experience in hunting and observing waterfowl over the course of a lifetime, which results in the shared knowledge and skills required to co-ordinate the collective strategies outlined above. But knowledge is only one of the prerequisites; local and regional co-operation among hunters is the other. While sport hunters occasionally achieve a level of knowledge and skill comparable to that of Cree, sport hunters tend to hunt in more atomistic units, and the use made of public hunting areas is the somewhat random outcome of individual choices. In our Euro-North American systems, we are therefore more dependent on centralized, bureaucratic systems to regulate hunting.

While the administrative means are different, there are some important similarities between the management practices of Cree and sport hunters. In both systems, areas of refuge are provided for, and hunting is banned from dusk to dawn. The 'split season' among sport hunters serves a function similar to the Cree practice of 'resting' the geese after large hunts. And sport hunters at private gun clubs, like Cree, do possess the local organization required to rotate hunting sites effectively. (I am indebted to Austin Reed for bringing these parallels to my attention.)

Certain Cree practices are difficult to justify, however, in the view of sport hunters, and of some scientific wildlife managers. One hears the argument, for instance, that females taken late in the reproductive cycle, toward the end of a demanding spring migration, are too costly in terms of eco-energetics. Yet native subsistence requirements have long been part of the ecosystemic equation, and their energy requirements should not be dismissed in this sort of accounting. The opportunities for Cree to harvest passing migrations are brief, compared to the more lengthy fall/early winter season of hunters in the south. And in spring, alternative harvestable sources of food are more limited than at any other time of year for Cree hunters. The bag limits applied to sport hunters would not be realistic or politically acceptable in this context, except perhaps where enforced limits were the only way to prevent the depletion of a valued resource.[6]

RITUAL AND SYMBOLIC ASPECTS

The harvest of the seasonal goose migration, successfully orchestrated according to the principles outlined, is an all-embracing and complex social process in which the community as a whole takes enormous pleasure (Feit 1978; Preston 1975, 1978; Scott 1983; Tanner 1979).

Each stage and aspect of the hunt is both a ritual enactment and a practical activity, symbolizing key relations in the structure of Cree society and its connection to the natural world. The all-important spring hunt is an annual renewal of the relationship between the Cree and the geese, a promise of abundance collectively shared, and the occasion for high-spirited celebration. The commencement of the spring season is marked by two stages of ritual feasting. A key message that emerges in the symbolism of these feasts is that the sacred gift of geese is intimately connected to human sharing and co-operation (Scott 1983: 134–5). This message is no mere fancy. Indeed, without the sharing of opportunities to shoot geese and of the product itself, co-operation would wane, and the communal management of the hunt would become impracticable. Hunting would become more individualistic and opportunistic; geese would become subject to random disturbance, would suffer in terms of stress, and would adjust their behaviour accordingly, avoiding prime feeding areas and reducing their accessibility to hunters. It would be more difficult for the geese, and bad for the hunters.

Everyday occurrences in goose hunting refer to the symbols and events of a rich oral tradition, and this interaction shapes the psychology of the maturing hunter. A two-fold attitude is engrained by these symbols: the hunter who wishes to survive must on the one hand practice efficiency and accuracy in the killing of geese; but must on the other hand practice self-restraint, to avoid excessive exploitation of the resource (Scott 1983: 126–32, 178–83).

On a deeply figurative plane, geese are human companions, from cradle to grave (Preston 1978). They play a central role in the 'Walking-Out' ceremony, an infant's rite of initiation into the Cree world, a preferred time for which is during the spring hunt. An adolescent boy's first goose is an occasion for celebration, and for lessons about the maturing hunter's responsibilities toward fellow Cree and toward the game. Geese are involved in the symbolism of courtship and marriage. The Canada Goose is among the most powerful of spiritual allies that a hunter may have. It frequents his dreams, and is involved in various significant encounters in waking life. The goose's special relationship to the hunter is often manifest by its presence at the time of his death. Human identification with geese is intimate, on occasion rapturous; and is surely fundamental to the deep respect shown toward the bird. At certain points in his writing, Lorenz (1979) evokes something of the same spirit from within a European cultural context.

CONCLUSION: THE ROLE OF NATIVE WATERFOWL MANAGERS

With reference to northern native people, we should certainly have no difficulty arguing the critical importance of waterfowl on economic and cultural grounds alone. But native peoples' involvement with wildlife represents an additional asset, in respect of their direct contributions to the stewardship of these resources.

Development in the north—ranging from industrial resource extraction, to new transportation corridors, to new direct competition for wildlife resources—is potentially disruptive to indigenous management systems. The Cree example supports the frequent assertion that the interaction of humans and animals in these environments is a sensitive affair. Hasty development, or ill-conceived interference with native systems, are almost certain to be detrimental to wildlife populations as well as to native societies themselves. Competition can arrive in many forms, including competition for management control of the resource. Freeman (1985) discusses cases in which native knowledge has proved more adequate than scientific management scenarios. If this knowledge is taken systematically into account, it yields important management information (Nakashima 1986).

Sport hunters and other recreationalists are, at the level of their fundamental interest in protecting and promoting healthy waterfowl populations, natural allies of native hunters. But there are potential areas of conflict. It is not difficult to imagine, for example, that non-native sportsmen who hunt individualistically, in a random and dispersed pattern, without knowledge of local behaviour cycles, and on vacations too short to wait for the right winds, tides, or concentrations of geese, could be detrimental to the harvests of the Crees and the staging of the waterfowl—if there were greater uncontrolled access to James Bay from the south.

Currently, most sport hunting at James Bay is confined to a few localized camps under the supervision of native proprietors or guides. In one such instance, local territory stewards deemed that pressure to take paying clients hunting when conditions were not correct resulted in excessive disturbance to flocks, and the camp was closed. Such experience is suggestive of the more serious conflicts that would be encountered if there were unrestricted access by non-native recreationalists, or if industry-related development were to intrude directly on the coastal area.

The James Bay and Northern Quebec Agreement, which accords Cree and Inuit exclusive or preferential use of wildlife resources for subsistence purposes, provides significant protection from direct competition on traditional native lands. Competition with user groups *elsewhere* on continental ranges, however, is a potentially greater threat. Some observers (e.g. Boyd 1977) predict increasing political pressure from sport hunting interests to restrict spring hunting and impose quotas on native subsistence hunters. Such measures would probably be considered illegitimate by native people, except where required to prevent the decline of a particular stock.

Moral and legal dimensions of aboriginal rights aside, the enforcement of policies which did not have the consent of native people would carry the real risk of dividing communities, disrupting indigenous management systems, and precipitating practices which would be counterproductive in conservation terms. While the indigenous system results in relatively high per capita kills for Cree, it does function in a variey of ways to ensure quality environmental conditions for migrating waterfowl. For instance, Cree say that their practices of hunting site rotation, no shooting on calm days or at night, and periodic 'resting' of territories is 'respectful' treatment, allowing geese to rest and feed peacefully, and to put on fat. The importance of the James and Hudson Bay Lowland in permitting geese to increase their bodyweights during both spring and fall migrations has been confirmed by Thomas (1982) and others. Adequate female bodyweight in spring is positively related to the reproductive output of arctic and subarctic geese; and the fall staging period is important to the growth of juveniles, as well providing the fat reserves necessary for migration.

Given that the native portion of the annual kill, according to estimates summarized earlier, is in the 15 to 25 percent range for geese, and much lower for ducks, measures to restrict native harvests would result in marginal increases at best in sport hunting bag limits. At worst, disruption of the indigenous management system could result in less favourable circumstances for migrating geese during the critical pre-nesting period, and lead to poorer reproduction rates of harvestable stocks.

Effective wildlife management requires building on indigenous systems if the objectives of wildlife managers—native and non-native— are to be realized in this period of rapid evolution in northern regions. It is significant that the excellent quantitative information gathered by the JBNQNHR Committee would not be available without the co-operation and direct participation of the great majority of Quebec Cree hunters. Cree and Inuit participation in wildlife research, planning and management depends on effective recognition in the James Bay and Northern Quebec Agreement of their preferential right to harvest and manage wildlife, according to custom (Anon. 1975; Boyd 1977; Boyd et al. 1982: 20; Reed 1983).

Sadly, sizeable sectors of the non-native public and even the social and biological scientific community resist the notion that native subsistence societies practice viable wildlife management. Certainly, ethnocentric bias is at the root of much of this resistance. Conservation is often regarded as a concept unique to literate science; and centralized, bureaucratic forms as the only assurance of regulatory efficacy. Native subsistence hunting is too often equated with episodes of unregulated sport or commercial hunting in Euro-North American history, and similar dire consequences are often feared.

Such perspectives neglect the fact that native subsistence hunters are uniquely equipped informationally, socially, and culturally for precisely the kind of community-sponsored wildlife management that seems impractical in our own highly individualistic, urban society. Native hunters observe animals daily over the course of lifetimes. Through their oral traditions, moreover, they are the recipients of knowledge developed through generations of observation and reflection. Given the tremendous importance of animal life to indigenous societies, it would indeed be surprising if they did not have a well-considered appreciation of the effects of their own hunting activities and of many other environmental factors on the availability and behaviour of the game. This expertise, together with the social co-ordination and regulation possible in small-scale co-operative societies, is fundamental to ecological adaptation in the north, a potential source of knowledge for all of us, and a line of defence for healthy wildlife populations.

FOOTNOTES

1. The JBNQNHR Committee's research was initiated prior to Canada's metrication policy, and their foodweight figures are expressed in pounds. Their original figures are given in the tables, but metric equivalents are provided in the text.
2. The JBNQNHR Committee used average foodweights of 4.7 pounds per Canada Goose and 3.5 pounds per Lesser Snow Goose, calculated at 70 percent of whole weights estimated at 6.7 pounds and 5.0 pounds respectively. These are very conservative estimates. The JBNQNHR Committee (1976 vol. 2: 123, 133, 153–4, 164–5, 167–8) acknowledges that less conservative estimates would be 8.0 pounds whole weight for Canada Geese and 5.7 pounds for Snow Geese, with foodweights of 6.0 pounds and 5.3

pounds, respectively, calculated at 75 percent of whole weight. Cree people eat portions of the viscera, head and feet that are normally discarded by non-Cree. Accepting the less conservative figures would boost foodweight figures by 28 percent for Canada Geese and 23 percent for Snow Geese.

3. Feit (1978: pages 593–667) provides nutritional breakdowns of Cree subsistence animals, including waterfowl. His research on Waswanipi Cree hunting groups indicates that protein, carbohydrates, fats, and most essential vitamins and minerals are from harvested animals, as opposed to purchased foods; and that a calorically-adequate diet based on bush foods generally meets or exceeds recommended intakes of the various nutrients. Geese, loons and ducks are better-than-average sources of certain vitamins and minerals.

4. The possibility that some health problems might also be associated with waterfowl consumption has been suggested. Fish-eating waterfowl in areas of industrial mercury contamination in northwestern Ontario have been found to accumulate sufficient mercury to interfere with their reproduction and to be considered unsafe for human consumption (Desai-Greenaway & Price 1976; Barr 1986; Alan Penn, pers. comm.). However, according to figures cited in Berkes (1977b: 54–57), mercury levels in James Bay area geese and most ducks appear to be well within a safe range. Some inland fish-eating ducks have mercury levels similar to those of predatory fish, but consumption of these particular species is low and occasional. Berkes (*ibid:* 57) concludes that 'mercury concentrations in James Bay area waterfowl are not high enough to cause health problems'. Also, according to Berkes (*ibid:* 54), 'it is quite certain that the levels of pesticides in (James Bay area waterfowl) are too low to cause reproductive failure in birds or health problems in humans'.

5. Most, but not all, Cree communities on the east coast of James Bay practise the steward/territory system for waterfowl harvesting. It is in use at the communities of Chisasibi, Wemindji, and Eastmain on the east coast of James Bay, and various other management features discussed are common at other Cree communities.

6. The level of Cree waterfowl utilization is probably at or near its limit, for a variety of reasons discussed in Berkes (1982). A growing population of materially better-equipped Cree hunters has not resulted in increased goose harvests, even where goose populations have been increasing. It cannot be taken for granted that population growth among native people will result in ever-escalating subsistence harvests of migrating waterfowl.

ACKNOWLEDGEMENTS

This work has benefited from the generous support of the Social Sciences and Humanities Research Council of Canada, and the *Direction générale de l'Enseignement supérieur* of Quebec; the J. W. McConnell Foundation, the Programme in the Anthropology of Development, and the Centre for Northern Studies and Research at McGill University; as well as the Department of Anthropology at McMaster University.

I wish to thank the Canadian Wildlife Service, the *Ministère du Loisir, de la Chasse et de la Pêche* of Quebec, the Hunting, Fishing and Trapping Coordinating Committee of the James Bay territory, and the Wemindji Band Council for special permits which made it possible to participate with and to learn from Cree hunters. My very special thanks to those who hosted my family and me at their hunting camps.

Comments from Austin Reed on the conference copy of this paper have been extremely helpful in improving the final version. Conversations with Fikret Berkes, Brian Craik, Rick Cuciurean, Charles Drolet, Harvey Feit, Bruce Hunter, Alan Penn, Dick Preston and others are gratefully acknowledged.

REFERENCES

ANON. 1975. *The James Bay and Northern Quebec Agreement.* Editeur officiel du Québec, Quebec City, Canada.

BARR, J. F. 1986. Population dynamics of the Common Loon (*Gavia immer*) associated with mercury contaminated waters in Northwestern Ontario. Occasional Paper No. 56, Canadian Wildlife Service, Ottawa, Canada.

BERKES, F. 1977a. Fishery resource use in a subarctic Indian community. *Human Ecology* **5**, 289–307.

BERKES, F. 1977b. *Waterfowl Resources and their Utilization by the Cree People of the James Bay Area.* Grand Council of the Crees (of Quebec), Montreal, Canada.

BERKES, F. 1982. Waterfowl management and northern native peoples with reference to Cree hunters of James Bay. *Musk-Ox* **30**, 23–35.

BERKES, F. & FARKAS, C. 1978. Eastern James Bay Cree Indians: changing patterns of wild food use and nutrition. *Ecology of Food and Nutrition* **7**, 155–72.

BOYD, H. 1977. Waterfowl hunting by Native peoples in Canada: the case of James Bay and Northern Québec. *Transactions of the XIII Congress of Game Biologists:* 463–73.

BOYD, H., SMITH, G. E. J. & COOCH, F. G. 1982. The lesser snow geese of the eastern Canadian Arctic: their status during 1964–79 and their management from 1981 to 1990. Occasional Paper Number 46, Canadian Wildlife Service, Ottawa, Canada.

CRAIK, B. 1975. The formation of a goose hunting strategy and the politics of the hunting group. *In:* Freedman, J. & Barkow, J. *Proceedings of the Second Congress, Canadian Ethnology Society.* Canadian Ethnology Service Paper No. 28. Vol. 2: 460–5. National Museum of Man Mercury Series, Ottawa, Canada.

DESAI-GREENAWAY, P. & PRICE, I. M. 1976. Mercury in Canadian fish and wildlife used in diets of native peoples. Canadian Wildlife Service, Toxic Chemicals Division, Manuscript Reports No. 35, Ottawa, Canada.

FEIT, H. A. 1973. The ethno-ecology of the Waswanipi Cree: or how hunters can manage their resources. *In:* Cox, B. *Cultural Ecology: Readings on Canadian Indians and Eskimos:* 115–25. McClelland and Stewart, Toronto, Canada.

FEIT, H. A. 1978. Waswanipi Realities and Adaptations: Resource Management among Subarctic Hunters. Ph.D. thesis, McGill University. University Microfilms International, Ann Arbor, U.S.A. & London, England.

FREEMAN, M. M. R. 1985. Appeal to tradition: Different perspectives on Arctic wildlife management. *In:* Brøsted, J., Dahl, J., Gray, A., Gulløv, H. C., Henriksen, G., Jørgensen, J. B. & Kleivan, I. *Native Power: The Quest for Autonomy and Nationhood of Indigenous Peoples:* 265–81. Universitetsforlaget, Bergen & Oslo, Norway.

JAMES BAY AND NORTHERN QUEBEC NATIVE HARVESTING RESEARCH COMMITTEE. 1976. *Research to Establish Present Levels of Harvesting by Native Peoples of Northern Quebec. Part I. A Report on the Harvests of the James Bay Cree.* James Bay and Northern Quebec Native Harvesting Research Committee, Montreal, Canada. 2 Vols.

JBNQNHRC. 1978. *Interim Report for Phase II, Year 1. Research to Establish Present Levels of Harvesting by Native Peoples of Northern Quebec. Part I. Harvests by the James Bay Crees.* James Bay and Northern Quebec Native Harvesting Research Committee, Montreal, Canada.

JBNQNHRC. 1979. *Harvests by the James Bay Cree—1976–77. Third Progress Report (Phase II, Year 2). Research to establish present levels of harvesting by Native peoples of Northern Quebec.* James Bay and Northern Quebec Native Harvesting Research Committee, Montreal, Canada.

JBNQNHRC. 1980. *Harvests by the James Bay Cree—1977–78 and 1978–79. Fourth Progress Report (Phase II, Years 3 and 4). Research to Establish present levels of harvesting by Native peoples of Northern Quebec.* James Bay and Northern Quebec Native Harvesting Research Committee, Montreal, Canada.

JBNQNHRC. 1982. *The Wealth of the Land: Wildlife Harvests by the James Bay Cree, 1972–73 to 1978–79.* James Bay and Northern Quebec Native Harvesting Research Committee, Quebec City, Canada.

JOHANNES, R. F. 1978. Traditional marine conservation methods in Oceania and their demise. *Annual Review of Ecology and Systematics* **9**, 349–64.

LEWIS, H. T. 1982. Fire technology and resource management in aboriginal North America and Australia. *In:* Williams, N. M. & Hunn, E. S. *Resource Managers: North American and Australian Hunter-Gatherers. American Association for the Advancement of Sciences, Selected Symposium No. 67:* 46–67. Westview Press, Boulder, U.S.A.

LEWIS, H. T. 1985. Burning the 'top end': Kangaroos and cattle. *In:* Ford, J. *WAIT Environmental Studies Group Report #14:* 21–31. Western Australian Institute of Technology, Perth, Australia.

LORENZ, K. 1979. *The year of the Greylag Goose.* Harcourt Brace Jovanovich, New York, U.S.A.

NAKASHIMA, D. J. 1986. Inuit knowledge of the ecology of the Common Eider in northern Quebec. *In:* Reed, A. *Eider Ducks in Canada:* 102–13. Canadian Wildlife Service Report Series No. 47, Ottawa, Canada.

NIETSCHMANN, B. 1972. Hunting and fishing focus among the Miskito Indians, eastern Nicaragua. *Human Ecology* **1**, 41–67.

NORREVANG, A. 1986. Traditions of seabird fowling in the Faroes: an ecological basis for sustained fowling. *Ornis Scand.* **17**, 275–81.

PRESTON, R. 1975. *Cree narrative: expressing the personal meaning of events.* National Museum of Man Mercury Series, Canadian Ethnology Service Paper No. 30, National Museums of Canada, Ottawa, Canada.

PRESTON, R. 1978. La relation sacrée entre les Cris et les oies. *Recherches amérindiennes au Québec* **8(2)**, 147–52.

REED A. 1983. Eider ducks in Ungava Bay: case history of a joint research project by the Inuit and government. *In:* Boyd, A. *First western hemisphere waterfowl and waterbird symposium:* 60–1. Canadian Wildlife Service, Ottawa, Canada.

REED, A. 1984. Harvest of waterfowl by the James Bay Cree in relation to the total kill of those stocks. Canadian Wildlife Service, Ste-Foy, Québec. Unpublished Paper.

REED, A. & DROLET, C-A. 1985. Waterfowl harvest by Native peoples of Northern Quebec in relation to the total kill. *In: Proceedings of the 1985 Northeast Fish and Wildlife Conference.* Hartford, U.S.A.

REICHEL-DOLMATOFF, G. 1976. Cosmology as ecological analysis: a view from the rain forest. *Man* **11(3)**, 307–18.

SCOTT, C. H. 1983. The Semiotics of Material Life Among Wemindji Cree Hunters. Ph.D. thesis, McGill University. University Microfilms International, Ann Arbor, U.S.A. & London, England.

SCOTT, C. H. 1984. Between 'original affluence' and consumer affluence: Domestic production and guaranteed income for James Bay Cree hunters. *In:* Salisbury, R. F. & Tooker, E. *Affluence and Cultural Survival: 1981 Proceedings of the American Ethnological Society:* 74–86. The American Ethnological Society, Washington D.C., U.S.A.

TANNER, A. 1979. *Bringing home animals: religious ideology and mode of production of the Mistassini Cree hunters.* Social and Economic Studies No. 23, Institute of Social and Economic Research, Memorial University of Newfoundland, St. John's, Canada.

THOMAS, V. G. 1982. The roles of the James and Hudson Bay Lowland in the annual cycle of geese. *Naturaliste Canadien* **109**, 913–25.

ICBP Technical Publication No. 6, 1987

SOCIO-ECONOMIC ASPECTS OF MUTTONBIRDING IN TASMANIA, AUSTRALIA

I. J. SKIRA

*Tasmania National Parks and Wildlife Service,
P.O. Box 210, Sandy Bay, Tasmania, Australia, 7005*

ABSTRACT

The Short-tailed Shearwater (*Puffinus tenuirostris*), known locally as the Tasmanian Muttonbird, is harvested only in Tasmania. From 27 March to 30 April commercial operators take 400,000 chicks annually and sell the meat for human consumption, feathers for bedding and oil for medicinal and stock use. This small cottage industry was begun by sealers and their Aboriginal wives in the 1820s. Carried on by their descendants, the taking of Short-tailed Shearwaters was very important to them socially and financially. Today, most of the people in the industry are Aboriginal Tasmanians and the social and financial aspects are still very important to many of them. In the 1985 season the industry employed 150 people and the gross cash value of Short-tailed Shearwaters and their products was $328,300. The industry also generated $18,000 worth of other business in freighting and further processing of birds. In terms of tourism, however, neither the industry nor the birds themselves have yet been of any monetary value.

Non-commercial or amateur muttonbirders take approximately 300,000 chicks each year for food only, in a season that begins on the last Saturday in March and ends in mid-April. In recent years it has come under close scrutiny due to problems of over-harvesting, physical damage to habitat, alleged cruelty to birds and general anti-social behaviour of mutton-birders caused partly by alcohol, particularly on opening day. These problems do not occur on colonies exploited commercially.

INTRODUCTION

The Short-tailed Shearwater (*Puffinus tenuirostris*), known locally as the Tasmanian Muttonbird, breeds only in southern Australia and is most abundant in Tasmania. In Tasmania it is a partly protected species subject to annual open seasons. Commercial operators, the persons in charge of operations, take chicks and sell the meat for human consumption, feathers for bedding and the oil for medicinal and stock use. Non-commercial or amateur muttonbirders take chicks for food only. Elsewhere in Australia Short-tailed Shearwaters are fully protected and not harvested.

The first use of the term muttonbird is on two plates in the Watling Drawings of the British Museum (Bowdler-Sharpe 1906). On Plate 280 there is a note 'Norfolk Island petrel or the mutton bird, in full feather'. Serventy (1958) suggests that this note was probably written by Surgeon-General John White who was in New South

Wales between 1788 and 1794. The term muttonbird probably originated in 1790 and originally applied to the Providence Petrel (*Pterodroma solandri*). In that year about 170,000 adult Providence Petrels were killed for food to ward off starvation by convicts and military personnel on Norfolk Island, 1500 km east of Sydney. A military officer mentioned that these birds tasted like mutton (Clark 1981). They were also called 'flying sheep' (Serventy 1968). However, John Gould (1865) considered that the term muttonbird originated because of the large amounts of fat in fledgling birds which looked like tallow around sheep carcasses. Whatever the etymology, the term is of Australian origin and now refers mainly to the Short-tailed Shearwater in Australia and Sooty Shearwater (*P. griseus*) in New Zealand.

METHODS

Research on the biology of Short-tailed Shearwaters began in 1947 and still continues (Serventy & Curry 1984; Wooller *et al.* 1986). The Tasmanian National Parks and Wildlife Service has monitored the extent of harvesting on colonies by monitoring burrow occupancy since 1977 (Skira & Wapstra 1980). Statistics on harvest figures and licence sales have been analysed and information on the industry has been obtained through interviews with most of the commercial operators.

RESULTS

Biology of the Short-tailed Shearwater
Most of the information on the biology of Short-tailed Shearwaters has been obtained from Fisher Island in the Furneaux Group (*Figure 1*). The small size of the island (1ha) has enabled all birds to be banded and their lives followed (Serventy 1967, 1977; Serventy & Curry 1984; Wooller *et al.* 1986).

The Short-tailed Shearwater is a circum-Pacific migrant spending the boreal summer in the region of the Aleutian Islands. It has a precise breeding regime and first appears at breeding colonies about the third week of September. One egg is laid between 19 November and 2 December, the peak of egg-laying being 24–26 November every year. The incubation period is 53 days and the chicks hatch from mid-January onwards. The chick is in the burrow for about 94 days and in early April is at its maximum weight of approximately 800 g (Lill & Baldwin 1983). Mean age at first breeding is 6 years. Mean life span is 21 years although birds can live for more than 36 years (Skira, pers. obs.). Annual mortality in adults is approximately 10 percent and at least 50 percent of chicks die before breeding.

Distribution and abundance
There are 167 known colonies around the coast of Tasmania and its near offshore islands. It is unlikely that many new colonies remain to be discovered. The total area of colonies is 1522ha and the number of burrows is estimated at 11.4 million. Commercial harvesting occurs on seven colonies (692ha), non-commercial harvesting on 110 (565ha) and harvesting is not permitted on 50 (265ha). The largest colony is on Babel Island with an estimated 2.86 million burrows (Towney & Skira 1985). In other Australian States Victoria has 1.45 million burrows (Harris & Norman 1981), South Australia 1.25 million burrows (A. C. Robinson, pers. comm.), New South Wales 25,700 breeding pairs (Lane 1979) and Western Australia 250 burrows (Lane 1983).

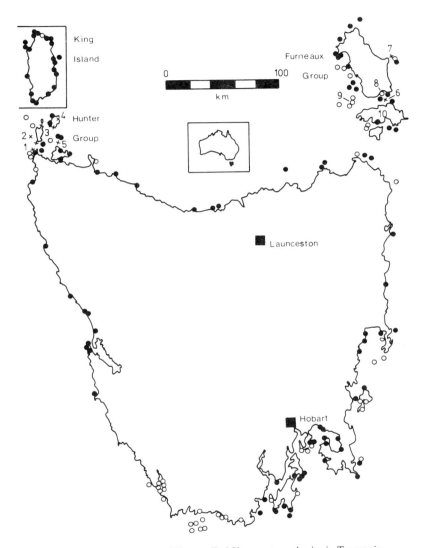

Figure 1: Distribution of Short-tailed Shearwater colonies in Tasmania.

x Commercial colony;   o Reserved colony;   • Unreserved

1. Trefoil Island
2. Steep Island
3. Hunter Island
4. Three Hummock Island
5. Walker Island
6. Great Dog Island
7. Babel Island
8. Fisher Island
9. Chappell Island
10. Cape Barren Island

Usually 80 percent of burrows contain eggs, and prior to the harvest season approximately 50 percent of burrows contain chicks. At many colonies exploited by amateur muttonbirders over 90 percent of shearwater chicks are taken. Calculated maximum sustainable yield (MSY) is 37 percent of available chicks aged 10 weeks, and is treated as a first approximation to provide a level to which current harvesting levels can be compared (Skira *et al.* 1986). The world breeding population of Short-tailed Shearwaters, based on a total 14.13 million burrows, is 11.3 million breeding pairs. Tasmania contains 81 percent of this total and of these, 4.4 million pairs (37%) breed on commercial colonies, 3.38 million pairs (30%) on non-commercial colonies and 1.58 million (14%) on colonies where harvesting is not permitted.

HARVESTING OF SHORT-TAILED SHEARWATERS

Pre-history
Prior to the settlement of Tasmania by Europeans in 1803, Aborigines collected Short-tailed shearwaters for food. They were hunter-gatherer people for whom the archaeological evidence indicates that the taking of shearwaters was probably incidental to the hunting of more important prey such as seals or wallabies (Bowdler 1974, 1984; Vanderwal & Horton 1984).

Nineteenth century
As an industry the harvesting of Short-tailed Shearwaters, or muttonbirding, began in the Furneaux Group in the early 1800s after fur sealing had become uneconomical because of over-exploitation. The transitory seal gangs were replaced by sealers, who took Aborigines for wives and made permanent homes on the various islands. However, through outside circumstances their descendants, sometimes known as Islanders and later Aboriginal Tasmanians, were forced on to Cape Barren Island (Murray-Smith 1974; Ryan 1981). The best accounts we have of this unique community are from the writings of Church of England missionaries, in particular Canon Brownrigg who visited the islands on 13 occasions between 1872 and 1885 (Brownrigg 1979a, b). A history of the muttonbird industry is in fact the main focus of the social history of this community.

The sealers bartered with passing ships shearwaters and the skins of wallabies (*Macropus rufogriseus* and *Thylogale billardierii*) and wombats (*Vombatus ursinus*) they collected (Begg & Begg 1979). One of the first comments on the industry was by John Boultbee, an educated English adventurer who arrived in the Furneaux Group in August 1823 and stayed several months. He mentioned that a black woman would pluck 500 birds per day for her work, and that the feathers were usually exchanged for flour, spirits etc. (Begg & Begg 1979). Who actually initiated the industry is a matter of conjecture. Some sealers would probably have known about the harvesting of Manx Shearwaters (*P. puffinus*) and other seabirds on the islands off the coast of Wales and England. Equally, the Aboriginal women may have shown sealers how to harvest the birds and then left it up to their menfolk to sell them.

In the early years, the industry mostly involved collecting eggs, fat, oil and feathers. Some chicks were salted and said to taste like red herrings (Backhouse 1843). Adult birds were caught only for their feathers, and the carcasses were discarded. The method involved digging a hole, approximately 2 metres square and about 60 centimetres deep (Backhouse 1843). From the two edges nearest the sea a brush fence was constructed up to 200 metres long. At pre-dawn, adult birds coming down to the shore to take off were herded along the fences and forced into the pit. Between 2000 and 2200 birds were generally taken in each drive and they died due to smothering. When the pit was full a brush mat or other covering was placed on top so no birds could escape. The fences were then taken down and the remaining birds allowed to escape (Elwes 1859).

Feathers were one of the most important products of the industry up to about the 1860s. However, because of their strong smell, which could not be removed, the demand for feathers declined. It was said that 'the perfume is not readily forgotten' (Brownrigg 1872). Chicks most likely became the mainstay of the industry when the market for feathers dropped. There is no documentary evidence to suggest that the muttonbirders realised that taking adults would cause the population to decline.

The season extended over a period of seven weeks and muttonbirding was a family affair for the Islanders. The men caught the birds, the children cut off wings and feet, and the women plucked, scalded, opened and packed the birds in brine. Muttonbirding was a very social occasion, an opportunity for families to renew friendships with other seldom-seen families. The strong social tradition continued even as late as the 1930s, when such activities as dances were still held on Saturday night on Great Dog Island during the season (Dorothy Cook, pers. comm.). Initially most went to Chappell Island with their goods, chattels, poultry, cats and dogs. Towards the latter part of the nineteenth century Babel Island became the centre of muttonbirding activities.

During the nineteenth century and the early decades of the twentieth century muttonbirding was the mainstay for the Islanders. Other employment came from hunting wallabies, sealing, making shell necklaces, shearing sheep and gathering resin from Grasstrees (*Xanthorrhoea australis*) for varnish. Occasionally whale strandings were utilized. In 1877, 1000 gallons of whale oil were obtained from 90 'blackfish', probably the Pilot Whale (*Globicephala melaena*) (*Launceston Examiner* 9 January 1877). The Islanders pursued a lifestyle based on elements from both traditional Aboriginal and nineteenth century European society (Ryan 1981). This seeming casual life style annoyed many people, particularly some missionaries and Government officials. Their attitude to the Islanders may be summed up by an observer who stated that the '. . . half-castes need boozing up to make them do anything. Their motto is Dolce fa Niente—sweet do nothing' (*Launceston Examiner* 26 May 1883).

Alienation of the islands in the Furneaux Group by European settlers began under the *Waste Lands Acts* of 1861–1870. In 1887 land on Flinders Island was made available for sale. These new settlers muttonbirded on the smaller colonies of Little Dog, Great Dog, Little Green, Big Green, East Kangaroo and Sisters Islands. To them the financial aspect overrode any tradition. In those days, however, the survival of everyone greatly depended on the income provided by muttonbirding. Australia was hit by a depression in the 1890s which meant 'no money in circulation and a good season of muttonbirds means little more cash passing from one to another' (*Launceston Examiner* 27 March 1895). One settler on Flinders Island was so badly off that he could remark that 'he had not had any sugar in his tea for over one month and no money to buy any with' (*Launceston Examiner* 11 February 1896).

Twentieth century

The present-day method of taking and processing birds is based on tradition and has not changed for over 100 years (Carter 1965). Chicks are taken from burrows by hand and their necks broken. They are then threaded by the lower mandible on to a long spit which holds about 50 birds and carried to the processing shed.

There the proventricular oil is drained into a drum and the birds are dry-plucked, scalded, and any remaining down and feathers brushed off. The bodies are then allowed to cool before being cleaned. They are then packed in cartons and sent away fresh, or are salted and packed in casks. In the 1940s and early 1950s many birds were canned and sold as 'squab-in-aspic'.

Muttonbirding developed purely as an exploitive industy and conservation measures developed through experience, practical sense and legislation. Legislation to protect colonies was first enacted in 1891 in which muttonbirding was permitted only between 20 March and 20 May (Tasm. Govt. Gaz. 15 Dec. 1891). Under the *Animals and Birds Protection Act* of 1928 there was much tighter control over exploitation of the birds. The Police Department was responsible for game regulations, so seasons were policed, fees were collected, and periodic inspections of harvesting operations were made. Currently, administration involves the Health Department and the National Parks and Wildlife Service. The erection of living quarters and processing sheds is subject to building regulations. For the colonies on reserves, operators require from the Service a temporary licence renewable annually to enable them to build and occupy sheds. This costs between $50 and $300. Once the Health Department passes the sheds, the Service issues a licence to the operator ($50) and his/her catchers ($10 each) to take birds. However, if the Service has grounds for not allowing a particular colony to open, or an operator to work it, no licences would be issued. Such grounds have included damage to colonies by fire killing chicks and destroying the vegetation, flooding of colonies, unsatisfactory condition of processing sheds and illegal occupation of colonies.

The first record of harvest is in 1831 when the Quaker missionary Backhouse stated that two and a half tons of feathers were sold at 6d. a pound in Launceston. He estimated that 20 birds yielded one pound of feathers, in other words 112,000 birds were killed (Backhouse 1843). In that year thousands of eggs were also gathered. The few harvest figures available for the nineteenth and early twentieth centuries should be taken only as a rough guide (*Table 1*). For example, Lord (1908) traced shipments to Launceston merchants for five seasons, 1904–8. However, he considered that he traced only some of the shipments and so, for 1908, he almost doubled his estimate of birds taken from 636,592 to 1,030,000.

Table 1: Short-tailed Shearwater statistics for the Furneaux Group in the nineteenth and early twentieth century

Year	Locality	Number of birds taken	Oil (gals)	Fat (gals)	Feathers	Eggs	Reference
1831	Furneaux Gr.				2.5 tons	1000's	Backhouse 1843
1858	Chappell I.	300,000	2000				Murray-Smith 1974
1864	Chappell I.					300,000	Lord 1908
1872	Furneaux Gr.	'millions'	3000				Brownrigg 1872
1876	Chappell I.	400,000	1000	4000			*Examiner* 8.2.1876
1883	Chappell I.	300,000	3000				*Examiner* 25.5.1883
1890	Chappell I.	204,000				*100s of dozens	Montgomery 1891
							Examiner 8.5.1890
1900	Furneaux Gr.	500,000					*Examiner* 2.6.1900
1904	Furneaux Gr.	379,804					Lord 1908
1905	Furneaux Gr.	459,094					Lord 1908
1906	Furneaux Gr.	493,777					Lord 1908
1907	Furneaux Gr.	572,671					Lord 1908
1908	Furneaux Gr.	1,030,000					Lord 1908
1911	Furneaux Gr.	800,000					Mollison 1974

The inconsistencies in the statistics reflect the unreliability of observers. Of all the nineteenth century observers Canon Brownrigg and Bishop Montgomery had the most experience with the Islanders. Brownrigg was not enthralled by the birds whereas Montgomery was, and published several articles on his experiences (Montgomery 1891, 1892, 1896, 1898). Now, almost 100 years later, it is extremely difficult to know how many shearwaters were once taken, but a truer estimate could lie between 200,000 and 300,000 chicks from Chappell Island alone.

Up to about 1925 the number of chicks taken each year in the Furneaux Group is thought to have been around one million. From 1928 more accurate estimates were made by the local policeman on Flinders Island, and since 1949 operators have been required to put in returns of how many birds they caught. Until recently harvesting centred on the Furneaux Group but limited commercial harvesting commenced in the Hunter Group around the mid 1800s, principally on Trefoil and Steep Islands (Buckby 1984). The colonies on Hunter, Walker and Three Hummock islands were non-existent or very small until the turn of the century (P. J. Macquire, pers. comm.; Burnie Advocate 26 March 1977). This period corresponded with a general expansion of the breeding range of the Short-tailed Shearwater in Tasmania (Serventy 1974; Sharland 1956). Overall, the annual harvest is estimated to have been around 100,000 or approximately one tenth of the Furneaux Group for many years.

Present commercial harvesting
The season runs from 27 March to 30 April and although there is no quota or daily bag limit the MSY is well below the maximum of 37 percent (Skira *et al.* 1986). An operator employs a number of catchers for gathering birds on a commercial colony and shed hands to process the birds. One operator may have more than one site, as in 1985 when the same operator worked Three Hummock Island and Steep Island. Boundaries of sites are usually defined by natural landforms and are well known to operators. Since 1978 there have been 15 or 16 operators, although in this paper I have grouped the four on Trefoil Island as one. Trefoil Island is run by Aboriginal Tasmanians as a co-operative, sharing any profits. Most of the people in the industry are Aboriginal Tasmanians whether they are operators, catchers, or shed hands. Of the 13 operators in 1985, seven were Aboriginal Tasmanians and the rest European. Altogether, approximately 150 people, of whom 64 were catchers, were employed in the industry in the 1985 season.

For the remainder of the year, the majority of people are unemployed. Two of the six European operators classed themselves as generally unemployed, and all the Aboriginal Tasmanian operators except one were unemployed, although two had intermittent work. In Australia, unemployment benefits can be claimed by unemployed people and the adult rate in March 1986 was $90 per week. Of the operators who had jobs, two were fishermen/farmers, two were farmers, one was an air charter pilot, and another one a labourer. Most catchers and shed hands are unemployed and receive unemployment benefits. The high Aboriginal unemployment in Tasmania is a major social problem and various programmes have been initiated to overcome it (Anon. 1982).

Total income derived from the sale of birds, feathers and oil in 1985 was $328,000. Approximately half the birds were sold locally and half exported to New Zealand. The gross income was higher for the Hunter Group because of the greater number of birds caught there (*Table 2*). After processing, birds were sold for $1.16 to $1.35 each. Operators on Great Dog Island in the Furneaux Group, who sold fresh birds for 70 cents each to a local fish processing factory, had the lowest gross income. Salted birds were 85 cents each. The factory, after paying for freight, casks and salt, sold the birds for $1.30 each.

Table 2:   Number of Short-tailed Shearwaters taken from each commercial colony,
1980–86

	Great Dog Island	Babel Island	Trefoil Island	Hunter Island	Three Hummock Island	Walker Island	Steep Island
1980	88,896	18,100	118,092	48,680	12,516	21,460	28,000
1981	116,355	34,290	134,200	15,000	22,100	30,100	17,040
1982	92,263	54,625	110,250	12,000	17,000	39,987	33,180
1983	104,100	58,000	134,685	5,600	35,000	41,160	34,100
1984	89,784	53,565	112,324	14,000	32,000	41,546	24,000
1985	88,724	47,605	83,210	3,000	33,500	42,540	26,000
1986	80,929	0	91,853	4,000	27,000	26,732	18,500

Very little supplementary business is generated by the muttonbird industry, and no one depends on it for a living. The largest business is in the freight of birds. Two air charter companies in Smithton grossed $15,000 in carrying birds, people and goods to and from the Hunter Group. In the Furneaux Group a fishing boat picks up fresh birds daily from Great Dog Island and salted birds at the end of the season from Babel Island. The value of this freight depends on the number of birds carried but is around $3000. The fish processing factory employs six extra staff during the season to process the birds, and in 1985 paid out $3000 in wages.

Profits vary considerably. In the Furneaux Group the profit for nine operators ranged between $2600 and $11,000 and averaged $5100 (*Table 3*). In the Hunter Group, with four operators, profit averaged $8800 and ranged between 'no profit' on Trefoil Island and $24,200. All operators except two regarded the profits to be very important to their annual income. The two exceptions were a fisherman/farmer and a farmer from the Furneaux Group. However, all operators go muttonbirding for financial reasons although to some Aboriginal Tasmanian operators tradition was their primary reason.

Main operating overheads are wages, food and freight, of which wages are usually two thirds of all expenses. Cost of maintaining sheds averages only several hundred dollars annually. Substantial costs of capital equipment such as stoves and electrical generators are periodic expenses. Few operators insure their sheds and if they are destroyed by fire, the cost of re-building would be considerable.

Wages vary greatly depending on experience and are paid on an agreed season, five-week contract. Catchers are paid between $700 and $1600, with the average around $1000. Shed hands generally receive less than $1000, the average being $700. Most sheds employ two or three catchers and one or two shed hands. On Trefoil Island, twenty catchers work in four sheds and another fifty people are paid anything between $400 and $1500 for the season. On Walker and Three Hummock Island there are only catchers and birds are killed, bagged and flown off the islands daily for processing in the small country towns of Smithton and

Table 3:   Value of the 1985 muttonbirding season in Tasmania

	Furneaux Group	Hunter Group	Total
Number of operators	9	4	13
Income ($)	119,500	208,800	328,300
Expenses ($)	73,400	173,400	246,800
Profit ($)	46,100	35,400	81,500

Boat Harbour respectively where they are sold locally as 'fresh' birds. Mutton-birders work a six-day week, taking Sunday off for washing clothes, resting and preparing for the next week. The work is generally regarded as hard, hot and dirty but the season is still classed as one of the main social events of the year.

The general decline in annual takes is due not to a diminishing resource but to a number of other reasons: changing eating habits in today's generation of Tasmanians who have not grown up with the tradition of muttonbirding; lack of interest in a greasy product which can be difficult to promote; ever-increasing expenses, and the decline of tradition in younger Aboriginal Tasmanians. The existence of the muttonbird industry today seems remarkable in a modern twentieth century western culture. Serventy *et al.* (1971) list five reasons why the industry ever existed and persisted in Tasmania. They are the large population of birds available; an egg-laying season of remarkable constancy enabling commercial operations to be carried out to a strict calendar; the shortness and ready accessibility of nesting burrows; easy landings and their close proximity to settlements. Serventy *et al.* (1971) also make the very valid point that had there been no vested interests in preserving the islands for muttonbirding, many of them may have been 'improved' for domestic stock, destroying colonies in the process. Muttonbirding could therefore be said to have a conservation role and not be such an anachronism.

Conflict in the use of some commercial colonies occurs between birders and graziers. It is not new but has been going on for many years (Lord 1908). Steep Head, Three Hummock and Babel Islands are not grazed. Sheep are run on Great Dog Island and some birders maintain that they damage burrows. Under current regulations grazing is permitted and has been traditional for well over 100 years. About 100 sheep are kept on Trefoil Island by the Aboriginal Tasmanians. Hunter Island is held under a grazing lease and cattle do occasionally wander over the shearwater colonies. Walker Island is privately owned and the owners rent out the muttonbirding rights each year. However, cattle have been allowed to wander over the colonies on Walker Island during the season to the anger of the catchers and operator. Physical damage to burrows by sheep is regarded as not detrimental to the breeding of Short-tailed Shearwaters (Norman 1970). Most damage by stock, particularly cattle, is through soil erosion and grazing, particularly after fire. On King Island some farmers with shearwater colonies on their land do not allow cattle on colonies during the breeding season.

Non-commercial muttonbirding

The season is from the last Saturday in March to mid-April. For a licence fee of $10, any person is entitled to a daily quota of 15 birds except on Bass Strait islands where the daily quota is 50 birds. The birds are taken for food only. The quota on Bass Strait islands differ because colonies are larger and fewer people are on them. The annual take is estimated at 300,000 birds. Non-commercial birders are not required to put in returns and this figure is based on number of licences sold and bag limits. Its accuracy can be measured only at considerable cost.

There is very little money generated by the season. In the past ten years there has been a general decline in the number of licences sold (*Table 4*). This is partly

Table 4:   Non-commercial licence sales, 1976–86

Year	1976	1977	1978	1979	1980	1981	1982	1983	1984	1985	1986
Number of licences sold	7401	7935	6633	6811	4644	4790	4326	3882	2269	3039	2865

Table 5:   Summary of offences for the 1982–86 non-commercial Short-tailed
Shearwater seasons

Year	Number of offenders	Number of charges	Number of convictions	Number of dismissals	Fines [$]
1982	21	47	44	3	1952
1983	70	147	137	10	5835
1984	32	58	42	9	2547
1985	35	88	76	2	4943
1986	37	75	70	0	4752

due to closer policing of the season, the ever rising expense of transport to colonies by car or boat, and over-harvesting of the birds. Any advantages, in fact, are greatly outweighed by the problems. These are over-harvesting, damage to habitat, alleged cruelty towards birds, litter, poaching, anti-social behaviour and general abuse of regulations.

The majority of colonies are <5ha in area and over 90 percent of chicks are taken. This is well above the MSY of 37 percent. Studies at Cape Queen Elizabeth near Hobart, a colony that has been heavily harvested for many years, have shown that over-harvesting has resulted in fewer birds breeding compared to colonies that are not harvested or are only lightly harvested (Skira & Wapstra 1980).

Illegal physical damage to burrows occurs on islands in Bass Strait and elsewhere. Burrows are ripped or dug up making them useless for breeding. It is almost impossible to catch people in the act of destroying burrows, and education through publicity pamphlets and press releases has failed. To overcome these problems the season was shortened in 1979, the bag limit reduced from 25 to 15 birds in 1984 and some colonies have been closed for one season. These measures have not been entirely successful and periodic closure of all colonies except those on Bass Strait islands has been accepted as a necessary step. These colonies will be closed in 1987.

Methods of killing birds vary. Commercial catchers hold the chick by the head and then, with a quick flick of the wrist, break the neck or crush the skull. These methods cause sudden and painless death. In contrast, a common method among non-commercial muttonbirders is to swing the birds around in the air in windmill fashion. This method is unlikely to cause instantaneous death and may cause needless suffering.

Muttonbirders leave litter and offal, often at picnic spots. Where muttonbirding takes place on reserved land, these actions are offences and offenders are prosecuted. Another problem is poaching which in itself could cause over-harvesting on small colonies and must be combatted (*Table 5*).

Most participants are of European descent, adults and children. The amateur season is in stark contrast to commercial muttonbirding. To many people, opening day is regarded as a day of sport and fun which, combined with effects of alcohol, often results in offensive behaviour. The taking of Short-tailed Shearwaters by amateurs is not a necessity and it is difficult to justify its continuance. In the last two years adverse media publicity and increased public criticism from groups such as Greenpeace have reinforced this. The Government has accepted this criticism and from 1987 it has closed the season indefinitely except on Bass Strait islands where the problems are not as acute.

Non-consumptive use of Short-tailed Shearwaters
Neither the industry nor the birds have had any tourism value although articles romanticising the industry in particular are frequently written. On the average, a

TV, radio or newspaper crew do a story every year on the industry or the birds. The Japanese have shown great interest in the shearwaters, for many young birds are beach-washed on their beaches (Oka & Maruyama 1985), while the Japan-Australia Migratory Birds Agreement has brought about exchange visits by biologists from both countries to study Short-tailed Shearwaters.

CONCLUSION

Commercial muttonbirding persists today because of social tradition and financial need. The tradition of muttonbirding, passing on through each generation as a way of life for the Bass Strait islands' community, changed only gradually until 40 years ago. Since the Second World War, cultural influences and modern life styles have altered the attitudes of the present generation, while increasing expenses and other factors are making muttonbirding less profitable. Most muttonbirders deem it inevitable that commercial muttonbirding will disappear, mainly because few young people are becoming involved in the industry.

The economic significance of the industry is small and its demise could be covered through other employment. The social loss is unknown. The concept of Aboriginal land rights in Tasmania is seen as the root of Aboriginality (Anon. 1982). Into this concept the tradition of muttonbirding is strongly linked. Specifically, Aboriginal Tasmanians are requesting several shearwater colonies including Great Dog and Babel Islands. In 1980 the Australian Government purchased Trefoil Island for muttonbirders. Although commercial muttonbirding will probably disappear, the existence of an aboriginal identity based on future recognition of land rights should allow Aboriginal Tasmanians to continue other traditional activities.

Non-commercial muttonbirding has come under close scrutiny in recent years and protests over the practices have led the Government to close the season from 1987. Policing the closure will be difficult due to a lack of enforcement officers. However, the take from poaching will be very much less than if colonies were open for harvesting. Destruction of shearwater colonies due to increased grazing is not expected. The majority of colonies that were open to amateur birding are already grazed, and grazing is not expected to increase when the amateur season is closed.

ACKNOWLEDGEMENTS

I would like to thank all the commercial muttonbird operators who kindly provided information. I thank Nigel Brothers and Rod Pearse of the Tasmanian National Parks and Wildlife Service, Phyllis Pitchford of Flinders Island and the referee Dr. Chris Feare for their comments on the manuscript. Special thanks go to Lynne Cullen for her typing.

REFERENCES

Anon. 1982. Tasmanian aboriginals and their struggle for recognition (1876–1982). In *Tasmanian Year Book No. 16 1982.*, pp. 510–27. Aust. Bureau of Statistics.
Backhouse, J. 1843. *A Narrative of a Visit to the Australian colonies.* Hamilton, Adams & Co. London.
Begg, A. C. & Begg, N. C. 1979. *The World of John Boultbee.* Whitcoulls. Christchurch.

BOWDLER, S. 1974. An account of an archaeological reconnaissance of Hunter Isles, North-West Tasmania, 1973/4. *Recs. Queen Vict. Mus. Launceston* **54**, 1–22.

BOWDLER, S. 1984. Hunter Hill, Hunter Island. *Terra Australis* **8**, 1–148.

BOWDLER-SHARPE, R. 1906. *History of the collections contained in the Natural History Department of the British Museum.* Vol. II.

BROWNRIGG, M. 1979a. *The Cruise of the Freak.* Author. Launceston.

BROWNRIGG, M. 1979b. *Mission to the Islands. The missionary voyages in Bass Strait of Canon Marcus Brownrigg,* 1872–1885. Ed. S. Murray-Smith. Cat and Fiddle Press. Hobart.

BUCKBY, P. Y. 1984. *Around Circular Head.* Denbar Publishers. Tasmania.

CARTER, I. F. 1965. The bird men of Bass Strait. *Blackwood Magazine* **298**, 166–73.

CLARK, R. 1981. *The Journal and Letters of Lt. Ralph Clark* 1787–1792. Eds P. G. Fidlon and R. J. Ryan. Australian Documents Library. Sydney.

ELWES, R. 1859. Notes on the breeding and mode of capture of the short-tailed petrel, or mutton bird *Puffinus obscurus,* in the islands in Bass's Straits. *Ibis* **1**, 397–9.

GOULD, J. 1865. *Handbook to the Birds of Australia.* Vol. II. Author. London.

HARRIS, M. P. & NORMAN, F. I. 1981. Distribution and status of coastal colonies of seabirds in Victoria. *Mem. Nat. Mus. Vict.,* **42**, 89–106.

LANE, S. G. 1979. Summary of the breeding seabirds on New South Wales coastal islands. *Corella* **3**, 7–10.

LANE, S. G. 1983. Short-tailed shearwater on Figure of Eight Island, Archipelago of the Recherche, Western Australia. *Emu* **83**, 37–8.

LILL, A. & BALDWIN, J. 1983. Weight changes and the mode of depot fat accumulation in migratory short-tailed shearwaters. *Aust. J. Zool.* **31**, 891–902.

LORD, J. E. C. 1908. Furneaux Islands: Report upon the state of the islands. Tasmania House of Assembly Parl. Paper No. 57.

MOLLISON, B. 1974. A chronology of events affecting Tasmanian Aboriginal people (1642–1974). Part 2 *Psychology Dept. Uni. Tasmania* **3** (36).

MONTGOMERY, H. H. 1891. Some account of the mutton birds, or sooty petrels (*Nectris brevicaudus*), as seen in their homes among the Furneaux Islands, Bass Straits, Tasmania from notes taken during a visit to the locality in March 1891. *Pap. Procs. Roy. Soc. Tasm.* 1891, 1–10.

MONTGOMERY, H. H. 1892. A mutton bird island. *New Review* (Lond). Aug. 227–35.

MONTGOMERY, H. H. 1896. A night in a petrel rooketry. *Pap. Proc. Roy. Soc. Tasm.,* v–vii.

MONTGOMERY, H. H. 1898. On the habits of the mutton-bird of Bass Strait, Australia (*Puffinus tenuirostris*). *Ibis* **7**, 209–16.

MURRAY-SMITH, S. 1974. Beyond the pale. The Islander community of Bass Strait in the nineteenth century. *Pap. Proc. Tasm. Hist. Res. Assoc.* **20**, 167–200.

NORMAN, F. I. 1970. The effects of sheep on the breeding success and habitat of the short-tailed shearwater, *Puffinus tenuirostris* (Temminck). *Aust. J. Zool.* **18**, 215–29.

OKA, N. & MARUYAMA, N. 1985. Visual evaluation of tibiotarsus and femur marrows as a method of estimating nutritive conditions of short-tailed shearwaters. *J. Yamashina Inst. Ornith.* **17**, 57–65.

RYAN, L. 1981. *The Aboriginal Tasmanians.* Univ. Q'land Press. St. Lucia.

SERVENTY, D. L. 1958. Recent studies on the Tasmanian mutton-bird. *The Australian Mus. Mag.* **12**, 327–32.

SERVENTY, D. L. 1967. Aspects of the population ecology of the short-tailed shearwater, *Puffinus tenuirostris. Proc. XIV. Int. Ornith. Congr.* 165–90.

SERVENTY, D. L. 1974. The biology behind the muttonbird industry. *Pap. Procs. Roy. Soc. Tasm.,* **107**, 1–9.

SERVENTY, D. L. 1977. Seabird Islands No. 49. Fisher Island. Tasmania. *Corella* **1**, 60–2.

SERVENTY, V. 1969. *Wildlife of Australia.* Nelson. Melbourne.

SERVENTY, D. L. & CURRY, P. J. 1984. Observations on colony size, breeding success, recruitment and inter-colony dispersal in a Tasmanian colony of short-tailed shearwaters *Puffinus tenuirostris* over a 30-year period. *Emu* **84**, 71–9.

SERVENTY, D. L., SERVENTY, V. & WARHAM, J. 1971. *The Handbook of Australian Sea-birds.* A. H. & A. W. Reed. Sydney.

SHARLAND, M. 1956. Population rise in two sea-birds. *Emu* **56**, 75–9.

SKIRA, I. J. & WAPSTRA, J. E. 1980. Occupation of burrows as a means of estimating the harvest of short-tailed shearwaters in Tasmania. *Emu* **80**, 233–8.

SKIRA, I. J., WAPSTRA, J. E., TOWNEY, G. N. & NAARDING, J. A. 1986. Conservation of the short-tailed shearwaters *Puffinus tenuirostris* in Tasmania, Australia. *Biol. Cons.* **37**, 225–36.

TOWNEY, G. N. & SKIRA, I. J. 1985. Seabird Islands No. 139. Babel Island, Furneaux Group, Tasmania. *Corella* **8**, 103–4.

VANDERWAL, R. L. & HORTON, D. 1984. Coastal Southwest Tasmania. *Terra Australis* **9**, 1–137.

WOOLLER, R. D., BRADLEY, J. S., SERVENTY, D. L. & SKIRA, I. L. 1986. Factors contributing to reproductive success in short-tailed shearwaters. *Proc. XIX Int. Ornith, Congr.* (in press).

ICBP Technical Publication No. 6, 1987

THE VALUE OF SEABIRDS AS A SOCIO-ECONOMIC RESOURCE IN JAMAICA

ANN M. HAYNES-SUTTON

Marshall's Pen, P.O. Box 58, Mandeville, Jamaica

ABSTRACT

Seabirds are a potentially valuable resource in Jamaica and other Caribbean islands. In Jamaica, they are exploited for food (mainly eggs, occasionally chicks and adults); as aphrodisiacs (eggs); and for fertilizer (guano). Fishermen also depend on seabirds as navigational aids, and use them to locate fishing grounds. Jamaican seabird populations have declined seriously in the last fifty years, through exploitation, habitat destruction and habitat disturbance. In the 1980s the Jamaican Government recognized that with proper management, seabird colonies could provide employment and revenue, with new uses such as tourism and education supplementing traditional uses. A programme of research into the management of seabird colonies was carried out, and new conservation measures were successfully introduced.

INTRODUCTION

Most fishermen in Jamaica are artisans; they fish opportunistically from motorized fibreglass canoes, exploiting whatever is available. Marine turtles, manatees and seabird eggs are taken occasionally to supplement the income and diet derived from fishing with pots and nets. Seabirds provide food in the form of eggs, chicks and adults; the eggs are eaten for their supposed aphrodisiac as well as nutritional qualities. Until the 1950s, guano deposits were mined for sale as fertilizer. The economic importance of these resources is hard to measure, but was undoubtedly much greater in the past. Since 1982, some success has been achieved with research into the management and conservation of Sooty Tern (*Sterna fuscata*) colonies in Jamaica. This experience is relevant to other tropical islands.

SEABIRDS AS FOOD

Of the twenty-six species of seabird that occur in Jamaica, eight are known to be exploited for food there. These are the White-tailed Tropicbird (*Phaethon lepturus*), exploited for eggs; Masked and Brown Booby (*Sula dactylatra* and *S. leucogaster*), for eggs, chicks and adults; Brown Pelican (*Pelecanus occidentalis*), for chicks; and Laughing Gull (*Larus atricilla*), Bridled Tern (*Sterna anaethetus*), Sooty Tern (*S. fuscata*) and Brown Noddy (*Anous stolidus*), for eggs (Haynes 1987a).

Larids

The collection of eggs of Sooty Terns and Brown Noddies is a tradition that began in pre-Columbian times (Lewis 1948), and Sooty Terns remain the most important producers of wild eggs, in Jamaica as in the world as a whole (Cott 1954). In the nineteenth century, eggs collected on offshore cays (Morant and Pedro groups) were 'of considerable economic importance' (Gosse 1847). Unfortunately Gosse gave no figures to indicate the monetary value of the 'schooner loads' of eggs to which he referred.

The first indications of the quantities collected date from the 1920s. At that time, between 400,000 and 600,000 eggs were being brought annually to Jamaica from the cays (Lewis 1947). Girls selling 'booby' eggs were one of the sights of Kingston from March to July (Clark 1927). Perhaps as many as 600 people were employed in the trade, including collectors, transporters, middlemen and street vendors. The eggs sold for 'a bit' per dozen in the 1890s (Field 1894), suggesting that sales may have amounted to about US$100,000 annually (at current values).

By the 1970s, the numbers of eggs reaching Kingston annually had fallen to between 60,000 and 80,000 (Haynes 1987a). Licences have been issued for egg collecting at the cays since 1882 (Haynes 1987a). The last year in which a licence was issued was 1985, and in that year, the licensee was estimated to have made a net profit of less than US$2000 on the 22,000 eggs collected.

In addition to the eggs transported to Jamaica, about 300 fishermen on the Morant and Pedro Cays regularly supplement their diets with tern eggs during the eight-week nesting season, from April to June. Eggs are also smuggled to the mainland for family, friends, and a very limited trade. Of the 2000 people who probably benefit from the eggs, perhaps only three or four fishermen collect enough eggs annually to profit from the trade. Tern eggs are also collected illegally from all accessible colonies around Jamaica; it is very difficult to estimate the scale of illegal collecting.

Tern eggs are very much in demand in Jamaica. They are sold for up to US$0.60 each (1986 prices)—three times the price of a hen's egg—and are often mixed with stout, wine, condensed milk and spices, to produce a punch which is regarded by men as an aphrodisiac. For the fishermen on the cays (and to a lesser extent their families on the mainland), eggs provide a welcome treat. The small number of eggs available diminishes their value as a protein source to the population as a whole, and in this respect, Jamaica apparently differs from other Caribbean islands where tern eggs may provide a cheaper source of protein than hens' eggs (Halewyn & Norton 1984).

Other seabirds

The eggs of White-tailed Tropicbirds are taken wherever their nests are accessible. Colonies are small, and exploitation is local; about 30 families benefit from this illegal subsistence activity.

Booby eggs, chicks and adults were eaten in the past at Pedro Cays (Lewis 1947). Today, other foods are more easily available to the fishermen, and only one or two of the several hundred fishermen on the cays eat sulids. A colony of about 440 nesting pairs of Masked Boobies coexists in close proximity to a settlement of about 200 fishermen on Middle Cay, Pedro group (Haynes 1986).

Brown Pelican chicks were eaten traditionally by the people of Port Royal, but the scale, extent and effects of this subsistence activity have not been investigated.

The Black-capped Petrel (*Pterodroma hasitata*) is eaten in Haiti and other parts of the Caribbean (King 1981). It is not known whether human exploitation contributed to the probable extinction of the Jamaican subspecies *P.h. caribbaea*.

SEABIRDS AS SOURCES OF FERTILIZER

Guano from the Morant and Pedro Cays was an important source of fertilizer in the nineteenth century. Mining continued into the mid-twentieth century (Zans 1958). In the 1940s there were manure houses on all the Morant and Pedro Cays, though some were in disrepair (Lewis 1947). No data appear to be available on the amounts extracted. Some reserves remain at the Pedro Cays (Zans 1958). The small size of the remaining reserves, combined with the ready availability of fertilizers from other sources and the severe effects of mining on the ecology of the cays, led to the end of mining in the 1950s.

The geological history of Jamaica's offshore cays has not been examined. Halewyn & Norton (1984) suggested that guano on the Caribbean cays was laid down in the Pleistocene by larger populations of sulids, and that no deposition is occurring at present. However, at the Pedro Cays, Zans (1958) found that there was more guano, with a higher average phosphate content, on the cay which then had the largest sulid population, suggesting that some deposition may still be occurring.

NAVIGATION

Many Jamaican fishermen operate in offshore waters without compasses. They report that they frequently follow boobies and terns, using them both as navigational aids when making for the cays and banks, and to locate schools of commercial fish. There have been no detailed studies of this behaviour, or of its value to the fishermen who practise it. The Jamaican cays would make a good site for such research.

TOURISM AND EDUCATION

Some Jamaican seabird colonies have potential as tourist attractions (Halewyn & Norton 1984; Haynes 1987a). It has been proposed that at least one cay from each group should be protected as a nature reserve (Haynes 1987a); controlled tourism could then help to support these reserves, as it does on Cousin Island in the Seychelles (Diamond 1985). The sustainable use of seabird nesting areas could provide an important demonstration of the ways in which conservation can benefit local communities. At the Morant Cays, the education programme has already played an important role in generating support for conservation measures from the fishing community and the general public.

CONSERVATION

All seabirds are fully protected under Jamaican law. Traditionally, a single licence was issued each year for the collection of eggs at the cays between April and June. This system was difficult to administer because of the remoteness of the cays. In 1982, the Natural Resources Conservation Division, with the assistance of the Jamaica Defence Force Coastguard and the University of the West Indies, began to protect one cay as a nesting sanctuary. Wardens were placed on the protected cay during the nesting season, and no egg collecting was allowed there. This is seen as the first step towards creating a system of reserves on Jamaica's cays

(Haynes 1987b). The Sooty Tern breeding population on the protected island has quadrupled after five years of protection (Haynes 1987b). The development of a similar system for cays on which sulids breed in Jamaica should be regarded as a priority (Haynes 1987a). Protection of the cays for seabirds will, of course, also benefit other marine resources, including turtles.

RESEARCH

Seasonal protection of the cays has provided the necessary conditions for research into the breeding ecology of Sooty Terns and Brown Noddies. The ecological effects of the traditional system of egg collecting have been evaluated, and improved techniques are being tested (Haynes 1987a). The results of this research will be of use wherever selected nesting areas of Sooty Terns can be managed for sustainable commercial egg collecting and tourism.

CONCLUSION

The collection of eggs is the most important form of exploitation of seabirds currently being carried out in Jamaica. Egg collection is regarded as a traditional right by many fishermen in Jamaica and the Caribbean (Halewyn & Norton 1984) and elsewhere (Cott 1954; Feare 1984). The catastrophic decline of tern populations in the last fifty years—attributed to over-collection of eggs and associated mismanagement of habitat (Haynes 1987a)—has resulted in the decline of the industry from an economically important practice to a relatively minor activity. Work in Jamaica suggests that tern populations can recover quickly if selected colonies are protected from egg collecting, and their habitats managed to promote nesting. Such protection need not be expensive or labour-intensive since it can draw on existing resources, such as coastguard patrols, university students, Government departments and volunteers from the public. The potential benefits are many, and include tourism, sustainable egg collecting, public education, improved safety and efficiency for fishermen, and provision of suitable conditions for research into tropical seabird ecology.

REFERENCES

CLARK, A. 1927. Kingston street cries c.1927 and something about their criers. Reprinted in *Jamaica Journal* **18**, 11–17.
COTT, H. B. 1954. The exploitation of wild birds for their eggs. *Ibis* **96**, 129–49.
DIAMOND, A. W. 1985. Multiple use of Cousin Island Nature Reserve, Seychelles. Pp. 239–51 *In:* Moors, P. J. (ed.). *Conservation of Island Birds. ICBP Tech. Publ. 3.* Cambridge.
FEARE, C. J. 1984. Human exploitation. Pp. 691–700 *In:* Croxall, J. P., Evans, P. G. H. & Schreiber, R. W. (eds.). *Status and Conservation of the World's Seabirds. ICBP Tech. Publ. 2.* Cambridge.
FIELD, G. W. 1894. Notes on the birds of Port Henderson, Jamaica, West Indies. *Auk* **11**, 117–27.
GOSSE, P. H. 1847. *The birds of Jamaica.* London.
HALEWYN, R. VAN, & NORTON, R. L. 1984. The status and conservation of seabirds in the Caribbean. Pp. 169–222 *In:* Croxall, J. P., Evans, P. G. H. & Schreiber, R. W. (eds.). *Status and Conservation of the World's Seabirds. ICBP Tech. Publ. 2.* Cambridge.
HAYNES, A. M. 1986. Masked Boobies nesting at Pedro Cays. *Gosse Bird Club Broadsheet* **47**.

HAYNES, A. M. 1987a. Human exploitation of seabirds in Jamaica. *Biol. Cons.* (in press).
HAYNES, A. M. 1987b. 'Booby' tern conservation, management and research—report on the 1986 season. Unpubl. report, 2 pp.
KING, W. B. 1981. *Endangered birds of the world.* Washington, D. C.
LEWIS, C. B. 1947. Inspection of the Morant and Pedro Cays 1947. Institute of Jamaica internal report. 7 pp.
LEWIS, C. B. 1948. The history of the Morant and Pedro Cays. *Jam. Hist. Rev.* **1**, 302–9.
ZANS, V. A. 1958. The Pedro Cays and Pedro Bank. Report on the survey of the cays 1955–7. *Geol. Surv. Dept. Jam. Bull.* **3**, 1–47.

ICBP Technical Publication No. 6, 1987

EGG AND IMAGE: NEW AND TRADITIONAL USES FOR THE MALEO (*MACROCEPHALON MALEO*)

RENÉ W. R. J. DEKKER & JAN WATTEL

Instituut voor Taxonomische Zoölogie, Universiteit van Amsterdam, Postbus 20125, 1000 HC Amsterdam, The Netherlands

ABSTRACT

Macrocephalon maleo, the endemic megapode of Sulawesi, Indonesia, is disappearing at an alarming rate. Man is the major cause of this decline, but will himself lose substantial economic and cultural benefits if it continues. The people of Sulawesi are unknowingly exterminating a natural resource with economic potential for tourism and trade. A combination of protection, regulated exploitation of its eggs, and marketing of its image will be beneficial for Maleo and man.

RINGKASAN

Maleo, burung megapode yang endemik dari Sulawesi, Indonesia, mulai punah dengan kecepatan yang mengkhawatirkan. Manusia adalah musuh utama dan walaupun kedengaran tidak masuk akal manusia adalah yang rugi. Masyarakat pulau Sulawesi tidak adar bahwa mereka sedang memusnakan satu sumbar daya alam yang mempunyai nilai ekonomi untuk parawisata dan perdagangan. Gabungan entara konservasi alam dengan pemanfaatan secara teratur daripada telur maleo serta memperkenalkan burung yang aneh ini akan menguntunkan manusia dan burung maleo.

INTRODUCTION

Megapodes have always attracted attention on account of their very large eggs and remarkable breeding behaviour. Travellers visiting Australasia in the last century were fascinated by the strange breeding biology of these birds, while local people used their eggs for consumption. The number of genera and species within this family is still a subject of discussion among taxonomists. Wolters (1976) recognized seven genera and twelve species: *Megapodius* (3), *Eulipoa* (1), *Macrocephalon* (1), *Talegalla* (3), *Aepypodius* (2), *Alectura* (1) and *Leipoa* (1).

Megapodes do not incubate their eggs themselves. They bury them in sand heated by the sun or by volcanic activity, or in mounds of forest litter heated by organic decomposition. *Talegalla, Aepypodius, Alectura* and *Leipoa* build mounds, are territorial, and expend a lot of energy in constructing the mound and regulating its temperature. *Macrocephalon* and *Eulipoa* lay their eggs in the sand at communal nesting grounds where the sun or volcanic activity provides the heat for incubation. Although they do defend a nesting hole during egg-laying, they do not care for the nesting hole or egg after laying has finished. Within the genus *Megapodius* we find both mound-builders and communal nesters. Even within one species, *Megapodius freycinet,* different populations use different strategies.

Megapode eggs are rich in yolk and big in relation to body size. Average egg weight varies between 75g for *Megapodius pritchardii* (Todd 1983) and 232g for *Macrocephalon maleo* (this study) and accounts for 10–17 percent of the female body weight (Clark 1964; Vleck *et al.* 1984). Yolk accounts for 50–67 percent of the egg contents (Meyer 1930; Todd 1983; Vleck *et al.* 1984). This makes megapode eggs very attractive for consumption compared with chicken eggs which weigh only about 50–60g and contain 30 percent yolk (Meyer 1930). Megapode egg consumption by man especially affects those species that make use of volcanic or solar heat and lay their eggs at communal nesting grounds. The territorial mound-builders suffer fewer egg losses from human consumption. Lister (1911) mentioned several cases of more or less complete domestication of megapodes by natives, all involving species of *Megapodius.* According to Lister (1911) man even played a role in the distribution of this genus over the islands of the Indo-Australian region.

MACROCEPHALON MALEO

Macrocephalon maleo, the endemic megapode of Sulawesi, Indonesia, lays its eggs in tropical rainforest close to hot springs or on beaches exposed to the sun. In former times, collecting eggs of this species was supervised by rajas (kings) or other local authorities. Nesting grounds were leased, and only a few people were allowed to collect the eggs (Rosenberg 1878; Stresemann 1941; Watling 1983). This system usually guaranteed that enough eggs were left to hatch, although Uno (1949) reported local overexploitation and consequent population declines in north Sulawesi at the beginning of this century. Although fully protected by Indonesian law (Surat keputusan menteri pertanian No. 421/Kpts/Um/8/1970 tentang Ordonansi Perlindungan Binatang Liar 1931), the eggs are still collected and sold on the Sulawesian markets for 500–750 Rupiah (1000 Rp = 1 US$) which is about five times the price paid for chicken eggs.

MacKinnon (1981) and Watling (1983) reported recent declines in Maleo populations caused not only by overexploitation of the eggs but also by destruction of the birds' nesting grounds and habitat. The human population on Sulawesi has increased sharply, both from the high birth rate and as a result of transmigration of people from the overpopulated islands of Java and Bali. New villages have been established and roads have been built, especially along the coast. The Maleo nesting ground of Bakiriang on the east coast of central Sulawesi, which produced about 100 eggs per day during the peak of the season only five years ago (Watling 1983), is now said to be abandoned because of the development of a new settlement area. The same happened to the coastal nesting ground of Batu Putih, north Sulawesi, between 1913 and 1919 (MacKinnon 1981). In 1947, 9705 registered eggs were collected at the Panua nesting ground on north Sulawesi (Uno 1949) where MacKinnon (1981) reported production of only 2–3 eggs per day 30 years later. New nesting grounds, previously hidden in the tropical rainforest, are discovered when the forest is logged and are subsequently harvested. The uprooting of ancient traditions and the social changes due to transmigration result in egg collecting being completely uncontrolled. The eggs are not for local consumption only, but even find their way to restaurants in

Jakarta. The eggs are eagerly sought after, especially around Christmas, and are often given as presents to friends, relatives, or persons in special positions. In captivity Maleos can reach 20 years or more of age and still produce eggs (D. Bruning pers. comm.). The adults do not have many natural enemies, and under natural circumstances they can become quite old. They are hunted by man, but only on a small scale. If pairs are faithful to a certain nesting ground this will mean that the results of overexploitation of the eggs at such a site are not noticeable in the short run. This is probably why Maleos still make use of the inland nesting grounds of Tambun and Tumokang in north Sulawesi where the ICBP and the University of Amsterdam began a joint research and management project in 1985 in co-operation with the Dumoga-Bone National Park. The Tambun and Tumokang nesting grounds, situated inside the National Park, suffered many years of egg collecting which reduced both Maleo populations considerably. The opening up of the Dumoga Valley for agriculture, the rapid increase in human population, and the continued deforestation at the edge of the valley in the 1970s caused a severe threat to both nesting grounds. The establishment of the Dumoga-Bone National Park in 1980 guaranteed the survival of the tropical rainforest surrounding the valley and the two nesting grounds, although large-scale egg collecting could not be stopped (Rodenburg & Palete 1982).

In 1985, population numbers at each of the two nesting grounds were estimated at between 150 and 200 pairs, with a maximum egg production of 10–15 eggs per day. An estimated 3500 eggs were laid during the 1985/86 egg-laying season (September to June) at the two nesting grounds taken together. The first months of the research showed that hatching success was close to zero. Stealing of eggs, and predation on eggs and chicks by dogs and monitor lizards (*Varanus salvator*), were responsible for this. Following the hatching experiments of Hatibe and MacKinnon at the Panua nesting ground (MacKinnon 1981) a protected hatchery was built on each of the two nesting grounds in which eggs collected by staff of the Dumoga-Bone National Park were re-buried. Hatching success of eggs in these hatcheries varied during the year and averaged 55 percent for Tambun and 75 percent for Tumokang. With the help of these hatcheries, and by patrolling at both nesting grounds, more than 700 young Maleos have already hatched.

WHERE DO WE GO FROM HERE?

Restoration of the population

If we concentrate our efforts on these two nesting grounds only, many other known nesting grounds will come under threat and be abandoned in the near future. Without the help of Indonesians who live in villages close to nesting grounds nothing will be achieved. Ignorance among local people is the major problem. Stories about the common Maleo and its big eggs pass from father to son, and sound more like fairy tales now. Everyone still believes that Maleos occur everywhere and that egg collecting does not matter. However, meetings with local authorities of villages close to nesting grounds showed that they are interested, understand the situation, and are prepared to help when properly informed.

With the construction of hatcheries at other nesting grounds, fully controlled by park authorities if the nesting ground is inside a National Park or by local authorities if the site is outside park borders, Maleo populations can be built up again. Egg collecting will have to stop for a number of years, and egg predators like lizards and dogs will have to be removed from the nesting grounds. Once the population has returned to an acceptable size, eggs can be used for consumption again—but under strict supervision. A certain percentage of the eggs must always be used for the hatchery, while the surplus can be used for consumption. Although further research is necessary, preliminary calculations made for the Tambun and Tumokang nesting grounds show that several million rupiah can be obtained per year in the future in an area where people earn 2000–3000 Rp per day. If properly managed by National Park staff, or by tenants supervised by park or local authorities, with a leasing system such as existed fifty or more years ago, nesting grounds on Sulawesi can again become beneficial for Maleo and man. Money from these projects may be used to pay the people who collect the eggs, for maintenance of the nesting ground, for other nature conservation projects in the area or for community purposes.

Tourism
The nesting grounds can, however, be more than 'egg farms' alone: they can become real tourist attractions, as has been proved already. Local people from as far away as Manado (250km) have organized excursions to the Tambun nesting ground, and two international travel agencies now plan to include a visit to the Maleo project in their tours to Sulawesi. A properly controlled nesting ground, with a hatchery, a hide and a healthy Maleo population, can reveal many of the secrets of this unique species to nature-minded tourists. It is obvious that tourism to Sulawesi, with trips to remote areas, will stimulate the local economy on all levels—from hotel and restaurant owners to taxi drivers and farmers. Tourism will increase the awareness among the people of Sulawesi towards the Maleo and nature conservation in general.

The use and exploitation of natural resources can go hand in hand with nature conservation: the two may even stimulate each other. This is especially important in developing countries. The people of Sulawesi would think twice if they only realized what a 'goose with a golden egg' they might unknowingly exterminate.

ACKNOWLEDGEMENTS

This project was supported by ICBP, the Zoological Museum of the University of Amsterdam, Lembaga Ilmu Pengetahuan Indonesia, Lembaga Biologi Nasional-Bogor, Directorat Jenderal Perlindungan Hutan dan Pelestarian Alam and WWF-Indonesia. Financial support was given by WWF-Holland, WWF-Indonesia, Grand Hotel Krasnapolsky Amsterdam, Dierenrampenfonds, The Netherlands Foundation for International Nature Protection, Dr J. L. Dobberke Stichting voor Vergelijkende Psychologie, Greshoff's Rumphius Fonds 1913 and the Netherlands Foundation for International Bird Protection. The Netherlands Society for the Protection of Birds donated two pairs of binoculars. I wish to thank Ir Ubus Wardju Maskar, Ir Raymond Palete, Ir Jan Wind, Dra Charlotte Vermeulen and my Indonesian counterparts who shared in the pleasure and hardships of the field work.

REFERENCES

Clark, G. A. 1964. Life histories and the evolution of megapodes. *Living Bird* 3, 149–67.
Lister, J. J. 1911. The distribution of the avian genus Megapodius in the Pacific Islands. *Proc. Zool. Soc. London,* 1911, 749–59.

MacKinnon, J. 1981. Methods for the conservation of maleobirds, *Macrocephalon maleo*, on the island of Sulawesi, Indonesia. *Biol. Conserv.* **20**, 183–93.

Meyer, O. 1930. Untersuchungen an den Eiern von *Megapodius eremita*. *Orn. Monatsber.* **38**, 1, 1–5.

Rodenburg, W. F. & Palete, R. 1982. *Proposed Dumoga-Bone National Park management plan 1982–1983.* WWF/IUCN Conservation for Development Programme in Indonesia. Bogor.

Rosenberg, H. von. 1878. *Der Malayische Archipel.* Gustav Wiegel, Leipzig.

Stresemann, E. 1941. Die Vögel von Celebes. *J. Orn.* **89**, 1–102.

Todd, D. 1983. Pritchard's megapode on Niuafo'ou Island, Kingdom of Tonga. *J. Wld. Pheasant Ass.* **8**, 69–88.

Uno, A. 1949. Het natuurmonument Panoea (N. Celebes) en het maleohoen *Macrocephalon maleo* Sal. Muller in het bijzonder. *Tectona* **39**, 151–65.

Vleck, D., Vleck, C. M. & Seymour, R. S. 1984. Energetics of embryonic development in the megapode birds, Malleefowl *Leipoa ocellata* and Brush Turkey *Alectura lathami*. *Physiol. Zool.* **57**, 4, 444–56.

Watling, D. 1983. Sandbox incubator. *Animal Kingdom* **53**, 28–35.

Wolters, H. E. 1976. *Die Vogelarten der Erde.* Paul Parey, Hamburg & Berlin.

THE CULTURAL AND ECONOMIC IMPORTANCE OF BIRDS AMONG THE BORAN PEOPLE OF NORTHERN KENYA

HUSSEIN ADAN ISACK

*National Museum of Kenya, Dept. of Ornithology, P.O. Box 40658,
Nairobi, Kenya*

ABSTRACT

The Boran people are pastoral nomads who keep cattle, camels, sheep and goats in an arid region of northern Kenya. Birds play an important role in many aspects of Boran life. Several species have direct effects on the economic welfare of the people. Many more play important roles in the cosmology, traditional medicine, religion and ceremonies of the Boran. Birds also feature in Boran songs, folktales and proverbs.

The roles that birds play in the ecosystem and in the socio-economic environment in which the Boran people live have moulded the attitudes of the nomads towards birds. The consequence has been the enhancement of bird conservation through a number of cultural rules and practices. (For a general view of the Boran traditional ethics of conservation, see Isack 1976).

Finally, the effects that changes in people's way of life has had on their attitudes towards birds is discussed.

INTRODUCTION

The Boran people display some practical, conscious relationship with, or use of, a number of bird species in their area. They also have strong beliefs and taboos about certain other birds. To understand the basis of their beliefs about birds and their use of birds it is necessary to take a brief look at some of the social and ecological constraints experienced by the Boran.

The Boran belong to the Cushitic group of nomads, and inhabit a large part of northern Kenya and southern Ethiopia. They comprise four major sub-groups: the Gabbra and Sakuyye, who rear mainly camels, sheep and goats; the Boran-gutu, whose main livestock are cattle; and the Watt, the smallest group, who traditionally do not keep domestic livestock, but instead live by hunting.

The traditional homeland of the Boran is characterized by low annual rainfall (less than 200mm per year) and high temperatures. For a people whose existence depends on livestock, the droughts that result from inadequate rain, or outright rain failures, bring human and animal sufferings of great magnitude. As a natural response to this ecological stress, the people lead a nomadic life, migrating over large areas as they search for pasture and water for their livestock.

In addition to their fear of rain failures, the people are constantly worried about the future of their prosperity—which includes wealth, reproductive success, manpower, peace and health. These uncertainties and other ecological factors have dictated the way the people relate to the environment, and in this instance, towards birds.

SOME DIRECT ECOLOGICAL AND ECONOMIC EFFECTS OF BIRDS

In this arid region, birds are of great ecological and economic significance. They participate in pollination and seed dispersal—a fact that is important in the maintenance and distribution of the flora of the area. Similarly, their predation on insects that often devastate the grass cover, and the foliage of trees that provide both food and shade, is of some considerable importance. On the other hand, the birds' depletion of seeds of annual grasses, especially in degraded areas, could have important ecological consequences for pastoral nomads.

Ticks (*Acaris* spp.) cause weakness in animals, often destroy their milk teats, and may transmit a number of diseases. Oxpeckers (Buphagidae) help rid the domestic livestock of tick infestation, but by pecking off and eating flesh from wounds on the backs of camels and donkeys, with which they associate closely, these birds may also facilitate wound infection and thereby incapacitate these beasts of burden on which the people depend for transportation of water and other loads.

The roles that vultures play in keeping the environment clean, and thereby in the control of epidemic diseases, cannot be over-emphasized. By contrast some eagles, notably the Tawny Eagle (*Aquila rapax*) and the Martial Eagle (*Polemaetus bellicosus*) are known to prey occasionally on lambs and kids of sheep and goats.

Birds as food
With the exception of the Watt (the hunter-gatherer group) the consumption of bird or any wildlife meat by the other three Boran groups was traditionally forbidden (Isack 1986). Though this is no longer wholly true today, the reason for the existence of the taboo is said to be the loss of good luck and spiritual powers by any person who happens to eat a bird. Such a person loses his unique natural powers to influence external forces to his advantage, and he becomes prone to misfortunes.

'Birds are birds', they also say, 'and because some of them eat human flesh [Vultures, Accipitridae] they are unclean'. However, for the Watt, the Ostrich (*Struthio camelus*) does provide a source of food. Except on occasions when a game-bird came in hand, smaller birds were traditionally ignored—even by the Watt.

Medicinal use of birds
Oil extracted from the fatty base of the Ostrich tail is bought from the Watt and used for the treatment of a number of ailments, especially chronic backaches and bone diseases. It is also said to be very good for post-natal 'womb cleaning' in women. The oil is also drunk as a laxative.

The quill feathers of large birds, especially those of birds of prey, are used for cleaning wounds. During the treatment, contact between wound and fingers is avoided. The feather is believed to stop the wound from becoming septic. The feather may also be burnt, ground into powder and, together with herb powder, applied to the wound.

Ceremonial importance
During his development, every male member of the Boran community goes through a number of initiation rites into age and generation groups. Among the Boran-gutu there are eleven different generations, each separated by a period of eight years. After this period, every individual moves up one step. The highest political office in Boran-gutu can be held only by a member of the 6th generation group. At the end of his era, and before he and his group move up to the 7th stage, the leader must officially hand over his office and powers to an elected member of the new 6th generation group. This is a very important ceremony, which cannot take place unless both the retiring and new leaders possess Ostrich feathers during the function.

In fact, the possession of an Ostrich feather is compulsory during most Boran ceremonies—for example, during the election of age-group leaders, during child-naming ceremonies, and during change-over ceremonies of the many different generation sets. For this reason, every family expecting to participate in these traditional functions keeps Ostrich feathers in the home, and the feathers are passed on from father to son. A man wears the feathers in his hair in order to let it be known that he is a brave man who has killed a lion, elephant, rhino, buffalo or giraffe.

Craft
Bird products are also put to other uses. If found intact, the Ostrich egg is perforated and the contents emptied out. The inside is thoroughly cleaned, then the whole shell is tightly covered with fresh (wet) cattle hide. The small opening is fitted with a lid, and the shell—now virtually unbreakable—is used as a container for hair oil and edible fats.

There is yet another, universally common use for bird feathers. The flight feathers of large birds are broken into suitable sized pieces and fixed to the wooden shafts of arrows in order to achieve more propulsion and accuracy when the weapon is fired.

Trade
Trade in bird products occurs to a very limited extent. The only products that are sold or exchanged for other items by the Watt are Ostrich feathers and oil. In return, the Watt receives a domestic animal (sheep or goat); other useful materials such as spears and arrows with which he can hunt; or any other gift of appreciation.

BIRDS AS A SOURCE OF INFORMATION

Revealing the whereabouts of honey
Known as Simpirre-Damma (honey bird), the Greater Honeyguide (*Indicator indicator*) has a special 'symbiotic' relationship with the Boran, as it does with several other peoples of Africa (Friedmann 1955). To make use of the bird's habit of leading man to wild bee hives, the Boran perform, in a suitable area, a number of activities that facilitate this co-operation. These include loud wood tapping, whistling, loud calling, and creating smoke—performed simultaneously or individually. Such self-advertisement by man results in a greater response by the

bird—which then guides him to a bee colony whose location the bird already knows.

After the man attacks the bees' nest for honey, the bird receives a reward of nutritious bee combs and larvae which would otherwise have been inaccessible. Without the help of the bird, the search by a honey hunter for bee hives is costly in both time and energy. Several days may pass before he locates a single new bee colony purely by chance. However, when a bird co-operates, a bee colony is almost certain to be located, and on average a man saves about 64 percent of the time he would have spent on unaided search (Isack, unpub.).

Honey plays a number of important roles in the lives of the Boran people. As food, it can be eaten on the spot. It can be diluted with water or milk to make a refreshing drink. Honey is used for the treatment of a number of diseases, such as malaria, chicken pox, pneumonia, stomach troubles and several other diseases. It is also used for brewing alcohol, and as a tea sweetener. When sold, honey can bring in a monthly cash income four times what a honey hunter can earn as a casual labourer for the same duration of time in northern Kenya (Isack, in prep.). Although specialist honey hunters search for honey only during certain periods of the year, herdsboys, herdsmen, and other opportunist honey collectors do use the bird and attack the bees all through the year.

Currently, the price of units of honey and sugar to sweeten equal volumes of tea are nearly the same (in northern Kenya). Honey is therefore not cheaper than sugar. However, wild honey is free, if one is prepared to face the bees, and available in remote areas where sugar is not. These facts probably mean that the nutritional importance of honey, and thus the role of the bird, was even more important for the Boran people in the past.

Indicating the coming of rain

Because rain is crucial for the survival and well-being of the Boran and their livestock, the anticipation of its arrival at the expected end of the dry season creates much anxiety amongst the people. To relieve the anxiety, the Boran resort to frequent consultations with experts, whose weather forecasting is based on the study of cloud formations, the configuration and positions of stars in the sky, the patterns of glands, veins and arteries on mammalian entrails, and the occurrence and behaviour of birds.

The Boran rely heavily on their powers of observation to speculate on the possibilities of rainfall. The arrival of migratory European Storks (*Ciconia ciconia*) and Abdim's Storks (*Ciconia abdimii*) is associated with the coming of the rain. Likewise, the appearance of Yellow Wagtails (*Motacilla flava*) announces that the rain is near. When many Cattle Egrets (*Bubulcus ibis*) turn up in an area and associate with cattle, the message is that one should expect a good (heavy) rain season. Other birds, such as the Black-bellied Bustard (*Eupodotis melanogaster*), Kori Bustard (*Otis kori*), and Blue-spotted Wood Dove (*Turtur afer*) emit calls that are used as indicators of rain.

It is interesting to note that the birds whose arrivals are associated with the coming of the rain (storks, wagtails) are migrants which normally arrive in northern Kenya at or just before the start of the short (Oct./Nov.) rain season. Thus, part of the Yellow Wagtail's local name, 'Hagayyole', may have been derived from the name of the short rain, Hagayy.

Indicating danger

Birds are widely used as indicators of potentially dangerous situations. Thus, whenever a travelling Boran hears the shrill 'Chirr . . .' cry of the Oxpecker, he knows that some large and possibly dangerous animal is nearby, and changes his route accordingly. Oxpeckers associate closely with rhinos, buffalos and several other large mammals from which they remove, and eat, ticks (Benson 1964; Attwell 1966; Mengesha 1978).

The Boran also respond to the harsh warning cries of several species of bird that congregate near snakes. The Superb Starling (*Spreo superbus*) is well known for this behaviour. Close to human settlement, the danger is usually investigated, and if a snake is found, it is killed. However, if this behaviour of the bird is observed in the bush, far from home, the site is usually avoided. In these circumstances, the benefit of finding and killing the snake would be lost if, during the confrontation, the snake managed to inflict a bite on the person.

As an adaptation to the problems of dessication in the desert, the Boran people tend to travel (on foot) during the night, when temperatures are low. This reduces the chances of suffering from dehydration. However, travelling at night also increases the risks of being harmed by several nocturnal animals, especially snakes, lions or often human beings. Plovers (*Vanellus coronatus* and *V. spinosus*) respond to disturbances at night by flying off and creating a lot of noise. Thus, night travellers use the birds as an indicator of the presence of other large mammals in the area in which they are travelling.

Giving a variety of information

Even before the arrival of the present-day ivory trade and the excessive poaching that accompanies it, the Boran people killed elephants (*Loxodonta africana*) as a means of proving their bravery and thereby raising their social status. In addition, the tusks, which are used as traditionally important ornaments, were sold to local buyers in exchange for up to thirty head of cattle per pair of tusks.

However, since elephants were hunted with spears, critically wounded individuals occasionally escaped from the hunters, only to die some hours or days later, hidden in the bush. These animals had to be caught, to secure the precious tusks, and to do this effectively the hunters would constantly watch the sky for vultures that may have been attracted to an elephant carcass.

In a similar way, a search party that is looking for a cow or camel that has gone astray will look out for, and investigate the site of, vulture activities in order to establish whether it is their animal that has died. If this is the case, they can return home immediately, and thereby save their time and energy.

The sighting of many vultures circling above a particular location, especially close to tribal boundaries, is given serious attention for the birds may have been attracted to a place where a party of approaching warriors from an enemy tribe has killed an animal and stopped to feed. A reconnaissance party of able-bodied men is usually sent to the site to investigate and report back to a Boran defence group monitoring the area. For this reason, people on a raiding mission always try to ensure that the vultures do not discover their food kills, usually by covering up the meat, or by performing some witchcraft intended to blind the vultures.

Sudden outbursts of the alarming 'Tit tit tit . . .' call of a woodpecker (*Campethera* spp.) is one of the most characteristic sounds in the dry bush country of northern Kenya. The metallic, ear-piercing call can easily stir panic in a lone traveller who is already worried about the possibilities of meeting with a dangerous animal or man (pers. obs.). Subtle call variations, and the direction from which one hears it, are believed to indicate whether the bird is warning of dangers, the location of potential prey such as a giraffe (*Giraffa camelopardalis*), or lost domestic animals.

Indicating water

The greatest enemy to a traveller in the desert is dehydration. Doves (*Streptopelia* spp.), and queleas (*Quelea* spp.) are known to concentrate at sources of water such as rain pools, springs or man-made wells, and this behaviour is exploited by the local people as they travel in unfamiliar areas. Such travel across unfamiliar terrain is a common feature of the nomadic life: the people constantly need to find new pastures and new sources of water, and also to occasionally make their way through unfamiliar lands as they head for other tribes. Although such travels are not usually undertaken unless there is a known source of water along the route, the roles played by these birds in saving peoples' lives could be quite significant.

Announcing an imminent war

During their migrations, Boran villagers often find themselves in vulnerable situations. A number of neighbouring tribes are bent on attacking the Boran and acquiring their livestock by force—and people are often killed in the attacks. Under these conditions, the villagers are naturally quite edgy.

There is a 'war bird' which in the dark of the night, emits a hair-raising, high pitched, 'Hirrrr . . .' sound which is perceived by the Boran people as being 'terrible to the ear'. It is possible that several species of bird are capable of emitting sounds that alarm the Boran during the night. I think one such group are the goshawks (*Melierax* spp.). The calls are perceived as being very similar to a shout of aggression emitted by a Boran in battle. The belief in the truth of the message is so strong that often a whole village migrates to another safer site, far from the potentially dangerous neighbouring tribe. Boran have a very strong fear of the implications of odd phenomena. An odd happening is always a sign of terrible news to come. Good examples are the eclipse of the sun or the moon. Likewise, the vocalization by a bird very late in the night, especially if it is high and shrill, is a sign of imminent calamity. This belief is so strong that a domestic cock (*Gallus gallus*) which crows at an odd hour of the night is often condemned to death the following day.

Birds as signs of bad omen

Verreaux's Eagle Owl (*Bubo lacteus*).   This owl is associated with death. If it sits near a home in the night and calls, it is believed that a member of the family will soon die. When the owl 'cries', it is believed to shed not 'water' but 'blood' as tears.

Marabou Storks (*Leptoptilos crumeniferus*) and vultures (*Gyps* spp.).   These scavengers flourish when other animals are dying, and for this reason, pastoral nomads associate them with the time of much death in domestic animals. The appearance of large numbers of these birds close to a human settlement is believed to forecast an approaching mass death of domestic livestock or people due to drought or war.

Yellow-necked Spurfowl (*Francolinus leucoscepus*).   In the wild, the spurfowl is considered harmless. However, it is believed that when this bird enters the animal 'boma' (night enclosure for domestic animals), the livestock will experience a tremendous reduction in numbers.

Fan-tailed Raven (*Corvus rhipidurus*).   The Fan-tailed Raven is a scavenger whose appearance in a cattle enclosure, or whose calls at dawn or dusk, are taken as signs of bad omen.

Plovers (*V. coronatus* and *V. spinosus*).   These plovers, known in Boran as 'Wiitu', often make calls which sound quite sorrowful. This is especially true during the night when one hears that prolonged, 'W-I-I-I-I-T, WIT-WIT-WIT . . .' call. If a plover makes such calls near one's home, it is believed that a close member of the family will die in the near future. If the bird calls close to a particular hut, it is very bad news for the owner of the hut. His life is in great danger.

Birds as signs of good omen

Hornbills (*Tockus erythrorhynchus* and *T. flavirostris*). The song of these hornbills, during which the bird spreads its wings and rocks its body up and down, is believed to forecast a time of plentiful resources and happiness for people. The performance of this dance in front of a family hut is a sign of wealth to come to that family.

Swallows (*Hirundinidae*). The construction and use of a nest by this bird (most likely *Hirundo abyssinica*) inside a human hut is a sign of a forthcoming baby in the family that owns the hut. For this reason, these birds are never molested in any way.

Birds with supernatural powers

A number of birds of prey are believed to possess immense supernatural powers. It is believed that a person who is struck by the wing of a raptor could die instantly or suffer some paralysis. Even one who is not affected immediately will eventually suffer from insanity, chronic headaches or fainting problems. The cause of the illness is not the physical force, but an evil spirit which the bird introduces into the body of the victim. It is believed that this introduction can take place even without actual physical contact between the bird and man.

For this reason, certain diseases are always associated with birds of prey, and their treatment is possible only through exorcism. The fear of these birds is so great that people often refer to them as 'The Winged Ones'. Their real collective Boran name, *Risa,* literally mean, 'the one that paralyses'. Saying to somebody, 'May you be struck by a raptor' is considered to be a terrible ill-wish.

The raptor with the most potent spiritual power is the Bateleur (*Terathopius ecaudatus*). When it flies over a village, a clay cup containing red-hot charcoal is placed outside. As an offering, animal fat or incense is put in the container in order to produce a smoke. As the smoke drifts up towards the sky, the person utters the words, 'Do not yearn for ours. Here is yours'. At other times, they say to the eagle, 'If you have any evil with you, please take it elsewhere'.

BORAN CULTURAL ATTITUDES THAT PROMOTE THE PRESERVATION OF BIRDS

A number of Boran cultural rules, beliefs and taboos have made significant contributions to the protection of birds. One most important attitude is the general avoidance of birds as a source of food. The hunting of some birds for food and other products was traditionally carried out only by the Watt. Furthermore, the Watt are a very small subgroup, and the Ostrich, which they mainly hunt, is a very difficult bird to kill. The hunting of birds as a sport by adult members of Boran society has never existed. Secondly, because the Boran are pastoralists, even those birds that are pests to agricultural farmers are harmless to them. There is therefore no reason to kill any bird. The only individuals who kill birds are young boys who have undergone circumcision and are waiting to heal. During this period, these boys hunt birds and small rodents using bows and arrows. For reasons discussed already, there is a positively strong avoidance of the molesting of birds of prey, and their nests sites are never approached too closely.

Equally strong security for eggs and nestlings is enjoyed by the small, defence-less species. This arises from the fact that Boran have great respect for birds' nests, especially if they occur in a colony. The helpless young in the nests represent new births, and therefore to kill them is tantamount to denouncing prosperity. This respect is strengthened by the structural similarity between a colony of birds' nests and a cluster of huts in a Boran village. Thus, even when there is a shortage of thorny trees with which to fence in the domestic animals at night, the cutting down of a tree bearing nests is strongly forbidden. Furthermore, there is a strong belief that any child who passes below such a tree will get a severe attack of fungal (ringworm) infection on the head. Birds' nests are therefore protected from interference by adults and children.

Some birds are accorded special protection. The killing of the Greater Honey-guide and the Oxpecker is forbidden, the former for its co-operation in finding honey, and the latter for its close, beneficial association with livestock. The killing of Oxpeckers is said to be 'bad for cattle'.

CHANGING ATTITUDES

The ever-increasing tendency of the people to change from nomadism to seden-tary life has led to the increased practice of subsistence agriculture and small-scale business. This is accompanied by a change from the traditional protein-rich staple diet of milk and meat to cereal foods, and to obtain the necessary protein, this section of the population eats chicken meat, as well as guineafowl and spurfowl.

In addition, religions like Islam and Christianity, which have been introduced into the area, claim that game-birds are good and clean to eat. Some Muslim teachers maintain that birds such as the Ring-necked Dove (*Streptopelia capicola*) whose collar mark signifies that the bird was symbolically slaughtered and made halal (pure) by God, is only waiting to be consumed by man. This has helped weaken the Boran taboo of avoiding bird meat. Equally significant is the influence of individuals from other tribes of Kenya who come into the area, happily eat game-birds, and suffer no ill effects. These individuals (usually Government officers, school teachers, etc) purchase these birds from young boys who are able to trap them. A full-grown guineafowl fetches about KShs 7.00 in Sololo, approximately equivalent to £0.35 sterling.

Two very important changes which have affected the traditions of the Boran people during the last twenty years are increased poverty (due to the combined effects of bandits, bad weather and politics) and increased numbers of educated people in the society (due to political independence from Britain). Poverty has made the Boran eat new foods, including guineafowl and spurfowl, and some people are already talking of the possibilities of eating doves. With the rationale gained from formal education and exposure to the outside world, these trends have no bounds and can only be expected to continue.

Nowadays, small numbers of Boran have started consuming Ostrich eggs as a source of food. As the number of people who consume the previously avoided chicken eggs increases, the exploitation of Ostrich eggs will not only be accepted, but will also increase—especially in view of the volume of the eggs' contents. In the long term, this could have serious effects on the breeding success of these birds.

The cultural beliefs about birds, and the people's dependence on them for information and other traditional functions, are clearly losing their importance. This is a result of formal education, cultural changes, and the emergence of other, more reliable and scientific sources of information in areas such as weather prediction and medicine.

To agriculturalists, birds are generally regarded as pests. For this reason, birds that were held in high esteem by pastoralists, as well as those which to them existed only passively, have suddenly become enemies to the new farmers.

These cultural and economic changes imply that birds are probably going to play an increased role in the diet, and a diminished role in the tradition and culture of the Boran. It is already noticeable that increasing numbers of guineafowl and spurfowl are consumed. I predict that this will be followed by an increase in the number of species that will be regarded as acceptable for human consumption.

Poverty, which by Boran standards means lack of sufficient domestic livestock, plus the switch to agriculture or employment in towns, has meant a reduction in the amount of animal protein, especially meat, that is available to these people. Wild birds are beginning to play an important role in fulfilling these needs. Even if one had to buy these birds from the children who are able to trap them, a guineafowl is currently 50 to 80 percent cheaper than a domestic chicken of equal weight. But when demands increase and adults begin to get involved in the capture and sale of these birds, the price will probably go up quite considerably.

Considering the strength of the Boran culture, the time when the people will exploit wild birds on a large scale appears still to be far off. However, cultural changes and their effects on the environment can be very rapid and destructive, and because of this, it is important that conservationists pay more attention to the traditional use of birds and how this is affected by cultural changes. Through this, it might be possible to understand and deal with the effects of these changes on bird populations.

Obviously, increased exploitation of any bird species will have a negative impact on its population unless some regulation is imposed. This is especially true if the local techniques of trapping birds (which at the moment are quite inefficient) are greatly improved. This will be analogous to the change from the traditional use of spears to the present-day use of automatic AK47 guns for hunting rhinos or elephants. In northern Kenya, rhinos are now virtually extinct.

In the same way, the association between man and honeyguide, which has gone on for thousands of years, will diminish as man depends less and less on the bird. The dependence of man on this bird is decreasing because:

– Specialist honey hunters are migrating to the towns for work. A regular salary is more reliable than hunting for honey in the bush; and is not prone to the effects of drought.

– The role of honey as a source of medicine has diminished because of the availability of modern drugs from Government, as well as Missionary hospitals.

– The rush of specialist honey hunters into the towns means that less honey will be available to the 'common man'. At the same time, the change in the economy has meant more possibilities for obtaining cash, for example, through employment or sale of livestock, and this in turn now enables many people to buy sugar from shops.

– The improvement in the cash economy has facilitated the establishment of small retail shops in many parts of northern Kenya. Thus, for those who can afford it, sugar has become more widely available.

– Due to Government requirements for sending children to schools, far fewer individuals are now recruited to be herdsmen or honey hunters. This has had a significant effect on the honeyguide–man association (Isack, in prep.).

– The local alcoholic drink, which is made using honey, is illegal in Kenya. This therefore affects the market and price of honey.

What the long-term effect of man's reduced co-operation will have on the future of the honeyguide population is unknown. However, it appears that where man has failed to co-operate with it, the bird has shown a tendency to abandon this aspect of its behaviour (Queeny 1952).

We do not know how the settled Boran communities, especially the farmers, are affecting bird populations adapted to living in lands that were formerly free from farming. This would be especially important for colonial nesting birds whose habitat (for example, the acacia tree) is frequently destroyed because it shades cultivated crops. In order to throw more light on the traditional and 'modern' interactions between birds and the Boran people, more studies and solid data are required. Through this, it might be possible to design a suitable—and still rational—use of birds under the new circumstances.

REFERENCES

ATTWELL, R. I. G. 1966. Oxpeckers and their association with mammals in Zambia. *Puku* **4**, 17–48.

BENSON, C. W. 1964. Birds associating with ungulates. *Auk* **81** (3), 346.

FRIEDMANN, H. 1955. The honeyguides. *U.S. Nat. Bull.* **208**.

ISACK, H. A. 1976. African ethics of conservation. *Nat. Hist.* Vol. LXXXV, Nov. p. 95.

ISACK, H. A. 1986. *Peoples of the north: Boran.* Evans Brothers (Kenya) Ltd. p. 26.

MENGESHA, Y. A. 1978. A study of oxpecker–mammal symbiosis in Ethiopia. *E.A. Agr. J.* **43**, 321–7.

QUEENY, E. M. 1952. The Wandorobo and the honeyguide. *Nat. Hist.* **61**, 392–6.

A GLOBAL VIEW OF CULTURAL AND ECONOMIC USES OF BIRDS

A. W. Diamond

Canadian Widlife Service, Ottawa, Ontario K1A 0H3, Canada

Several papers in this volume describe socio-economic studies which show unequivocally that people in modern industrialized societies value birds very highly, and for a variety of reasons (Clark; Jacquemot & Filion; Schultz. See also Kellert 1980a,b; Anon. 1982). Yet those of us who make our living studying birds often have the impression that important sections of society view a pre-occupation with birds as an amusing pastime rather than as a subject of real importance. The favourable views towards birds and other wildlife that people express in socio-economic surveys do not seem to translate into a general societal attitude, nor into political realities. This discordance between public perceptions and political policy persists in spite of solid demonstrations of the economic value of the non-consumptive uses of birds (Kellert 1980a; Anon. 1982; Filion *et al.* 1983).

The surveys described elsewhere in this volume are of recent origin, and have been carried out in industrialized nations of the northern hemisphere. They are, therefore, open to the objection that favourable and caring attitudes to birdlife are characteristic of countries whose people have time and money to spare, and are not likely to apply to countries in which the day-to-day struggle for existence is paramount. However, some very recent studies in developing countries suggest that peoples' attitudes to wildlife there are not much less sympathetic than attitudes in more affluent societies (Pennington 1983; Weber 1981, 1986 in Harcourt *et al.* 1986). These surveys in developing countries did not specifically address attitudes to birds *per se*, but there is no reason to suppose these attitudes would differ from those to wildlife in general.

Lacking any surveys of the uses of birdlife in the world in general, I can examine this question only by reviewing descriptive accounts of other societies, and of early stages of our own. This examination shows that birds are and have been useful to people in many different ways; that mankind has always had a very special relationship with birds, and that it is societies that do not recognize this, rather than those that do, that are aberrant.

I shall make my case by reviewing the range of economic and cultural uses to which birds are, or have been, put, concentrating on aspects or societies that have not been subjected to the kind of professional survey that other contributors have described. For convenience I use discrete subject headings, but these divisions are conceptual rather than real because birds—even of a single species—are used and valued for many different reasons. This holistic view of bird-use is illustrated by the most widely-used of all birds, the domestic fowl. Although it is now kept almost exclusively for its meat and eggs (see below), it was first valued for its sacrificial and religious significance and for cock-fighting, and it has been suggested that these uses were more responsible for the species' distribution by man than was its potential for producing food (Wood-Gush 1985). My approach is hardly different from earlier treatments of the subject (e.g. Hartley 1922) in being essentially descriptive, though I have quoted figures where I could find them.

BIRDS AS A FOOD RESOURCE

Domesticated birds

Poultry meat accounts for about 18 percent of all meat produced for human consumption, while the meat and eggs of birds together provide at least 15 percent of the total animal protein produced by mankind (Bowman 1977, *Tables 2* and *5*). These figures are derived from the *FAO Production Yearbook* and undoubtedly underestimate backyard production of poultry, especially in the developing world. Chickens have been domesticated for at least 4500 years, and are more widely distributed throughout the world than any other domestic animal except the dog. They are small, easy to keep, will eat almost anything, and are very hardy, so they can be kept by the poorest people, on very little land. Because of their availability to the least privileged members of human society, chickens are the single animal species contributing most to mankind's consumption of protein.

Many other species of bird have been domesticated for their food value. Turkeys (*Meleagris gallopavo*) were domesticated in North America before Columbus arrived, and are widely farmed now as the centrepiece of traditional festivals such as Christmas and Thanksgiving. Ducks and geese are also common as domestic stock, and Ostriches (*Struthio camelus*) are farmed in southern Africa not only for feathers and leather but also for their famous eggs, which begin as the world's largest single animal cell and end as its biggest breakfast.

Pigeons (*Columba livia*) housed in dovecotes in mediaeval Europe (and later) were an important year-round source of food for many communities. The dovecotes were often elaborate structures of stone, with a moveable wooden stage in the centre from which access could be gained to the hundreds of nesting niches built into the inside of the walls. The central 'keep' of many fortified castles was often equipped with a dovecote; the pigeons could feed in the surrounding countryside and return to the keep inside the castle, enabling the inhabitants to prolong their resistance to seige.

For centuries, Mute Swans (*Cygnus olor*) have been—and still are—'farmed' by monks at Abbotsbury in England, originally for food, while the 'Royal' swan has a long history of providing gourmet meals. Other tasty species that have been domesticated in various parts of the world, partly if not solely for their value as food, include Egyptian Geese (*Alopochen aegyptica*), Peafowl (*Pavo cristatus*), Guinea Fowl (Numididae), Quail (*Coturnix coturnix*) and even Little Egrets (*Egretta garzetta*) (Wood-Gush 1985).

Several kinds of game-bird, notably Ring-necked Pheasants (*Phasianus colchicus*) and Red Grouse (*Lagopus lagopus*) are intensively farmed, if not actually domesticated. Their cultivation is not strictly for food, being primarily for sport, but they nonetheless do provide significant nutritional benefit (lawful and otherwise) to the communities in which they are raised and hunted.

Wild birds

Wild birds provide food in a host of different societies throughout the world. They contribute 2.5–3.0 percent of all food to forest-dwelling peoples of Amazonia; the main groups involved are guans and curassows (Cracidae), tinamous (Tinamidae), doves (Columbidae), trumpeters (Psophiidae) and quail

(Phasianidae) (Pierret & Dourojeanni, quoted by Dourojeanni 1985). In Europe, Rook (*Corvus frugilegus*) and pigeon pies are traditional favourites of country people, and small songbirds on migration are still trapped and shot for food on a large scale. The eggs of quail, guinea fowl and plovers support specialized markets as delicacies in richer countries, while there and in many poorer lands the eggs of gulls and terns often make important contributions to human diets. In the Seychelle Islands of the Indian Ocean, the eggs of Sooty Terns (*Sterna fuscata*) have traditionally been harvested from the outlying islands, and provide such a welcome change from the usual diet of dried fish that people still fight for a place at the dock-side when the egg-boats come in. Sooty Terns are probably the commonest and most widely distributed of all tropical seabirds, and nest in such huge colonies that even though each pair lays only one egg, hundreds of thousands of eggs can be cropped in a season without reducing the population of terns (Ridley & Percy 1958; Feare 1976).

The egg production of such abundant colonial species, if properly managed, offers one of the clearest opportunities for sustained-yield harvesting of a wild bird resource. Skira (this volume) describes perhaps the best-documented example in which management of a colonial seabird for sustained yield seems to work tolerably well in practice. Seabirds offer the best opportunities for this kind of harvesting, because they tend to breed in large numbers in concentrated colonies at predictable seasons, and colonies of seabirds have been exploited in this way for many generations in several parts of the world (e.g. Faeroe Islands (Norrevang 1986), many islands in the South Pacific (Allen 1976; Chapman 1985), Outer Hebrides, Greenland, Iceland, Aleutian Islands, Japan and the Pelew Islands (Jones 1985)) and in some cases they have actually been the key resource for an entire human community (e.g. St. Kilda). Such societies have developed similar cultural traditions to control ownership of nesting cliffs and to regulate cropping, and most have apparently had little effect on the size of the seabird populations that they crop.

Birds as a human food resource have played a big enough part in human history to justify a book on that subject alone. Seabird colonies—and landbirds that were tame, abundant and tasty—have played significant roles in human exploration and colonization of the remotest parts of the planet. Lord Howe Island in the South Pacific and Funk Island in the North Atlantic were both important victualling stations for European explorers, who for decades—and in Funk's case, for centuries—found their tame, abundant bird-life a welcome source of fresh meat after the wearisome diet that sailors had to endure in the days before steam-engines and refrigeration. Funk Island was often the first landfall after leaving Europe on the westward crossing of the Atlantic, and the immense colonies of Great Auks (*Alca impennis*) which bred there provided the first fresh meat that west-bound sailors had seen for several weeks, and probably saved the lives of many a starving shipload of stormbound sailors. The distribution of Great Auks at sea was used by European fishing fleets as an indicator of their position on the Newfoundland Banks, and by the 1580s the French fishing fleet was so confident of the Great Auks' ability to support them that they took little fresh meat with them from Europe (Nettleship & Evans 1985).

Other colonial birds that can be exploited sustainably are the various species of cave-nesting swiftlets (*Collocalia* spp.) in south-east Asia, whose nests are fixed to the roofs or walls of caves by their own saliva (Harrison & Becking 1985). Birds'-nest soup is the 'caviar of the East', and many members of several societies in Indonesia and Malaysia make their living by selling swift spit. The trade has been carried on probably since pre-historic times, and has also involved protection and regulated harvesting of the colonies (Harrison & Becking 1985).

There are more subtle uses of birds to provide food, in which the bird itself is not eaten but either brings food to people, or leads them to it. In China and in Japan, Cormorants (*Phalacrocorax carbo*) are domesticated and trained to catch fish and return them to their owners; a collar around the bird's neck (usually attached to a leash) ensures that the bird does not swallow the fish for itself. In this case the birds are thoroughly domesticated, but there are several instances of wild birds being used to find food. In many parts of the world, seabirds—especially those that feed in flocks—are used by knowledgeable fishermen to locate schools of fish. This relationship (referred to in this volume by Haynes) is widely mentioned in an anecdotal fashion but has not yet attracted scientific investigation. In oceanic-island communities of very long standing—such as in the southwest Pacific—it was probably this use of birds to locate fish-schools that led to their less obvious use as aids in trans-oceanic navigation.

The well-known behaviour of the Greater Honeyguide (*Indicator indicator*) of Africa in guiding people to wild bees' nests has become a stock ingredient of the natural-history literature, and is evidently of real nutritional and economic value to the people who use it (Isack, this volume).

The American West was settled with the assistance of vast hordes of flocking birds that provided a cheap and reliable food supply to sustain the first settlers, and later the burgeoning human populations spreading from the east. Passenger Pigeons (*Ectopistes migratorius*), Carolina Parakeets (*Conuropsis carolinensis*) and Eskimo Curlews (*Numenius borealis*) certainly did their bit for the settlement of America by providing an (at first) unlimited supply of cheap food both for west-bound pioneers and for the East Coast markets which sprang up to feed the expanding population of immigrants (Peterson 1964).

Birds can not only provide food, or lead people to it, but can also help to grow it. Seabird guano—derived from Guanay Cormorants (*Phalacrocorax bougainvillii*), Peruvian Boobies (*Sula variegata*) and Brown Pelicans (*Pelecanus occidentalis*) on the Chincha Islands off the coast of Peru—was one of the Incas' most valuable commodities, and has been used as an agricultural fertilizer for hundreds if not thousands of years. Highland communities in the Andes took guano from the seabird islands off Peru and transported it to their fields in the mountains to grow maize and hot peppers. The guano islands and the industry they supported were central to the war involving Spain, Chile and Peru that was concluded 100 years ago. The guano industry still thrives—or at least continues—in South America, on Christmas Island in the Indian Ocean, in South Africa, and in the western Indian Ocean. Unfortunately, though of all commercial uses of birds guano-mining is surely the one best suited to sustained-yield, non-destructive harvesting, it has almost always been treated by its practitioners in the same way that industry treats anything else that is dug out of the ground—as a non-renewable resource to be mined rather than an indefinitely sustainable yield to be intelligently fostered (Stoddart *et al.* 1970).

HUNTING BIRDS FOR SPORT

Species once hunted for food are often hunted for sport by richer societies—or sections of society—which do not need the food. Sport hunting such as wildfowling in North America and grouse and pheasant shooting in Britain is of major economic and social importance in many developed countries, and often has a well-developed culture associated with it. The socio-economic benefits of sport hunting include its value to the hunter (i.e. how much he is prepared to spend in order to hunt); economic impacts on the local economy; the creation of employment; the creation of revenue for governments; the ability to fund conservation programmes from user licences etc.; and political benefits to conservation-minded politicians who derive support from sport-hunters. The need to provide for sport hunting can be a major influence in shaping the laws relating to land-use as well as wildlife; and wherever it is socially or economically important, it plays a dominant role in determining the legal and ethical concepts of wildlife as human property.

Falconry is a special form of hunting which has been practised for centuries and has spawned elaborate rituals and distinctive cultural practices in the many societies in which it has been adopted. Falconry hovers on the borderline between subsistence and sport hunting, since the quarry brought down by the falcon is often eaten and the sport was no doubt developed originally as an innovative way of catching food (Glasier 1978).

In view of the frequently adversarial relationship between hunters and other conservationists, it is worth noting that surveys of sport hunters in North America (Anon. 1982; Filion *et al.* 1983; Jacquemot & Filion, this volume) show that hunters engage in a great many other, non-consumptive uses of wildlife as well as in hunting. Filion & Parker (1987) demonstrated that 97 percent of all recreational hunters of migratory birds in Canada are also involved in non-consumptive activities (i.e. those that do not include killing birds). They also found that the commitments of hunters—expressed as the time and money they are willing to spend on wildlife-related activities—increase dramatically with the diversity of the activities pursued. These findings are entirely consistent with the theme of this paper—that human uses of birds (consumptive as well as non-consumptive) reflect a fascination with birds that seems to be fundamental to the human psyche.

BIRDS AS SOURCES OF ORNAMENTATION

To people without chemical dyes, the brilliant colours of birds are matched only by those of flowers, and are much more permanent. The use of feathers as human ornamentation has a special place in any discussion of this topic in a conservation context, because it was the drive to stop the international trade in feathers for the millinery industry that led to the formation of the major national and international conservation bodies of the western world. That trade, which was mainly in egrets (Ardeidae), birds of paradise (Paradisaeidae) and hummingbirds (Trochilidae), was a response to a basic human fascination with feathers which has sprung up in many different societies across the world. Feathers have of course been used for many purposes other than ornamentation: as insulation (see below); to stuff mattresses; the quills, for writing; to trim the flight of arrows and shuttlecocks; and for making artificial flies for angling (Jones 1985).

A few examples will demonstrate the worldwide extent of the use of feathers for human ornamentation; they are taken chiefly from Turner (1985) and Grossman & Hamlet (1964) who give many other striking cases. They include the elaborate feather-work of Californian Indians, and the social importance of war-bonnets of feathers to the Plains Indians; the intricate feathered headgear of Maya and Aztec nobles in classical Mexico; the spectacular feather cloaks, many made from species of honeycreeper that are now extinct, of Hawaiian nobles; and the magnificent feathered clothes and head-dresses used by many tribes in New Guinea and Borneo, which are associated with rituals and traditions in which birds figure very prominently. Further north, feathers become valued as insulation as well as ornament, and Common Eiders (*Somateria mollissima*) are still farmed for their down in Iceland (Doughty 1979). The use of feathers as ornamentation is likely to decline as other forms of brightly-coloured clothing become available; feather ornaments are often worn in inverse ratio to the amount of other clothing, in the jungle as well as in the cabaret.

THE ROLE OF AVICULTURE

Birds have been kept in captivity for many different reasons, and in most societies. The modern lucrative international trade in cage-birds, like the trade in skins and feathers of a hundred years ago, is an extreme distortion of what is evidently a deep-felt and almost universal human desire to have a bird or two about them. Captive birds are not always kept just for companionship; a utilitarian motive is often involved too. The bird is often raised for food or, for example, as a potential letter-carrier; pigeons are well-known examples of this skill, and were used as messengers by the British in both World Wars, but Lesser Frigatebirds (*Fregata ariel*) are also raised for this purpose (as well as for food) in some islands of the South Pacific. Domestic Pigeons are kept for racing as much as for fancy breeding; the ubiquitous practice of keeping small songbirds in Latin America and parts of the Caribbean is associated with singing 'contests' between teams of rival owners; and in south-east Asia small birds are often caged temporarily (though often repeatedly) for the spiritual benefit that is conferred on one who releases a captive bird.

BIRDS IN RELIGION AND MYTHOLOGY

Birds have played a sufficiently prominent role in human folklore, mythology and religion for the topic to have been explored fairly thoroughly, notably by Armstrong (1958).

The earliest art shows that veneration of animals is an ancient form of human worship. Many early peoples, and some recent societies, practised animist religions in which birds figured prominently. Most eastern religions have retained the respect for other forms of life that is implicit in animism; Judeo-Christian beliefs, on the other hand, seem to be unique in the little they have to say about mankind's relationship with his fellow creatures. Some scholars have traced this approach to the biblical injunction to, 'subdue (the earth), and have dominion over the fish of the sea, and over the fowl of the air, and over every living thing that moveth upon the earth' (Genesis 1: 28). It would perhaps be instructive to re-examine the original text to see whether there was not an alternative translation of the word that has been translated as 'dominion' that was more sympathetic to other forms of life and thus more consistent with the environmental awareness demonstrated by other religions.

Birds—especially birds of prey—played a significant part in our early spiritual strivings (see especially Grossman & Hamlet 1964, from which most of this section is taken). The legend of a huge raptor with flashing eyes and rushing wings, bringing storms and welcome rain, occurs in the thunderbird of the American Indians, the Voc of Central America (messenger to the tempest god Hurakan, who gave us the word *hurricane*), the Caribs of Brazil, the Basuto of Africa, the Karen of Burma and the Cook Islanders of Australasia. Such a thunderer seems to have been ancestral to the God of Hosts—also known as Jehovah—who was revealed to Hebrew prophets 2700 years ago (Grossman & Hamlet 1964; Turner & Armstrong 1985).

One of the earliest birds to appear in religious fable was Garuda, the great Hindu god of the sky, who bore the sun on his wings. Hindu (or possibly Buddhist) migrations took his worship east as far as Japan; and he is now the national symbol of the Moslem state of Indonesia. His statue still stands in the ruined temples of Angkor Wat, and his worship survives among Brahmans for whom he has the red wings and a white face of the Brahminy Kite, a real and common raptor of modern India.

It is easy to see why birds of prey impressed our forebears, for they were predators too and must have envied the birds' speed and power. Wooden masks and totems of birds, and especially birds of prey, were important religious symbols in many cultures; the removal of the bird-mask during a dance often symbolized mankind's transition from a lowly animal state.

Raptors also have martial connotations, and representations of eagles, or eagle feathers, were used as military banners or as imperial symbols by peoples as different as Babylonians in the sixth century BC, the Plains Indians of North America, the Aztecs of Montezuma's court, roman legions, the armies of Charlemagne and the Holy Roman Empire, and present-day Americans. Roman soldiers marched to war bearing bronze or golden eagle standards, but often decided whether or not to give battle on the basis of auguries from domestic chickens which they carried with them for the purpose. The Aztec emperors of Mexico were protected by a bird of prey—probably a hawk—caged in the temple, and the eagle was the totem of one of their elite soldier societies.

Vultures are venerated by the Parsees of India, who do not bury or burn their dead, but expose them on a tower for vultures to consume. Vulture feathers were used as propitious charms by midwives in ancient Greece and Rome, and vultures were symbols of childbirth to the Mayas of Yacatan and to ancient Egyptians whose goddess Nekhebt was represented as a vulture. The Egyptians deified many birds, especially ibises (*Threskiornis aethiopicus*) which were farmed specifically for entombment and are still known as the Sacred Ibis, and the god Horus, chief god of the sun-cult of Heliopolis, was represented as a falcon.

Owls have a chequered reputation in human folklore, and are feared as birds of ill-omen as often as they are respected for their fabled wisdom. The Greek goddess Athene (Minerva to the Romans) was a goddess of wisdom, and was represented on coins by an owl. She gave her name both to the city of Athens and to the Little Owl (*Athene noctua*).

Mankind has always been preoccupied with his part in the relationship between heaven and earth. The freedom with which birds pass between the two has given them a special place in human folklore and religion, while their beauty of movement, form and voice has given them a prominent role in the arts.

BIRDS IN CULTURE AND THE ARTS

The treatment of birds in literature, music and the pictorial arts is a vast subject which I can touch on only briefly, using Lambourne & Tudor's (1985) account as my main source.

Early European art was dominated by religion, so birds were used as religious symbols until the Renaissance; Lambourne & Tudor (1985) give a number of examples of the symbolic uses of a variety of species of bird in European religious art. There was little interest in showing birds in their own right until the nineteenth century in Europe, whereas in early Chinese art, by contrast, birds were often shown for their own sake, often as individual portaits of great beauty. Birds are also important motifs in Hindu art, and some (notably cranes (Gruidae) and Peafowl) have been extremely important in the development of Indian dance (A. J. Gaston, pers. comm.).

Shakespeare—the 'Swan of Avon'—was evidently a capable birdwatcher (unusually for his time). Birds appear in all his major works, in which over 60 species can be identified. Most poets have used birds as symbols of their own feelings, rather than observing and interpreting the birds themselves. Musical composers have often used birds as sources of inspiration, though direct use of recognizable bird sounds is limited to a few species. Most composers probably have preferred not to attempt to compete with bird song (Hall-Craggs & Jellis 1985).

Birds have been particularly important to the cultural, religious and aesthetic sides of human life from the earliest times of which we have any record. Their prominence in the life of ancient Egypt, for example, is amply attested to in the art and hieroglyphics of that culture (Houlihan 1986). Their importance stems from the same attribute that makes them so useful in the modern world as indicators of the health of our natural environments; their powers of flight allow them to move easily between earth and sky, and yet they are also perfectly adapted to every environment that man inhabits.

BIRDS AS A MEANS OF PEST CONTROL

One of the most striking manifestations of the human affinity for birds is man's compulsion to take familiar birds with him to unfamiliar parts of the world. Birds of over 400 species have been introduced to at least 100 regions which they had not reached by themselves (Long 1981). Usually these transplantations were made for aesthetic reasons, or to fulfill the third and fifth of Maslow's 'human needs' (see Filion, this volume), but often they have been made for the strictly utilitarian purpose of controlling pests. Common Mynas (*Acridotheres tristis*) and Cattle Egrets (*Bubulcus ibis*), for example, were introduced to Mauritius shortly after it was settled, to control insect pests (Long 1981).

Perhaps the most spectacular example of a successful introduction is the case of the House Sparrow (*Passer domesticus*) brought to North America to control dropworm (the larva of the moth *Ennomos subsignarius*) and other insect pests. The birds did not control the pests, but they did colonize the continent with unseemly speed (Long 1981). Meanwhile the California Gull (*Larus californicus*), a native of North America, acquired a considerable reputation in the Plains States and Prairie Provinces for its effectiveness in controlling grasshoppers and other agricultural pests.

In Europe, the value of insectivorous songbirds in limiting damage by insect pests of forests is sufficiently well established for the maintenance of high populations of some of these birds to be one of the objectives for which many forests are managed (Bruns 1960; Takekawa *et al.* 1982). Such intensive management for insectivorous birds is practised very rarely, if ever, in North America, despite a number of demonstrations of the effectiveness of birds in keeping pest populations at low levels, and particularly in lengthening the period between pest outbreaks. Over 60 years ago, Forbush (1921) estimated that birds saved the United States timber industry at least $444 million by reducing insect pests; and in northern Washington State, bird predators on Western Spruce Budworm (*Choristoneura occidentalis*) are worth at least $1820 per km^2 in an outbreak year (Takekawa & Garton 1984). One species alone—the Evening Grosbeak (*Hesperiphona vespertina*)—has an effect on budworm populations equivalent to spraying at a cost of $800–1300/$km^2$ (Takekawa & Garton 1984). There is clearly considerable potential value in using birds as controllers of insect damage in commercial forests, though this potential remains largely untapped (DeGraaf 1978; Otvos 1979; Crawford *et al.* 1983; Takekawa *et al.* 1982).

BIRDS AS BIOLOGICAL INDICATORS

Birds are among the most sensitive and valuable indicators of the health of our natural environment. This topic is explored in detail in Part II of this book, so here I will mention just two comparisons, one in time and one in space.

Compare the Greek soothsayers of three thousand years ago, who predicted the future by poking about in the entrails of birds, with today's environmental toxicologist who also pokes about in the entrails of birds. He uses expensive analytical machinery as well as his brain, but he is essentially a modern-day oracle using birds in a twentieth-century version of augury. Birds have already proved extremely valuable indicators of environmental pollution, and the new breeds of chemical pollutants—which leave no residue and so can be detected *only* by their biological impact—raise the prospect that birds will soon graduate from the status of 'useful' to that of 'essential' as environmental indicators (Peakall & Boyd, this volume).

The second comparison I offer is between the Kelabit tribe of the remote highlands of central Borneo, who determine their cycle of planting rice by the arrival of a series of species of bird migrating from the far north, and after whom they also name their winter months; and the subject of another ICBP Symposium, in which the fortunes of species breeding in North America appear to be beginning to reflect the increasingly damaging effects of agricultural practices on their tropical wintering grounds. The concept of birds as environmental indicators is one which our ancestors, and our more 'primitive' contemporaries, understood perhaps a lot better than we do. Their potential value as an early-warning system of environmental damage is perhaps the strongest utilitarian argument to be made for birds today.

POSTSCRIPT

This review is far from comprehensive. Many uses of birds remain unexplored—notably, for example, their enormous scientific value, which ranges from evolutionary, ecological and behavioural advances to biomedical research, where they are prominent in genetic studies, the development of vaccines, and the discovery and exploitation of retroviruses. My intention has been chiefly to remind those concerned with bird conservation of the value of what they do to humanity as a whole. Mankind has been fascinated by birds, observed them, used them, painted, written and sung about them, kept them, protected and revered them, since the earliest times of which we have any record. Our concern for birds is an unbroken link with our earliest ancestors; it is a major theme in mankind's cultural, aesthetic and spiritual development as well as a source of vital insight into the contemporary environments which we share with birds. Socio-economic surveys of industrial societies, and this essentially anecdotal gallop through past and present societies as yet unsurveyed, agree in suggesting that mankind's affinity for birdkind is an integral part of human nature.

ACKNOWLEDGEMENTS

I thank Fern Filion, Tony Gaston and Tony Keith for helpful comments on the manuscript, which is an amplification of ideas developed for Chapter 5 of Diamond *et al.* (1987).

REFERENCES

ALLEN, R. 1976. Ecodevelopment and traditional resource management in the South Pacific. South Pac. Comm. IUCN, Apia, Western Samoa (quoted by Chapman 1985).

ANON. 1982. 1980 national survey of fishing, hunting, and wildlife-associated recreation. U.S. Dept. Interior, Wildl. Serv. and U.S. Dept. of Commerce, Bureau of the Census. U.S. Govt. Printing Office, Washington, D.C.

ARMSTRONG E. A. 1958. *The folklore of birds.* London.

BOWMAN, J. C. 1977. *Animals for man.* London.

BRUNS, H. 1960. The economic importance of birds in forests. *Bird Study* 7, 193–208.

CHAPMAN, M. D. 1985. Environmental influences on the development of traditional conservation in the South Pacific region. *Biol. Cons.* 12, 217–30.

CRAWFORD, H. S., TITTERINGTON, R. W. & JENNINGS, D. J. 1983. Bird predation and spruce budworm populations. *Jour. For.* 1983, 433–5, 478.

DeGRAAF, R. M. 1978. *The importance of birds in ecosystems.* U.S.D.A. For. Serv. Gen. Tech. Rep. PNW-64. 5–11.

DIAMOND, A. W., SCHREIBER, R. L., ATTENBOROUGH, D. & PRESTT, I. 1987. *Save the Birds.* Cambridge.

DOUGHTY, R. W. 1979. Eider husbandry in the North Atlantic: trends and prospects. *Polar Rec.* 19, 447–59.

DOUROJEANNI, M. J. 1985. Over-exploited and under-used animals in the Amazon region. *In:* Prance, G. T. & Lovejoy, T. E. (eds.). *Amazonia.* Oxford.

FEARE, C. G. 1976. The exploitation of Sooty Tern eggs in the Seychelles. *Biol. Cons.* 10, 169–81.

FILION, F. L. & PARKER, S. A. D. 1987. *Human dimensions of migratory game-bird hunting in Canada.* Can. Wildl. Serv. Occ. Pap. No. 51. Ottawa.

FILION, F. L., JAMES, S. W., DUCHARME, J.-L., PEPPER, W., REID, R., BOXALL, P. & TEILLET, D. 1983. *The importance of wildlife to Canadians: highlights of the 1981 national survey.* Can. Wildl. Serv., Ottawa.

FORBUSH, E. H. 1921. The utility of birds. Bull. No. 9, Mass. Dept. Agr., Boston.

GLASIER, P. 1978. *Falconry and hawking.* London.

GROSSMAN, M. L. & HAMLET, J. 1964. *Birds of prey of the world.* New York.

HALL-CRAGGS, J. M. H. & JELLIS, R. E. 1985. Article 'Birds in music' *In:* Campbell, B. & Lack, E. (eds.). *A dictionary of birds.* Calton (UK) and Vermillion, SD (USA).

HARCOURT, A. H., PENNINGTON, H. & WEBER, A. W. 1986. Public attitudes to wildlife and conservation in the third world. *Oryx* 20, 152–4.

HARRISON, T. H. & BECKING, J. H. 1985. Article 'Edible nests' *In:* Campell, B. & Lack, E. (eds.). *A dictionary of birds.* Calton (UK) and Vermillion, SD (USA).

HOULIHAN, P. F. 1986. *The birds of ancient Egypt.* Warminster, U.K.

JONES, E. L. 1985. Article 'Utilisation by man' *In:* Campbell, B. & Lack, E. (eds.). *A dictionary of birds.* Calton (UK) and Vermillion, SD (USA).

KELLERT, S. 1980a. Contemporary values of wildlife in American society. *In:* Shaw, W. W. & Zube, E. H. (eds.). *Wildlife values.* U.S. For. Serv. Cent. for Assessment of Noncommodity Natl. Resour. Values, Fort Collins, CO.

KELLERT, S. 1980b. Americans' attitudes and knowledge of animals. *Trans. North Am. Wildl. and Nat. Resour. Conf.* 45, 111–24.

LAMBOURNE, L. & TUDOR, R. O. 1985. Article 'Birds in art' *In:* Campbell, B. & Lack, E. (eds.). *A dictionary of birds.* Calton (UK) and Vermillion, SD (USA).

LONG, J. L. 1981. *Introduced birds of the world.* London.

NETTLESHIP, D. N. & EVANS, P. G. H. 1985. Distribution and status of the Atlantic Alcidae. *In:* Nettleship, D. N. & Birkhead, T. H. (eds.). *The Atlantic Alcidae.* London and New York.

NORREVANG, A. 1986. Traditions of sea bird fowling in the Faeroes: an ecological basis for sustained fowling. *Orn. Scand.* 17, 275–81.

OTVOS, I. S. 1979. The effect of insectivorous bird activities in forest ecosystems: an evaluation. Pp. 341–74 *In:* Dickson, J. G., Conner, R. N., Fleet, R. R., Kroll, J. C. & Jackson, J. A. (eds.). *The role of insectivorous birds in forest ecosystems.* New York.

PENNINGTON, R. H. 1983. A living trust: Tanzanian attitudes towards wildlife conservation. M.Sc thesis, Yale Univ., New Haven.

PETERSON, R. T. 1964. *Birds over America.*

RIDLEY, M. W. & PERCY, LORD R. 1958. The exploitation of sea-birds in the Seychelles. *Colon. Res. Stud.* **25**, 1–78.

STODDART, D. R., BENSON, C. W. & PEAKE, J. F. 1970. Ecological change and effects of guano mining on Assumption Island. *Atoll Res. Bull.* **136**, 121–45.

TAKEKAWA, J. Y. & GARTON, E. O. 1984. How much is an Evening Grosbeak worth? *Jour. For.* 1984: 426–8.

TAKEKAWA, J. Y., GARTON, E. O. & LANGELIER, L. A. 1982. Biological control of forest insect outbreaks: the use of avian predators. 47th North Am. Wildl. Conf.: 393–409.

TURNER, G. E. S. & ARMSTRONG, E. A. 1985. Article 'Birds in folklore' *In:* Campbell, B. & Lack, E. (eds.). *A dictionary of birds.* Calton (UK) and Vermillion, SD (USA).

WEBER, A. W. 1981. Conservation of the Virunga gorillas: a socio-economic perspective on habitat and wildlife preservation in Rwanda. M.Sc thesis, Univ. Wisconsin, Madison.

WEBER, A. W. 1986. Socioecological factors in the conservation of afromontane forest reserves. *In:* Gartlan, J. S., Marsh, C. W. & Mittermeier, R. A. (eds.). *Primate conservation in tropical rain forest.* New York.

WOOD-GUSH, D. G. M. 1985. Article 'Domestication' *In:* Campbell, B. & Lack, E. (eds.). *A dictionary of birds.* Calton (UK) and Vermillion, SD (USA).

PART II
BIRDS AS BIO-INDICATORS OF
ENVIRONMENTAL CONDITIONS

BIRDS AS BIO-INDICATORS OF ENVIRONMENTAL CONDITIONS

CHAIRMEN'S INTRODUCTION

DAVID B. PEAKALL & HUGH BOYD

National Wildlife Research Centre, Canadian Wildlife Service, Ottawa, Ontario, Canada K1A 0H3

There are a number of reasons why birds are an attractive choice as bio-indicators. First, they are one of the best-studied groups of organisms from the viewpoint of both physiology and ecology. Second, there are large collections of museum specimens, particularly of eggshells and skins. This has enabled a historical record to be compiled both for organochlorines extracted from eggshell membranes and for heavy metals analysed in feathers. Third, there is a large amateur interest in birds which can be channelled into an effective mechanism to obtain information on species number, distribution, reproductive success etc. 'Amateur', here, is used in its older definition: a person who does something for the love of it, rather than in the more modern pejorative sense of doing something unskilfully. This use of volunteers was pioneered by the British Trust for Ornithology with such programmes as the nest record card scheme, common bird census and atlas projects (Hickling 1983), which have since been copied in many other countries. The uses made of these programmes in the United Kingdom are illustrated in the paper presented at this symposium by Hardy *et al*. Atlas studies and nest record card programmes have been undertaken in other parts of the world, including North America, but the full potential for using amateurs has not been realized outside Great Britain.

Perhaps the greatest strength of birds as monitors is that people care about them. They will more readily pay attention to the 'Plight of the Peregrine' than to chemical data or to the impoverishment of invertebrate faunas. This strong public interest in birds tends to provoke defensive responses from government officials, but may nevertheless be politically effective. This theme is explored more thoroughly in Part I of this book.

Birds have long been used as a source of material for the chemical analysis of environmental pollutants. Avian eggs, in particular, have been widely used for the analysis of residue levels of organochlorine. Innumerable studies have been carried out since their first use—the analysis of an egg of a Peregrine Falcon (*Falco peregrinus*) collected in Britain in 1961 (Moore & Ratcliffe 1965). Collection of eggs is less destructive than that of adults, as birds will frequently re-lay during the course of the breeding season, and the percentage of eggs that result in adult birds is small. As reproductive failure was one of the major concerns during this period, the levels of residues in eggs were relevant both to embryotoxic effects and to the body burden of the female. That this is still a valuable approach for monitoring the temporal trends of organochlorines is clearly shown by the paper by Gilbertson *et al.* in this Symposium. One of the major limitations of the use of eggs is that it is valid only for compounds with a high affinity for lipids.

The heavy metals are another class of pollutants of major interest. With the exception of organic derivatives such as methyl mercury, the heavy metals are not deposited into eggs. One approach is obviously to measure levels in tissues, but a much less destructive approach is the use of feathers as the monitoring device. Using this method Swedish workers were able, in the early 1960s, to demonstrate a marked increase in the levels of mercury in the feathers of Goshawk (*Accipiter gentilis*), Osprey (*Pandion haliaetus*) and Great Crested Grebe (*Podiceps cristatus*) following the introduction of mercury fungicides in Sweden in the 1950s (Johnels & Westermark 1969). In that study, feathers from museum specimens were used to track the changes in the levels of mercury. The importance of understanding the moult sequence is clearly demonstrated by the work of Ellenberg & Dietrich (1982) who found a variation of up to 25-fold for lead and 8-fold for cadmium in feathers from the same bird. It is difficult to relate levels in feathers to levels in internal organs. The levels in internal organs are the balance between ingestion and excretion; the levels in feathers are an expression of the circulating levels at the time of feather formation. Nevertheless, if care is taken to use comparable feathers, the technique can be used for temporal trends, e.g. the study by Appelquist *et al.* (1985) on the levels of mercury in Common Guillemot (*Uria aalge*) feathers over a period of 150 years. If the details of the moult are known, the technique can be used to demonstrate the different geographical sources of heavy metals in migratory birds (Lindberg & Odsjo 1983). The advantages of using feathers to monitor levels of heavy metals in seabirds are discussed by Furness (this Symposium). He points out the analytical difficulties in measuring the very low levels in water or ice samples and the availability of museum specimens to give long temporal trends.

This meeting, however, is focused not on the conventional approach of using avian tissues for chemical analysis, but on using birds as bio-indicators of environmental problems. One of the first bio-indicators was eggshell thinning, first demonstrated to have occurred dramatically in the Peregrine and European Sparrowhawk (*Accipiter nisus*) starting in 1947 (Ratcliffe 1967). The correlation between eggshell thinning in the Peregrine and the presence of DDE was soon demonstrated (Cade *et al.* 1971; Peakall *et al.* 1975) and direct correlation between the degree of eggshell thinning found both under experimental conditions and in field situations was demonstrated for the American Kestrel (*Falco sparverius*) by Lincer (1975). Soon after the discovery of eggshell thinning, the biological consequences were examined by Hickey & Anderson (1968). A recent review of the data for the Peregrine Falcon (Peakall & Kiff, in press) has clearly demonstrated that the initial suggestion of Hickey and Anderson that eggshell thinning of 20 percent or more was associated with population declines was correct. The degree of eggshell thinning has been used as an important management tool to maintain the population of the Peregrine in California and the Rocky Mountain states by removing eggs from the nests of females known to lay thin-shelled eggs, incubating them artificially, and returning the young to the wild (Walton, in press).

The studies of environmental pollutants in the Great Lakes of North America have had an important avian component. These studies are summarized in this volume by Fox & Weseloh. For a more detailed account the reader is referred to Mineau *et al.* (1984).

While our concerns in the toxic chemicals field were limited largely to organochlorines and heavy metals, bioeffects studies appeared largely as an adjunct to chemical analysis. In some cases biochemical measurements were more convenient than chemical analysis, e.g. inhibition of the enzyme amino levulinic acid dehydratase instead of determining lead levels, and in other cases, e.g. induction of metallothionein, they provided a preliminary answer to the question of what was the effect on the organism. In recent years we have become increasingly concerned with the impact of persistent use of the non-persistent materials that were substituted for the organochlorine pesticides, at least in the highly industrialized countries, in response to public objection to the use of long-lasting compounds.

The first major classes of less persistent pesticides that were introduced, the organophosphates and carbamates, blocked the central nervous system. It was soon accepted that inhibition of acetylcholinesterase (AChE) was the analytical system of choice to demonstrate exposure of organisms to these classes of compounds (Bunyan & Taylor 1966). This approach had the additional advantage that the degree of inhibition could be related to the degree of harm to the organism. Zinck *et al.* (1979) concluded that a 20 percent reduction in AChE activity was a clear indication of exposure, and that 60 percent inhibition was an indicator of chronic and 80 percent of acute mortality. Some of the complications of using the AChE methods under field conditions (e.g. behavioural changes and the difficulty of finding affected birds) have been considered by Mineau & Peakall (in press).

Looking back at the history of the development of bio-indicators, the use of the inhibition of AChE for the monitoring of organophosphates and carbamates seems clearly to have been a special case. The highly specific mechanism of action was known at the time these materials were introduced and thus there was no problem in the acceptance of the biochemical approach. Most of these compounds were highly toxic to birds and we were concerned with the direct mortality, rather than looking for subtle ecosystem effects.

The induction of hepatic mixed function oxidases (MFOs) is another system that has been widely studied since their serendipitous discovery, following the use of chlordane in animal rearing facilities (Fouts & Rogers 1965). Recent reviews on the environmental aspects of this subject include those by Payne (1984) and Walker (1980). This system is known to be induced by a wide variety of compounds, including such major classes of environmental pollutants as the organochlorines and polynuclear aromatic hydrocarbons. One value of studies on this system is to demonstrate that an organism is, or has been, exposed to a sufficiently high concentration of an environmental contaminant to cause a physiological change. Studies are also useful in determining clearance rates because MFO activity levels affect the rate of metabolism and excretion of pesticides and other man-made compounds (Walker 1978).

Until recently, bioeffects studies were directed towards the effect of the chemical directly on the target organism. In this way chemical analysis and biochemical/physiological changes were used to measure very similar things. Chemical analysis of the residue levels determined the amount remaining in the animal, the balance between exposure and excretion. The level might be due to massive exposure some time ago, to chronic low level exposure or to some more complex regime. In the same way a biochemical change could have been due to a massive change some time in the past followed by recovery, or to the effects of chronic effects.

The introduction of the synthetic pyrethroids and increasing use of herbicides has added a new dimension to our studies of the effects of pesticides on wildlife. The major effect on wildlife from these chemicals occurs via the food-chain, and so it is necessary to take an ecosystem approach. A compound such as deltametrin can, without leaving measurable residues or causing any mortality of warm-blooded animals, cause major effects on aquatic food-chains. The approach detailed in this Symposium by Mineau *et al.* is a radical departure from classical studies of chemical residues and mortality. It bears close examination as we are going to be making increasing use of the approach of considering the ecosystem as a functioning whole, examining toxic chemicals as merely one stress to which the system is exposed.

Another major problem that affects wildlife via the food chain is that of acidification, which occurs as a result of production of the oxides of sulphur and nitrogen, popularly referred to as 'acid rain'. Four papers on the effects on aquatic systems and one on terrestrial systems were presented at this workshop. McNicol & Blancher's paper examined the invertebrate composition of lakes of different pH and their effect on the waterfowl that were dependent on them. A major factor is the change in predator-prey relationships caused by the elimination of fish stocks as pH decreases. Not only are piscivores affected, but the changes have impact on such generalist feeders as Ring-necked Duck (*Aythya collaris*) and Common Goldeneye (*Bucephala clangula*). Ormerod & Tyler were able to demonstrate that breeding distribution of Dippers (*Cinclus cinclus*) in Wales correlated strongly with the abundance of macroinvertebrates in rivers, and also correlated well with stream acidity. Temporal relationships between increasing acidity and decreasing breeding abundance of Dippers were demonstrated. Eriksson reviewed the situation in Sweden, which has a long and distinguished history of studies in this field. His conclusion is worth quoting: 'I think that birds can be a good complement to other organisms, such as fish and aquatic inverte-brates, used as indicators of freshwater acidification, but the complex pattern behind the fluctuations in density and production of young makes it difficult to work with birds only. In addition, monitoring programs should include routines for traditional measurements of water chemistry in the lakes and streams con-cerned'.

These field studies, which show significant effects on the ability of aquatic birds to obtain enough food to breed successfully, were supported by experimental studies presented by Haramis. Using paired artificial ponds he was able to demonstrate that changes in the aquatic food-chain lead to an inability of young Black Duck (*Anas rubripes*) to obtain enough food to sustain growth.

The studies are of importance in demonstrating the biological consequences of long-term acidification which is affecting large areas of the globe. They may well provide good bio-monitors of the impact of anthropogenic input of the oxides of sulphur and nitrogen in the environment.

In recent years there has been increasing concern over the effects of air-borne pollutants on forests, especially in central Europe. The exact role of the direct effect of pollutants, especially ozone, on the foliage and the effect of acidification of the soil have not been determined. In North America the dieback of Sugar Maples, especially in Québec, has caused concern. Studies of the effect of these diebacks on avian populations were presented at this meeting by DesGranges. Whether these changes have value as a bio-monitor remains to be seen, as they do not appear to precede, nor are the changes easier to establish than, the dieback of the trees themselves. This topic was also discussed in conjunction with Welsh's paper on the effect on avian communities of the changes to the forest caused by Spruce Budworm (*Choristoneura fumiferana*). The possibility of interaction between disease and air-borne pollutants in affecting the health of forests needs to be borne in mind. The role of birds in affecting insect outbreaks, and the effect on avian communities of changes to the forest caused by both disease and pollutants, are important topics; but the case that birds can be used as bio-indicators of these effects remains to be proven. Another factor that can be affecting populations of highly migratory song-birds in Canada is the destruction of their wintering habitat in Latin America. This topic was also discussed at ICBP's Symposium on 'Migratory bird populations and the loss of wintering habitat in the Western Hemisphere'. Once more this brings us back to the importance of the holistic approach.

The use of animals as indicators of ecosystem responses to airborne pollutants has recently been reviewed by Newman & Schreiber (1984). Most of the studies refer to acid deposition, but the list also includes fluoride and a number of metals. In one study, Newman *et al.* (1985) demonstrate that air pollution from pulp mills can be correlated with the nesting density, colony size and occupancy rate of House Martins (*Delichon urbica*).

It may be appropriate to offer a few additional comments on two questions about bio-monitoring, raised most clearly in the papers by Rutschke and by Welsh, viz. Who needs it? And for what? In some OECD countries, including Canada, 'state-of-the-environment' reporting is the vogue; nevertheless few governments are willing to devote sufficient resources to long-term monitoring of environmental conditions to allow reliable studies to be carried out. Researchers work hard, as this workshop showed, to produce and test measuring devices. When they hand over the new devices and procedures to operational units, in their own or in other government departments, they frequently find that the necessary support is lacking.

One of the weaknesses of bio-monitoring is that it tends to be welcomed more by the critics of industry and government than by the industrialists and regulators themselves. Many professional gatherers of physical environmental data, such as air and water quality, are unwilling to treat biological data seriously. If the data are collected by amateurs, often at considerable expense of their own time, effort and cash, this problem is exacerbated. This anti-amateur bias seems likely to persist amongst professional civil servants, however much their political masters may seem to encourage 'public participation' in environmental issues.

Several of the studies presented in this Symposium—those concerned with acidification and the use of herbicides—have demonstrated that birds can be used as effective bio-indicators of environmental change. The field has come a long way since canaries were first used in coal mines. In other cases—Rutschke's work on the response of wintering waterfowl to eutrophication; Welsh's on the effect of budworm outbreaks; and DesGranges' on the effect of die-off of maple forests on boreal bird populations—it is not obvious that monitoring with birds is more effective than direct inspection of trees and crops. Nevertheless, this work helps to answer the question 'So what?' which should be, but all too frequently is not, asked when studying environmental problems. In the acid rain issue, for example, it is more important to know what is the effect of acidification on the ecosystem than to document the pH of the rain and water bodies. Yet the amount of funding for biological studies is small compared to that spent on water chemistry. Much remains to be done to convince regulators and policy-makers of the importance of bio-monitoring. Otherwise it will remain under-funded and be mainly used for waving yellow, red and, with luck, green environmental flags.

REFERENCES

Appelquist, H., Drabaek, I & Asbirk, S. 1985. Variation in mercury content of guillemot feathers over 150 years. *Mar. Poll. Bull.* **16**, 244–8.

BUNYAN, P. J. & TAYLOR, A. 1966. Esterase inhibition in pheasants poisoned by O,O-diethyl-S-(ethylthiomethyl)-phosphorodithioate (Thimet). *Agric. Food Chem.* **14**, 132–7.

CADE, T. J., LINCER, J. L., WHITE, C. M., ROSENEAU, D. G. & SWARTZ, L. G. 1971. DDE residue and eggshell changes in Alaskan falcons and hawks. *Science* **172**, 955–7.

ELLENBERG, H. & DIETRICH, J. 1982. The Goshawk as a bioindicator. *In: Understanding the Goshawk.* (Eds.) Kenward, R. E. & Lindsay, D. Int. Ass. Falconery, Oxford. No pagination.

FOUTS, J. R. & ROGERS, L. A. 1965. Morphological changes in the liver accompanying stimulation of microsomal drug metabolising enzyme activity by phenobarbital, chlordane, benz(a)pyrene or methyl cholanthrene in rats. *J. Pharmacol. Expt. Therp.* **147**, 112–19.

HICKEY, J. J. & ANDERSON, D. W. 1968. Chlorinated hydrocarbons and eggshell changes in raptorial and fish-eating birds. *Science* **162**, 271–3.

HICKLING, R. 1983. *Enjoying ornithology: A celebration of fifty years of the British Trust for Ornithology 1933–1983.* Pp. 296. T. & A. D. Poyser, Calton.

JOHNELS, A. G. & WESTERMARK, T. 1969. Mercury contamination of the environment in Sweden. *In: Chemical Fallout. Current research on persistent pesticides.* (Eds.) Miller, M. W. & Berg, G. G. Pp. 221–41. Charles C. Thomas, Springfield, Ill.

LINCER, J. 1975. DDE-induced eggshell thinning in the American Kestrel: A comparison of the field situation and laboratory results. *J. Appl. Ecol.* **12**, 781–93.

LINDBERG, P. & ODSJO, T. 1983. Mercury levels in feathers of Peregrine Falcon (*Falco peregrinus*) compared to the total mercury in some of its prey species. *Environ. Pollut.* (Ser. B.) **5**, 297–318.

MINEAU, P., FOX, G. A., NORSTROM, R. J., WESELOH, D. V., HALLETT, D. J. & ELLENTON, J. A. 1984. Using the herring gull to monitor levels and effects of organochlorine contamination in the Canadian Great Lakes. *Advances Environ. Sci. Technol.* **14**, 425–52.

MINEAU, P. & PEAKALL, D. B. (in press). An evaluation of avian impact assessment techniques following broadscale forest insecticide sprays. *Environ. Sci. Technol.*

MOORE, N. W. & RATCLIFFE, D. A. 1962. Chlorinated hydrocarbon residues in the egg of a Peregrine Falcon (*Falco peregrinus*) from Perthshire. *Bird Study* **9**, 242–4.

NEWMAN, J. R., NOVAKOVA, E. & McCLAVE, J. T. 1985. The influence of industrial air emissions on the nesting ecology of the House Martin (*Delichon urbica*) in Czechoslovakia. *Biol. Conserv.* **31**, 229–48.

NEWMAN, J. R. & SCHREIBER, R. K. 1984. Animals as indicators of ecosystem responses to air emissions. *Environ. Manage.* **8**, 309–24.

PAYNE, J. F. 1984. Mixed-function oxygenases in biological monitoring programs: Review of potential usage in different phyla of aquatic animals. Vol. 1: 625–55. *In: Ecotoxicological testing for the marine environment.* (Eds.) Persoone, G., Jaspers, E. & Claus, C. State Univ. Ghent, Bredene, Belgium.

PEAKALL, D. B., CADE, T. J., WHITE, C. M. & HAUGH, J. R. 1975. Organochlorine residues in Alaskan Peregrines. *Pesticide Monitoring J.* **8**, 255–60.

PEAKALL, D. B. & KIFF, L. F. (in press). Organochlorines in Peregrines and Kestrels and their effects on reproduction. *In: Peregrine Falcon Populations: Their Management and Recovery.* (Eds.) Cade, T., White, C., Enderson, J. & Thelander, C. Sacramento, Calif.

RATCLIFFE, D. A. 1967. Decrease in eggshell weights in certain birds of prey. *Nature* **215**, 208–10.

WALKER, C. H. 1978. Species differences in microsomal monoxygenease activity and their relationship to biological half-lives. *Drug Metabolism Rev.* **7**, 295–323.

WALKER, C. H. 1980. Species variations in some hepatic microsomal enzymes that metabolize xenobiotics. *Progr. Drug Metabolism* **5**, 113–64.

WALTON, B. J. (in press). Peregrine management in the Pacific coast states. *In: Peregrine Falcon Populations: Their Management and Recovery.* (Eds.) Cade, T., White, C., Enderson, J. & Thelander, C. Sacramento, Calif.

ZINCK, J. G., HENNY, C. J. & SHEA, P. J. 1979. Brain cholinesterase activities of passerine birds in forests sprayed with cholinesterase inhibiting insecticides. Pp. 356–65. *In: Animals as Monitors of Environmental Pollutants,* Natn. Acad. Sci., Washington D.C.

BIRDS AS INDICATORS OF THE INTENSITY OF USE OF AGRICULTURAL PESTICIDES IN THE UK

A. R. Hardy[1], P. I. Stanley[2] & P. W. Greig-Smith[3]

1 *Ministry of Agriculture, Fisheries and Food, Research and Development Service, Worplesdon Laboratory, Tangley Place, Worplesdon, Guildford, Surrey GU3 3LQ, United Kingdom*
2 *Ministry of Agriculture, Fisheries and Food, Research and Development Service, Slough Laboratory, London Road, Slough, Berkshire SL3 7HJ, United Kingdom*
3 *Ministry of Agriculture, Fisheries and Food, Research and Development Service, Tolworth Laboratory, Hook Rise South, Surbiton, Surrey KT6 7NF, United Kingdom*

ABSTRACT

Birds are among the most conspicuous, attractive and numerous fauna that may be at risk from the use of agricultural pesticides. They have been used extensively as both indicators and predictors of environmental impact. In the development of a pesticide and the assessment of wildlife hazards in the United Kingdom, captive birds are used in laboratory toxicity tests, wild bird populations are monitored during field trials, and bird deaths on farmland are investigated as part of the general post-registration surveillance of commercial pesticide use. Examples of environmental impact assessment are discussed to emphasise the central role that birds occupy as indicators of environmental safety.

INTRODUCTION

Modern intensive agriculture relies heavily on the use of a wide range of chemicals including fertilizers, herbicides, insecticides, fungicides and other crop protection chemicals. There has been considerable public concern since the early 1960s (Carson 1963) over the potential adverse effects of the widespread use of pesticides on the environment. Birds form a significant and very obvious part of the fauna, and as such have been used extensively as both indicators and predictors of environmental impact (Hill & Hoffman 1984). This paper will review the use of birds to assess pesticide impact on the environment and will outline the approaches taken in the United Kingdom.

Though a small country, approximately 76 percent of the land surface of the UK is used for agriculture. Permanent pasture and rough grassland account for 60 percent of this, while 37 percent is under arable crops (MAFF 1986a): cereals are grown on some 76 percent of the total tillage. Rather than continuous, unbroken cultivation, much of this farmland is a rich mosaic of different habitats with woods, copses, hedges, marsh and bog amidst cropped and grassed fields.

119

Farmland thus provides the largest area of bird habitat available in the UK, and Moore (1980) estimated that it is used by between 50 and 100 million pairs of breeding birds of about 130 species.

Ornithological interest within the UK is and has traditionally been very strong. Birds are conspicuous, attractive, often abundant and comparatively easily observed and, as a result of the high human population density, there is widespread amateur interest in birds and the countryside in general. Professional and amateur workers have collaborated in the long-term monitoring of bird populations, together with detailed studies of individual species. Reliable data are therefore available for such species as the Grey Heron (*Ardea cinerea*) and various geese, since the early part of this century. By virtue of its geographical position in the palaearctic migration system, large numbers of birds pass through on migration in the fall and spring and substantial populations overwinter in the UK. Through their ecological exploitation of food resources on agricultural land, it is apparent that large numbers of birds may come into contact with agricultural operations including pesticide use. For these combined reasons, birds are a very useful indicator of environmental health, and yield valuable data on the potential hazards to wildlife from the use of agricultural pesticides.

PESTICIDE USE

There have been dramatic changes in the UK in both the type and scale of use of pesticides during the last 45 years. Synthetic organic pesticides were first used in the UK following the discovery in Switzerland of DDT in 1939. Introduction into agriculture was rapid, with extensive use particularly in orchards and on brassica crops. The cyclodiene insecticides, aldrin, dieldrin and heptachlor, were introduced as cereal seed treatments in the mid-fifties. However, as a result of unacceptable environmental problems, progressive restrictions were placed on their use from 1962 until the final withdrawal of aldrin and dieldrin from agricultural use in 1975. Their withdrawal was made possible by the development and introduction of the more toxic but less persistent organo-phosphorus insecticides and the subsequent introduction of the carbamates. DDT was finally withdrawn from agricultural use in the UK in 1984. As the spectrum of pesticide chemicals and their use pattern have continuously changed during the last forty years so have the potential hazards to wildlife associated with agriculture. For example, total pesticide use on cereals doubled between 1977 and 1982 (Sly 1986).

By 1985 the total pesticide market in the UK was worth £345 million, 90 percent of which related to agricultural and horticultural use (BAA 1986). In the same year, 84 percent of agricultural pesticides were applied to cereal crops. It was estimated in 1982, from the most recent survey figures available, that 16,708 tonnes of active ingredients were applied in England and Wales to 17.75 million treated hectares of cereals (Sly 1986).

REGISTRATION AND CONTROL OF PESTICIDES IN THE UK

The aim of pesticide registration is to safeguard human beings, livestock, domestic animals, beneficial insects, wildlife and the environment in general from risks that could arise from the use of pesticidal products. After parliamentary debate of the environmental problems caused by the organochlorine pesticides in the early fifties, the Pesticides Safety Precautions Scheme (PSPS) was established in 1957. The PSPS was a formally negotiated agreement between the Government

Agricultural and Health Departments and the Trade Associations representing industry. Though a non-statutory scheme, pesticide manufacturers and distributors agreed to comply with the requirements as conditions of membership of their Trade Associations. The PSPS has recently been replaced by legislation with the introduction of the Food and Environment Protection Act (1985) and an attendant revision of data requirements for registration (MAFF 1986b). Risk evaluation of any new pesticide involves the assessment of safety to users and bystanders, to consumers of food, and to the environment. This is based on information derived from the combination of laboratory tests, field evaluation and environmental monitoring (Bunyan & Stanley 1979). Potential effects on bird species are an important part of this assessment process which is designed to allow the stepwise introduction of new pesticides on to the market as information becomes available to provide the necessary assurance that the proposed use is safe.

Evaluation of environmental safety involves initial toxicity tests in the laboratory to identify the inherent properties of the pesticide. If these properties and the intended use of the pesticide indicate that wildlife may be at risk from toxic residues then further laboratory tests followed by a programme of field trials are carried out to assess the likely hazards under field conditions (Stanley & Hardy 1983).

LABORATORY TOXICITY TESTS WITH BIRDS

Since it is clearly impractical to test a given pesticide against all species likely to be exposed to it under field conditions, a representative range of organisms are used in the laboratory to provide information that indicates the potential risks to wildlife. Birds are an important part of this first stage of testing in view of their prominence in the environment. International agreement between authorities— including those in the UK, the Environmental Protection Agency in the USA, the Organisation for Economic Cooperation and Development and the European Economic Community (EEC) in Europe, and the (UN) Food and Agriculture Organisation based in Rome—has led towards the harmonization of data requirements and the standardization of test criteria and the species most frequently tested. A recent literature review for the European Commission revealed that 50 different species of bird have been used in various toxicity studies (Goldstein *et al.* 1984). However, only a few species are used commonly since adequate background information is necessary on maintenance conditions, breeding data etc: these are Bobwhite Quail (*Colinus virginianus*) (not used in the UK), Japanese Quail (*Coturnix coturnix japonica*), Feral Pigeon (*Columba livia* var.) and Mallard (*Anas platyrhynchos*).

The range of laboratory tests conducted at this stage includes acute, sub-acute and chronic toxicity tests, teratogenicity and reproductive tests and bioaccumulation tests. The results form an essential part of the basic data package for each pesticide. More specialized tests have been developed for chemicals with obvious risks to non-target species in certain situations. Thus the secondary poisoning potential of rodenticides for predators can be determined in the laboratory or aviary using predatory gulls (the Laughing Gull (*Larus atricilla*); Fink & Jaber 1981) or owls (the Tawny Owl (*Strix aluco*); Townsend *et al.* 1981).

On the basis of the inherent properties of a pesticide and knowledge of its intended use pattern, it is then possible to predict those field situations and crops where wildlife may be at risk and where further information is required to provide relevant data for safety evaluation. Birds are again a very important part of the fauna that may be at risk in the field and therefore methodology must be adequate to provide sufficient data on which to base the hazard assessment.

FIELD ASSESSMENT OF ENVIRONMENTAL HAZARD TO BIRDS

This second phase of environmental testing is tailored to the particular pesticide under scrutiny. Whilst there is broad guidance available on the data that should be collected, the exact requirements will depend on the specific characteristics of the pesticide (identified during laboratory tests) and its intended use pattern (Stanley & Hardy 1983). For example, the crop, target pest, time of year, formulation and application rate all have a bearing on the potential risk to non-target wildlife and the spectrum of species, including birds, that may be affected. Knowledge of the toxic mode of action can be used in selecting suitable parameters for monitoring during field studies (Bunyan & Stanley 1982). Although some harmonization of approach is possible, flexibility is paramount and therefore standardization of field protocols is neither feasible nor desirable. Each field assessment must be directly relevant to the particular pesticide under examination.

The field assessment of environmental hazard to birds has historically depended on the application of the experimental material followed by casualty searches to identify and quantify direct mortality. This rather crude approach, though still included in the basic methodology, has been superseded by a comprehensive package of observations and measurements intended to describe the environmental behaviour of the candidate pesticide following application, to detect exposure in wildlife species and to estimate any effects at the level of both the individual and the population.

As a result of the need to monitor local population levels, census techniques have been developed to provide suitable methods for detecting sudden population declines that might be caused by a toxic pesticide. During the breeding season, while birds are resident and territorial, census methods can be easily applied. The sensitivity of one bird census technique was tested in the field to determine whether simulated local mortality after a 'toxic pesticide' application could be detected. Resident farmland passerines were censussed by mapping observations of territorial activity (IBCC 1970). Birds were captured in mist-nets during a 24-hour period and removed temporarily from the sites in order to reduce the local population. Census studies were then continued for 60 days to detect this reduction and to determine the rate of reinvasion from adjacent habitats. Sufficient data were collected for four species which showed that the territory mapping method was sensitive enough to detect sudden changes in bird populations such as might occur after a toxic pesticide application (Edwards et al. 1979). However, the choice of species selected for monitoring is important. For example, there was a wide range of variation in the speed of reinvasion over the 60-day 'post-treatment' period, from the Chaffinch (*Fringilla coelebs*) which showed none, to the Dunnock (*Prunella modularis*) and the Song Thrush (*Turdus philomelos*) which both showed some, to the Blackbird (*T. merula*) where a proportion of the population is non-territorial and does not breed. Any gaps in the territorial system through loss of resident adult Blackbirds are rapidly filled, thereby interfering with the detection of short-term change. The validity of the territory mapping technique to census resident passerines was shown in a separate exercise comparing maps derived from observations of individually colour-ringed birds and those from an independent census using the standard method. Outside the breeding season most birds are not sufficiently territorial for rigorous mapping methods to be relevant. It may then be necessary to use a risk index based on numbers of birds seen at the field trial site in order to identify those species most at risk (Bunyan *et al.* 1981).

A comprehensive range of techniques will be used in the field to assess the risk to local bird populations using the trial sites. These would usually combine observations of birds feeding in the areas; regular casualty searches to detect direct mortality; census studies of resident territorial species and the monitoring of the breeding success if appropriate; and positive sampling of birds on site for biochemical tests and pesticide residue analysis. It should be pointed out that the level of searching activity should be kept low enough to avoid undue disturbance of the study sites which might prevent wildlife from using the test areas. Risk to wildlife may be assessed by in-depth study at a single or few sites or may involve less intensive surveillance at many sites with fewer measurements allowing a greater range of field conditions. Sometimes it is necessary to combine both approaches (Bunyan *et al.* 1981). When the granular formulation of the carbamate, aldicarb, was introduced in the UK, an intensive single-site field trial was carried out which demonstrated two particular hazards to birds, namely the ingestion of granules left on the soil surface particularly at the edges of fields, and the ingestion of contaminated worms coming to the surface following wet weather soon after application. A surveillance exercise was subsequently carried out at eight sites under commercial conditions to assess the practical significance of these findings (Bunyan *et al.* 1981). This resulted in the modification of the applicator to prevent granules being left on the surface, and better advice to farmers concerning the risks from using granules under wet soil conditions. These measures reduced the environmental hazard to birds from extensive commercial use of this pesticide.

Tests undertaken in the laboratory and in the field provide data for the assessment of the environmental risk presented by a new pesticide product. If on the basis of these laboratory and field tests, it is concluded that the risk to non-target wildlife is low, then the new pesticide may be commercially introduced on to the UK agricultural market. Since such tests have been carried out on a relatively restricted range of organisms and under a limited range of environmental conditions, it is essential that the early years of commercial introduction are monitored in order to confirm the predictions of environmental safety made during the assessment stages of development.

POST-REGISTRATION SURVEILLANCE

In the UK, biologists and veterinarians and chemists within the Ministry of Agriculture, Fisheries and Food (MAFF) collaborate under the Wildlife Incident Investigation Scheme (WIIS) to determine the causes of death of wildlife found on farmland in order to identify any involvement of agricultural pesticides. Experience gained over the last 25 years has led to a sophisticated but flexible procedure being adopted by the Tolworth Laboratory for the investigation of wildlife incidents. Any reports of wildlife mortality on or near farmland, and thought to involve agricultural chemicals, are investigated in the field to determine the scale of the problem and all relevant details including evidence of local pesticide use. Any casualties are subjected to a thorough post-mortem examination at a Veterinary Investigation Centre to screen out disease and trauma as likely causes of death. Tissues from any cases where cause of death has not been determined are then sent to the Tolworth Laboratory for extensive biochemical and residue studies. Analyses are carried out for a wide range of pesticides (including organochlorines, organophosphorus, carbamates, rodenticides, pyrethroids and several vertebrate toxicants). Brain acetyl cholinesterase activity, measured and compared with control values (Westlake *et al.* 1983), may be used to support residue measurements of compounds whose mode of action is to inhibit AchE activity, e.g. organophosphorus and carbamate pesticides (Martin *et al.* 1981). The identities of any detected pesticide residues are confirmed by independent analysis. A final report summarizing evidence from the field, pathological examination, biochemical and residue studies is circulated to those concerned in the investigation and at the same time to the regulatory authorities and the chemical company responsible for the pesticide. A significant problem involving a pesticide in the field may require revision of the regulatory approval in an attempt to avoid a recurrence.

Since 1964, some 2500 suspected wildlife incidents have been investigated in England and Wales by MAFF (a parallel scheme is run in Scotland by the Department of Agriculture and Fisheries for Scotland). Approximately 45 percent were identified to have involved agricultural chemicals, 11 percent involved disease and trauma and in 44 percent of incidents no cause of death was established (Hardy *et al.* 1986). Birds as prominent animals in the agricultural ecosystem were involved in 51 percent of incidents investigated in the last three years. Reports of wildlife deaths on farmland may be received from a variety of sources including conservation organizations, animal welfare organizations, farm workers, members of the public, representatives of agrochemical manufacturers and Ministry staff. Whilst such monitoring cannot be complete, coverage is considered adequate to allow the detection of significant problems with individual pesticides. For example, incidents involving the death of geese have been reported within a few days by up to eight independent sources, permitting some confidence in the extent of post-registration surveillance.

The value of monitoring the early commercial use of a pesticide in order to identify environmental problems that were not predicted during the evaluation stages is emphasized by two examples. Wheat Bulb Fly (*Delia coarctata*) is perhaps the most important economic pest of winter wheat in eastern counties of Britain and is controlled most effectively by insecticide seed treatments. In the 1950s the persistent cyclodiene pesticides, aldrin, dieldrin and heptachlor were used but as early as 1956 large numbers of seed-eating birds were reported to be dying as a result of this use (Turtle *et al.* 1963). Predatory birds were also killed through eating prey poisoned by dieldrin and this led to serious population declines of, for example, Sparrow Hawks (*Accipiter nisus*) and Peregrine Falcons (*Falco peregrinus*). The use of these organochlorine seed treatments was progressively restricted as a result of several reviews of their environmental problems until dieldrin and aldrin were withdrawn from use in 1975. The phasing out of these pesticides was made possible by the development and introduction of the more toxic but relatively less persistent organophosphorus insecticides, carbophenothion and chlorfenvinphos in the late sixties. However, in the early 1970s, carbophenothion seed treatments resulted in a number of serious poisoning incidents involving wintering geese (Stanley & Bunyan 1979). At least 1500 Greylag (*Anser anser*) and Pinkfooted (*Anser brachyrhynchus*) geese died in eight incidents between 1971 and 1975 (Bailey *et al.* 1972; Hamilton & Stanley 1975; Hamilton *et al.* 1976). The common link between all these incidents was that carbophenothion seed treatments had been used, and either grain on the surface had been consumed or seedlings had been uprooted under wet soil conditions. In further laboratory research, toxicity tests with five species of geese revealed that the grey geese (*Anser*) are more susceptible to carbophenothion poisoning than the Branta geese e.g. the Canada Goose (*Branta canadensis*) (Westlake *et al.* 1978) on which the original laboratory test was conducted during pesticide development (Jennings *et al.* 1975).

As a result of the incident investigations, carbophenothion appeared to present an unacceptable hazard to wintering grey geese in the UK, and action was taken to reduce the risks. In 1975, 85 percent of the world Pinkfoot population and 65 percent of the world Greylag population wintered in Britain with the majority in Scotland and others near estuaries in eastern England. Carbophenothion was voluntarily withdrawn from use as a seed treatment in Scotland and in Wheat Bulb Fly areas further south where geese are still at risk, farmers were and still are advised to use an alternative insecticide, e.g. chlorfenvinphos, which does not cause the same problems to geese. This largely overcame the environmental problems associated with this pesticide. However, wintering Brent Geese (*Branta bernicla*) have changed their feeding behaviour during the last few years and now exploit farmland, regularly grazing cereals. This change of feeding habit may put them at risk from pesticide use on cereals. In the winter of 1982–83, some 110 geese (mainly Brent) died in East Anglia after grazing fields previously sown with carbophenothion-treated grain. The geese were able to uproot the germinating seedlings because of the very wet soil conditions and thus gained access to the treated seed coats not usually available to them. Similarly 25 swans, principally Bewick's (*Cygnus bewickii*), died after feeding on treated grain left exposed on the surface of fields adjacent to a refuge. Better advice to farmers by MAFF and conservation organizations should avoid further problems of this kind.

The second example worthy of note concerns the introduction of the carbamate, aldicarb, as a granular nematicide for use on potatoes and sugar beet. In 1975 and 1976 deaths of up to 100 gulls, chiefly Black-headed Gulls (*Larus ridibundus*) were reported following the application of aldicarb granules. In many cases granules were applied to wet soil and not immediately incorporated. Investigations revealed aldicarb residues in the gulls which also exhibited depressed brain AchE activity. It appeared that the gulls died after consuming aldicarb either directly as granules or through ingesting contaminated earthworms. In order to overcome these risks the application equipment was modified to reduce the chances of leaving granules on the surface and farmers were advised of the hazard to wildlife. This approach was successful and carbamate insecticides are extensively used today in vegetable crops with a high degree of environmental safety.

Investigations under the WIIS have demonstrated that since the withdrawal of organochlorine seed-treatments in the mid-seventies there have been relatively few incidents arising from the recommended agricultural use of pesticides (Hardy *et al.* 1986). Early problems associated with the introduction of organophosphorus seed treatments and granular carbamates were identified and resolved following incident investigations (Hardy & Stanley 1984). Half those incidents identified to involve agricultural chemicals involved the deliberate misuse of pesticides used as toxic baits to protect crops and game or stock rearing interests (Brown *et al.* 1977). Mortality from this cause has serious implications for long-lived raptors with small populations since these birds show deferred maturity and have low replacement rates, e.g. Red Kite (*Milvus milvus*) and Golden Eagle (*Aquila chrysaetos*).

Measurement of residue levels in particular wildlife species is another way of environmental monitoring in which birds can be indicators of pesticide problems. Widespread use of the organochlorine DDT has led to extensive contamination in many ecosystems (e.g. Bailey *et al.* 1970, 1974). Persistent lipophilic residues accumulate up the food chain with deleterious effects on predatory bird populations (Walker & Stanley 1986). In the UK, monitoring has been conducted by the

Natural Environment Research Council since 1963 with the analysis of tissues and/or eggs of ten species: Grey Heron (*Ardea cinerea*), Sparrowhawk, Kestrel (*Falco tinunculus*), Kingfisher (*Alcedo atthis*), Golden Eagle, Rough-legged Buzzard (*Buteo lagopus*), Peregrine and Long-eared Owl (*Asio otus*). Levels of residues of pp-DDE (the principal metabolite of DDT) and dieldrin have, in general, slowly declined in most species in line with the progressive restrictions of use (Cooke *et al.* 1982). However, there are exceptions; for example, DDE residues in Sparrowhawks have not declined during 20 years although the population has recovered since the trough of 1957–63 (Newton & Haas 1984).

DDT sprays have been used extensively on a variety of crops, particularly in orchards and on vegetable crops. Its use was progressively reduced in the UK until it was withdrawn completely in 1984. Since Woodpigeons (*Columba palumbus*) feed largely on brassica crops and are easily collected, intermittent monitoring of residue levels in this indicator species has provided valuable information to the regulatory authorities in the UK on the extent of environmental contamination with DDT/DDE. In view of continuing DDE levels in Sparrowhawks, it was considered possible that migrant thrushes coming to winter in the UK might be a major source of contamination. Residue analysis of tissues from birds collected in two years suggested that Redwings (*Turdus pilaris*) may arrive in the UK in late autumn with appreciable body burdens of organochlorine pesticides (Fletcher *et al.* 1986).

Contamination with alkyl mercury used as a fungicide resulted in widespread mortality of raptors in both Europe and North America in the fifties and sixties (Borg *et al.* 1969; Fimreite *et al.* 1970; Fuchs *et al.* 1971; Koeman *et al.* 1971). As part of a long-term pollution monitoring exercise in the UK, tissues of Tawny Owls and Barn Owls killed in traffic accidents were examined between 1967 and 1973 for mercury residues. Very low residue levels were found and it was concluded that the use of mercurial fungicides in the UK, where only aryl mercury is used, has not led to significant environmental contamination (Stanley & Elliott 1976).

ENVIRONMENTAL IMPACT ASSESSMENT

Sophisticated biochemical and histopathological techniques have been developed to complement sampling programmes in the field. These can be supported by additional laboratory studies necessary to interpret the field results as part of the assessment of the environmental impact of a pesticide. This detailed multidisciplinary approach may include studies of birds to monitor exposure to pesticides where direct mortality is not apparent.

Methiocarb is a non-systemic carbamate insecticide and acaricide which has been used as a bird repellent in a number of countries but which is not approved for use in the UK. A field trial was conducted by MAFF in 1980 to assess the environmental impact of experimentally spraying methiocarb on ripening cherries to reduce damage by Starlings (*Sturnus vulgaris*). Nest boxes were erected throughout the study area, a cherry orchard in south-east England, to establish breeding populations of tits, sparrows and Starlings. Resident birds were caught in mist-nets and individually ringed prior to the trial to permit their identification when caught subsequently during the spraying regime. Ripening cherries were sprayed with methiocarb on five separate days, starting in late May, so that each tree received three applications. Regular searches of the orchard were made for any wildlife casualties, and natural and artificial nest sites were checked regularly to monitor the breeding success of resident passerines. Mist-nets were operated continuously and more than 2000 birds of 42 species were caught during the 70-day trial. Blood samples were collected from thrushes, Starlings and House Sparrows (*Passer domesticus*) at intervals for biochemical measurements including esterase activity. Thrushes were released after sampling, but sparrows and Starlings were collected for further biochemical and residue studies and histological examination of selected tissues.

Measurements showed that 60 percent of the spray was deposited on the trees and that residue levels on cherries declined at a similar and rapid rate after each of the three applications. No effect that could be attributed to methiocarb was found on the breeding success of birds resident in the orchard. Young birds fledged from 95 successful nests in boxes and natural sites. Extensive casualty searches revealed a small number of dead birds in the orchard but laboratory investigations confirmed that most of these resulted from trauma or natural causes. Methiocarb was thought to have possibly contributed to the deaths of only three birds.

Significant decreases in blood plasma AchE activity, indicating exposure to carbamate pesticides (Westlake *et al.* 1981a) were found in individual House Sparrows immediately after the five sprays. Residues of methiocarb detected in breast muscle were correlated with these plasma AchE activity decreases but lack of depression of brain esterase activity reflected the transient nature of this plasma esterase response. In contrast, many Starlings which fed on cherries showed greater depression of brain AchE activity, indicating a progressive inhibitory effect during the trial. Residue levels in Starling breast muscle were variable but low. Measurements on blood from Blackbirds and Song Thrushes did not demonstrate overall esterase inhibition though a few individuals caught several times during the trial showed temporary inhibition of plasma esterases (*Figure 1*). This useful technique allows the repeated sampling and assessment of exposure of individual birds over a suitable time period in the field and has obvious advantages over the alternative of collecting and removing birds from the population for sampling purposes. It was concluded that the biochemical changes detected in the birds during this trial were significant but transient and there was no evidence that they influenced the survival of the birds.

Measurement of esterase activity can therefore be a valuable tool for estimating the exposure of birds to certain pesticides in the field, and when combined with detailed ecological studies can provide data essential for the assessment of environmental impact (Westlake *et al.* 1981b; Hill & Fleming 1982). The control of important economic insect pests of forestry has led particularly in North America to the development of the aerial application of certain pesticides. Monitoring studies have relied heavily on birds as an important part of the forest fauna potentially at risk (Busby *et al.* 1981, 1983; Zinkl *et al.* 1984). In the UK, aerial applications of the organophosphorus pesticide fenitrothion to forestry have been on a more limited scale but have also been closely monitored for environmental effects. After the spraying of Lodgepole Pine (*Pinus contorta*) in Scotland to control Pine Beauty Moth (*Panolis flammea*), resident Chaffinches, Coal Tits (*Parus ater*) and Willow Warblers (*Phylloscopus trochilus*) showed severe depression of brain AchE activity and detectable residues of fenitrothion in the first few days after-spraying (Hamilton *et al.* 1981). Some birds exceeded 50 percent inhibition, which may cause death resulting from continuous exposure (Zinkl *et al.* 1979) but if resulting from a single exposure should not incapacitate birds (Ludke *et al.* 1975). Up to 7 days after spraying, 80 percent of Chaffinches showed severe depression of esterase activity. Recovery varied with species, and some individuals still had depressed activity another 14 days later. Further

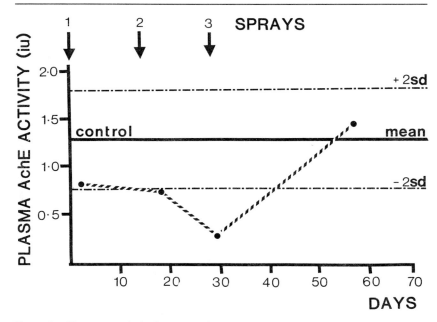

Figure 1: Plasma acetyl cholinesterase (AchE) activities of a single female Blackbird retrapped and blood-sampled in a cherry orchard in relation to three experimental spray applications of methiocarb. The incubating bird was sprayed on its nest on the first spray date and successfully reared its brood and completed its annual wing moult during the observation period.
AchE activities are compared with control values (mean 1.31 International units per gram tissue ± 2SD).

ecological studies of breeding success of small forest birds did not reveal significant effects of the annual spray programme (Spray *et al.* 1987).

Several workers have determined the effects of sub-lethal exposure to an organophosphorus pesticide in passerines by experimentally dosing birds to achieve 50 percent brain esterase inhibition. Grue, Powell & McChesney (1982) and Grue, Powell & Gorsuch (1982) have shown that such exposure has relatively little effect on breeding success and subsequent survival of captive and free living Starlings. Complementary work at the Worplesdon Laboratory (MAFF) in the UK is examining the behavioural responses of individual Starlings dosed at this level.

Studies of birds associated with field crops have been less successful in demonstrating the biological effects of exposure to such pesticides. In the US, overall reproductive success was unaffected in the Red-winged Blackbird (*Agelaius phoeniceus*) exposed to fenthion, another organophosphorus insecticide, which locally decreased the birds' food supply (Powell 1984). Also in the US, Niethammer & Baskett (1983) found significantly different inhibition of brain esterase activity in Red-winged Blackbirds and Dickcissels (*Spiza americana*) collected from wheat fields treated with methyl-parathion and toxaphene. There was no apparent difference in the insect diets of the two species and no explanation was found to explain the esterase results. This may be another example of the wide species variation in biochemical responses to various organophosphorus pesticides (Westlake *et al.* 1978).

An insectivorous passerine, the Tree Sparrow (*Passer montanus*), is being used as a model in the UK to determine whether biochemical parameters are sufficiently sensitive to detect exposure to an organophosphorus aphicide applied to adjacent wheat fields during its breeding season. As part of the Boxworth Project, MAFF is investigating the comparative ecological effects of different pesticide treatment regimes in winter wheat production (Stanley & Hardy 1984; Hardy 1986). Adult Tree Sparrows feed principally on aphid species within the wheat crops which may receive pesticide treatments. Breeding success and adult foraging behaviour is monitored from nest boxes provided, while insect food is monitored in the crops and as nestling diet. Nestlings are blood-sampled for electrophoretic analysis of plasma esterase enzymes (Martin *et al.* 1983) whose activities are inhibited by the aphicide demeton-S-methyl. Supported by laboratory dosing studies, it is hoped that at the end of the five-year treatment phase of the project, this field study will provide a realistic model of exposure in a free-living passerine to determine whether direct or indirect (through depletion of local insect food supply) effects are more significant to the survival of a small farmland bird.

Another major study in the UK is the Game Conservancy's work on the decline of the Grey Partridge (*Perdix perdix*). The survival of partridge chicks is closely dependent on the availability of suitable insect food, and local reductions of insects through pesticide use are thought to have adversely affected partridges (Potts & Vickerman 1974; Potts 1986). New crop management techniques are being developed to reduce the impact of pesticides on insect populations and to increase partridge populations.

CONCLUSION

Birds are important indicators of environmental health, and this paper has so far considered the important part they play in the assessment of environmental risks from pesticide use. There is no doubt that, in the UK, the investigations of field effects and wildlife incidents, together with the assessment of their significance, have greatly benefited from the wealth of both long-term population data and specific studies providing a deep understanding of the basic ecology of the bird species involved. In addition to the detailed research and monitoring studies outlined above, bird populations are regularly monitored in a number of other ways in the UK. The British Trust for Ornithology (BTO), through its largely amateur membership, maintains continuous monitoring of breeding farmland and woodland bird populations through the Common Bird Census. Annual indices are calculated from this information and used to identify changes in populations (e.g. Marchant 1983). Together with the Nest Recording Scheme, which annually documents breeding success of many species, this work provides a valuable source of information to assess the influences of changing agriculture in the UK and the impact of agricultural chemicals (O'Connor & Shrubb 1986). Publication by the BTO of the detailed *Atlas of Breeding Birds in Britain and Ireland* (Sharrock 1976) and its recent sequel, the *Atlas of Wintering Birds in Britain and Ireland* (Lack 1986) provide important baseline references for impact assessment.

The Wildfowl Trust monitors the numbers of wintering wildfowl, many of which feed on farmland, and records of game-birds are maintained by the Game Conservancy. Other long-term census studies, funded by the Natural Environment Research Council, cover heron and raptor populations and all contribute to the wealth of sound monitoring population data available in the UK. Additional information is derived from the national bird-ringing scheme run by the BTO. The level of surveillance of vertebrate populations, particularly birds, is considered to be adequate to detect the adverse effects arising from pesticide use (Bunyan & Stanley 1983). Environmental hazard assessment in the UK will continue to exploit birds as vulnerable and highly visible indicators of environmental health in order to minimise the effects of intensive pesticide use.

REFERENCES

BAA 1986. *Annual Report and Handbook 1985–86*. British Agrochemicals Association Ltd., London.

BAILEY, S., BUNYAN, P. J., HAMILTON, G. A., JENNINGS, D. M. & STANLEY, P. I. 1972. Accidental poisoning of wild geese in Perthshire, November 1971. *Wildfowl* **23**, 88–91.

BAILEY, S., BUNYAN, P. J., JENNINGS, D. M. & TAYLOR, A. 1970. Hazards to wildlife from the use of DDT in orchards. *Pestic. Sci.* **1**, 66–9.

BAILEY, S., BUNYAN, P. J., JENNINGS, D. M., NORRIS, J. D., STANLEY, P. I. & WILLIAMS, J. H. 1974. Hazards to wildlife from the use of DDT in orchards: II. A further study. *Agro-ecosystems* **1**, 323–38.

BORG, K., WANNTORP, H., ERNE, K. & HANKO, E. 1969. Alkyl mercury poisoning in terrestrial Swedish wildlife. *Viltrevy* **6**, 301–79.

BROWN, P. M., BUNYAN, P. J. & STANLEY, P. I. 1977. The investigation and pattern of occurrence of animal poisoning resulting from the misuse of agricultural chemicals. *J. forensic Sci. Soc.* **17**, 211–21.

BUNYAN, P. J. & STANLEY, P. I. 1979. Assessment of the environmental impact of new pesticides for regulation purposes. *Proc. Br. Crop Prot. Conf. Pests Dis.*, **10**th, 881–91. British Crop Protection Council, Croydon.

BUNYAN, P. J. & STANLEY, P. I. 1982. Toxic mechanisms in wildlife. *Regul. Toxicol. Pharmacol.* **2**, 106–45.

BUNYAN, P. J. & STANLEY, P. I. 1983. The environmental cost of pesticide usage in the UK. *Agriculture, ecosystems and environment* **9**, 187–209.

BUNYAN, P. J., VAN DEN HEUVEL, M. J., STANLEY, P. I. & WRIGHT, E. N. 1981. An intensive field trial and a multi-site surveillance exercise on the use of aldicarb to investigate methods for the assessment of possible environmental hazards presented by new pesticides. *Agro-ecosystems* **7**, 239–62.

BUSBY, D. G., PEARCE, P. A. & GARRITY, N. R. 1981. Brain cholinesterase response in songbirds exposed to experimental fenitrothion spraying in New Brunswick, Canada. *Bull. Environm. Contam. Toxicol.* **26**, 401–6.

BUSBY, D. G., PEARCE, P. A., GARRITY, N. R. & REYNOLDS, L. M. 1983. Effect of an organophosphorus insecticide on brain cholinesterase activity in white-throated sparrows exposed to aerial forest spraying. *J. anim. Ecol.* **20**, 255–63.

CARSON, R. 1963. *Silent Spring*. Hamish Hamilton, London.

COOKE, A. S., BELL, A. A. & HAAS, M. B. 1982. *Predatory birds, pesticides and pollution*. Institute of Terrestrial Ecology, Cambridge.

EDWARDS, P. J., BROWN, S. M., FLETCHER, M. R. & STANLEY, P. I. 1979. The use of a bird territory mapping method for detecting mortality following pesticide application. *Agro-ecosystems* **5**, 271–82.

FIMREITE, N., FYFE, R. M. & KEITH, J. A. 1970. Mercury contamination of Canadian prairie seed eaters and their avian predators. *Can. Field Nat.* **84**, 269–74.

FINK, R. J. & JABER, M. J. 1981. The laughing gull (*Larus atricilla*) as a model for the assessment of secondary poisoning. *In: Avian and Mammalian Wildlife Toxicology:* 2nd conference ASTM STP 757, (eds.) Lamb, D. W. & Kenaga, E. E. American Society Testing and Materials, 66–71.

FLETCHER, M. R., HARDY, A. R. & HOODLESS, R. A. 1986. Organochlorine residues in migrant thrushes in Britain. VI IUPAC Meeting, Ottawa, 1986; *Abstracts*.

FUCHS, P., DE VOS, R. H. & ZWIERS, J. H. L. 1981. Mercury in owls and birds of prey. *T.N.O. Nieuws* **26**, 413–14.

GOLDSTEIN, E., AMAVIS, R., CABRIDENC, R., GILLIARD, C. & SCHUBERT, R. 1984. Prevention des effets ecotoxicologiques dans l'environment terrestre bilan des methodes disponibles pour les oiseaux. Symposium International 'Ecotoxicologie Terrestre', Les Arcs 12–14 December 1984.

GRUE, C. E., POWELL, G. V. N. & GORSUCH, C. H. 1982. Assessing effects of organophosphates on songbirds: comparison of a captive and a free-living population. *J. Wildl. Manage.* **46**, 766–8.

GRUE, C. E., POWELL, G. V. N. & McCHESNEY, M. J. 1982. Care of nestlings by wild female starlings exposed to an organophosphate pesticide. *J. appl. Ecol.* **19**, 327–35.

HAMILTON, G. A. & STANLEY, P. I. 1975. Further cases of poisoning of wild geese by an organophosphorus winter wheat seed treatment. *Wildfowl* **26**, 49–54.

HAMILTON, G. A., HUNTER, K., RITCHIE, A. S., RUTHVEN, A. D., BROWN, P. M. & STANLEY, P. I. 1976. Poisoning of wild geese by carbophenothion treated winter wheat. *Pestic. Sci.* **7**, 175–83.

HAMILTON, G. A., HUNTER, K. & RUTHVEN, A. D. 1981. Inhibition of brain acetylcholinesterase activity in songbirds exposed to fenitrothion during aerial spraying of forests. *Bull. Environm. Contam. Toxicol.* **27**, 856–63.

HARDY, A. R. & STANLEY, P. I. 1984. The impact of the commercial agricultural use of organophosphorus and carbamate pesticides on British wildlife. *In: Agriculture and the Environment,* (ed.) Jenkins, D., 72–80. (ITE Symposium no.13). Institute of Terrestrial Ecology, Cambridge.

HARDY, A. R. 1986. The Boxworth Project—a progress report. *Proc. Br. Crop Prot. Conf. Pests Dis.* 1986, 1215–24. British Crop Protection Council, Croydon.

HARDY, A. R., FLETCHER, M. R. & STANLEY, P. I. 1986. Twenty years of vertebrate wildlife incident investigations by MAFF. *Veterinary Journal* **40**, 182–92.

HILL, E. F. & FLEMING, W. J. 1982. Anticholinesterase poisoning of birds: field monitoring and diagnosis of acute poisoning. *Environ. Toxicol. Chem.* **1**, 27–38.

HILL, E. F. & HOFFMAN, D. J. 1984. Avian models for toxicity testing. *J. Amer. Coll. toxicol.* **3**, 357–76.

INTERNATIONAL BIRD CENSUS COMMITTEE 1970. Recommendations for an international standard for a mapping method in bird census work. *Bull. Ecol. Res. Comm.* **9**, 49–52.

JENNINGS, D. M., BUNYAN, P. J., BROWN, P. M., STANLEY, P. I. & JONES, F. J. S. 1975. Organophosphorus poisoning: a comparative study of the toxicity of carbophenothion to the Canada goose, the pigeon and the Japanese quail. *Pestic. Sci.* **6**, 245–57.

KOEMAN, J. H., GARSSEN-HOEKSTR, J., PELS, E. & DE GOEIJ, J. J. M. 1971. Poisoning of birds of prey by methyl mercury compounds. *Meded. Fac. Landbouwwet. Rijksuniv. Gent.* **36**, 43–9.

LACK, P. 1986. *The atlas of wintering birds in Britain and Ireland.* Poyser Ltd., Calton.

LUDKE, J. L., HILL, E. F. & DIETER, M. P. 1975. Cholinesterase (ChE) response and related mortality among birds fed ChE inhibitors. *Arch. Environm. Contam. Toxicol.* **3**, 1–21.

MAFF 1986a. UK Food and farming in figures. Ministry of Agriculture, Fisheries and Food, Alnwick.

MAFF 1986b. Data requirements for approval under the Control of Pesticides Regulations 1986. Ministry of Agriculture, Fisheries and Food, Pesticides Branch, London.

MARCHANT, J. H. 1983. Bird population changes for the years 1981–1982. *Bird Study* **30**, 127–33.

MARTIN, A. D., NORMAN, G., STANLEY, P. I. & WESTLAKE, G. E. 1981. Use of reactivation techniques for the differential diagnosis of organophosphorus and carbamate pesticide poisoning in birds. *Bull. Environm. Contam. Toxicol.* **26**, 775–80.

MARTIN, A. D., BLUNDEN, C. A., FLETCHER, M. R., FLETCHER, W. J., STANLEY, P. I. & WESTLAKE, G. E. 1983. Electrophoretic profiles of esterases in starling (*Sturnus vulgaris*) plasma: an apparent simple genetic variant. *Bull. Environm. Contam. Toxicol.* **30**, 373–7.

MOORE, N. W. 1980. How many wild birds should farmland support? *In: Bird Problems in Agriculture,* (eds.) Wright, E. N., Inglis I. R. & Feare, C. J. pp. 2–6 (Monograph 23). British Crop Protection Council, Croydon.

NEWTON, I. & HAAS, M. B. 1984. The return of the sparrowhawk. *Brit. Birds* **77**, 47–70.

NIETHAMMER, K. R. & BASKETT, T. S. 1983. Cholinesterase inhibition of birds inhabiting wheat fields treated with methyl parathion and toxaphene. *Arch. Environm. Contam. Toxicol.* **12**, 471–5.

O'CONNOR, R. J. & SHRUBB, M. 1986. *Farming and birds.* Cambridge University Press, Cambridge.

POTTS, G. R. & VICKERMAN, G. P. 1974. Studies on the cereal ecosystem. *Adv. ecol. Res.* **8**, 107–97.

POTTS, G. R. 1986. *The partridge: pesticides, predation and conservation.* Collins, London.

POWELL, G. N. 1984. Reproduction by an altricial songbird, the red-winged blackbird, in fields treated with the organophosphate insecticide fenthion. *J. app. Ecol.* **21**, 83–95.

SHARROCK, J. T. R. 1976. *The atlas of breeding birds in Britain and Ireland.* British Trust for Ornithology, Tring.

SLY, J. M. A. 1986. *Pesticide usage survey report 35: arable farm crops and grass 1982.* Reference book 535. Ministry of Agriculture, Fisheries and Food, Alnwick.

SPRAY, C. J., CRICK, H. Q. P. & HART, A. D. M. 1987. Effects of aerial applications of fenitrothion on bird populations of a scottish pine plantation. *J. Appl. Ecol.* **24**, 29–47.

STANLEY, P. I. & ELLIOTT, G. R. 1976 An assessment based on residues in owls of environmental contamination arising from the use of mercury compounds in British agriculture. *Agro-ecosystems* **2**, 223–34.

STANLEY, P. I. & BUNYAN, P. J. 1979. Hazards to wintering geese and other wildlife from the use of dieldrin, chlorfenvinphos and carbophenothion as wheat seed treatments. *Proc. R. Soc. Lond. B.* **205**, 31–45.

STANLEY, P. I. & HARDY, A. R. 1983. Methods of prediction of environmental effects of pesticides. Field trials to assess the hazard presented by pesticides to terrestrial wildlife. *In: Proc. Int. Congr. Plant Protection,* **10**th, Brighton, 1983, 2, 692–701. British Crop Protection Council, Croydon.

STANLEY, P. I. & HARDY, A. R. 1984. The environmental implications of current pesticide usage on cereals. *In: Agriculture and the Environment,* (ed.) Jenkins, D., 66–72. (ITE Symposium no.13). Institute of Terrestrial Ecology, Cambridge.

TOWNSEND, M. G., ODAM, E. M., STANLEY, P. I. & WARDALL, H. P. 1981. Assessment of secondary poisoning hazard of warfarin to Tawny Owls. *J. Wildl. Manage.* **45**, 242–7.

TURTLE, E. E., TAYLOR, A., WRIGHT, E. N., THEARLE, R. J. P., EGAN, H., EVANS, W. H. & SOUTAR, N. M. 1963. The effects on birds of certain chlorinated insecticides used as seed dressings. *J. Sci. Fd. Agric.* **14**, 567–77.

WALKER, C. H. & STANLEY, P. I. 1986. Organochlorine insecticide residues in predatory birds—long term trends and bioaccumulation. *In:* Greenhalgh, R. & Roberts, T. R., (eds.) *Pesticide Science and Biotechnology,.* Blackwell Scientific Publications, Oxford.

WESTLAKE, G. E., BUNYAN, P. J. & STANLEY, P. I. 1978. Variation in the response of plasma enzyme activities in avian species dosed with carbophenothion. *Ecotox. Environ. Safety* **2**, 151–9.

WESTLAKE, G. E., BUNYAN, P. J., MARTIN, A. D., STANLEY, P. I. & STEED, L. C. 1981a. Carbamate poisoning. Effects of selected carbamate pesticides on plasma enzymes and brain esterase of Japanese quail (*Coturnix coturnix japonica*). *J. Agric. Food Chem.* **29**, 779–85.

WESTLAKE, G. E., BUNYAN, P. J., MARTIN, A. D., STANLEY, P. I. & STEED, L. C. 1981b. Organophosphate poisoning. Effects of selected organophosphate pesticides on plasma enzymes and brain esterases of Japanese quail (*Coturnix coturnix japonica*). *J. Agric. Food Chem.* **29**, 772–8.

WESTLAKE, G. E., MARTIN, A. D., STANLEY, P. I. & WALKER, C. H. 1983. Control enzyme levels in the plasma, brain and liver from wild birds and mammals in Britain. *Comp. Biochem. Physiol.* **76**, 15–24.

ZINKL, J. G., HENNY, C. J. & SHEA, P. J. 1979. Brain cholinesterase activities of passerine birds in forests sprayed with cholinesterase inhibiting insecticides. *In: Animals as monitors of environmental pollutants,* 356–365. Academy of Sciences, Washington.

ZINKL, J. G., MACK, P. D., MOUNT, M. E. & SHEA, P. J. 1984. Brain cholinesterase activity and brain and liver residues in wild birds of a forest sprayed with acephate. *Environ. Toxicol. Chem.* **1**, 79–88.

PESTICIDES AND WATERFOWL ON THE CANADIAN PRAIRIES: A PRESSING NEED FOR RESEARCH AND MONITORING

P. Mineau[1], P. J. Sheehan[2] & A. Baril[1]

1   *Canadian Wildlife Service, National Wildlife Research Centre,*
Ottawa, K1A 0H3, Canada
2   *Aqua Terra Technologies, 3490 Buskirk Ave. Suite A, Pleasant Hill,*
California 94523, USA

ABSTRACT

Approximately one-quarter of the total North American duck population breeds in Canada's breadbasket—the prairies. Encroachment of agriculture on the waterfowl resource has been extensive and shows no sign of abating. Whereas physical disruption of the wildlife habitat has been all too visible, the possibly more insidious impact of pesticides on the quality of the wildlife habitat needs to be determined. As the habitat base keeps shrinking, the emphasis of managers will gradually change from the quantity of habitat remaining to the quality of what is left.

We propose that studies of prairie-nesting ducks could be used with considerable success to answer questions relating to the broad range of possible environmental impacts resulting from the use of pesticides. Ducks are an obvious choice as monitor species because their habitat requirements include both dry upland sites and small prairie wetlands. Furthermore, the numerous duck species are broadly distributed and in intimate contact with agriculture, and they are susceptible to both direct toxicological impacts and ecological effects mediated through their nesting requirements or food supply. Finally, waterfowl are more extensively monitored than other species, and using them to study the environmental consequences of pesticide use represents a small incremental increase in current survey efforts.

INTRODUCTION

As we move away from the use of highly persistent and bioaccumulatory insecticides, such as organochlorines, to the current North American arsenal of organophosphates, carbamates, and more recently synthetic pyrethroids, it stands to reason that our approach to monitoring environmental quality has to change. No longer are measurable residue levels commensurate with probable impact (Peakall & Boyd, this volume). Therefore, the use of any species as a bio-indicator of environmental conditions becomes almost exclusively an exercise in population surveying and modelling.

A great deal of energy has been expended on looking at the possible impacts of forest insecticide spray programmes on a variety of non-target populations, especially small migratory songbirds (Mineau & Peakall, in press). Unfortunately, the impacts of modern pesticides on species that are heavily dependent on the agricultural landscape for their survival have been largely ignored (but see Hardy, this volume). The reason for this is largely the prevailing view that today's agricultural landscape is a hostile environment to birds and beyond redemption for most species.

The prairie pothole region covers approximately 777,000 square kilometers, 64 percent of which lies in the Canadian provinces of Saskatchewan, Alberta and Manitoba. It was created after the departure of the last continental ice sheet and is characterized by millions of poorly drained, small depressions which collect water and are known as sloughs. Approximately 85 percent of these sloughs are less than 0.5 hectares in area and therefore subject to wide temporal fluctuations in their water levels. The pothole region is of vital importance to a large number of bird species which use these wetlands either for nesting or for feeding. Approximately one-quarter of the total North American waterfowl production originates from this area. The total duck population breeding in the North American prairies, averaged between 1970 and 1983, stands at 22 million, 16 million of which nest in Canada. More than 20 duck species use this habitat, 11 of which have breeding populations in excess of 100,000. Dabbling ducks (*Tribe Anatini*) are clearly the dominant group, comprising more than 80 percent of the duck population. Approximate population numbers are given in *Table 1*.

The region is also of vital importance to agriculture. As of 1981, approximately 34 million hectares were under crop or fallowed (placed out of production for a year as a water conservation measure). Cereals, principally wheat, accounted for 78 percent of the agricultural production of the three prairie provinces. This intensive agricultural development has not been without an impact on the waterfowl and other waterbird communities, but this impact has yet to be adequately quantified. The only solid information available at this time is on wetland disappearance or degradation. Since the early 1960s, Canadian prairies have been undergoing a loss similar to that which occurred in the US at the turn of the century. It was estimated, for example, that the cumulative loss of wetlands in Iowa since the mid-1800s was 94 percent in 1981 (USNRC 1982).

Wetland drainage is a very visible form of habitat disturbance and has therefore received a lot of attention. Pesticide use, on the other hand, has the potential to affect wildlife and wildlife habitat in much more subtle ways. As the habitat base continues to shrink, we will be forced to consider much more carefully the quality of the habitat remaining.

The Wildlife Toxicology and Surveys Branch of the Canadian Wildlife Service looked at what is currently known of the impacts of pesticides on waterfowl, and tried to assess probable impacts based on a knowledge of waterfowl biology and on the properties of pesticides currently in use (Sheehan *et al.* 1987, where full details of the analyses described here are presented). Here, we present a summary of these findings as well as a list of recommendations which in many cases address the usefulness of waterfowl as bioindicators.

WHY WATERFOWL?

As a result of sport hunting, more interest has been generated about this group of species than any other prairie nester. United States and Canadian Federal, State and Provincial Governments, as well as private organizations, expend a considerable effort each year to monitor duck populations in the prairies and throughout the North American continent. Prairie ducks, therefore, fulfill one of the criteria for successful indicators: that their biology, distribution and status be relatively well known. As outlined above, waterfowl populations are large and extensively

Table 1: Population estimates of ducks and American Coot in the prairies. These estimates (in thousands of breeding ducks) are based on 14-year averages for each species over the period 1970–1983, and are compared to current Canadian and US population levels of the same species (from Cooch 1981).

No.	Species	Population in Canadian prairies	Percentage of total surveyed population present in Canadian prairies	Percentage of total surveyed population present in combined Canadian and US prairies
1	Mallard (Anas platyrhynchos)	3,983.2	51.1	67.4
2	Pintail (Anas acuta)	2,826.6	49.4	65.7
3	Blue-winged Teal (Anas discors)	2,746.6	55.6	87.9
4	American Coot (Fulica americana)	1,445.3	59.0	86.4
5	Northern Shoveler (Spatula clypeata)	1,145.8	53.6	80.7
6	American Wigeon (Mareca americana)	1,092.7	33.1	47.2
7	Scaup (primarily Lesser) (Aythya affinis)	1,093.4	14.4	16.9
8	Gadwall (Anas strepera)	968.0	60.7	93.8
9	Green-winged Teal (Anas carolinensis)	678.2	28.2	36.1
10	Redhead (Aythya americana)	452.9	57.1	87.7
11	Canvasback (Aythya valisneria)	346.6	59.6	67.5
12	Ruddy Duck (Oxyura jamaicensis)	312.4	48.7	88.5
13	Bufflehead (Bucephala albeola)	103.2	11.7	12.1
14	Ring-necked Duck (Aythya collaris)	74.2	12.2	16.8
15	Goldeneye (Bucephala clangula)	64.6	8.5	8.7
16	Scoters (Melanitta sp.)	24.5	1.7	1.7
17	Mergansers (Mergus sp.)	21.0	3.3	3.6
18	Black Duck (Anas rubripes)	0.7	0.8	0.8
19	Oldsquaw (Clangula hyemalis)	.1	—	—
20	Eiders (Somateria, Polysticta)	.1	—	—
	Total dabbling ducks	13,441.8	48.0	67.9
	(84.4% of Canadian prairie population)			
	Total diving ducks	1,967.1	16.2	21.2
	Total ducks	15,934.6	36.7	51.3

distributed throughout the prairies. This fulfills a second criterion, that of widespread availability.

Breeding waterfowl have two basic requirements critical for successful recruitment: a complex of shallow water-bodies for providing food throughout the breeding season, and adequate vegetative cover in close proximity for successful nesting. Dabblers (*Tribe Anatini*) prefer shallow temporary or seasonal wetlands, while divers (*Tribe Aythyini*) are usually found on deeper, larger and more permanent sloughs. Also, it has become clear that for dabblers at least, a complex of different wetlands may be essential to their success. Shallow ephemeral ponds provide abundant food early in spring, and deep ponds, which thaw later, provide invertebrate food to the ducklings when other ponds have dried up. The latter requirement is especially critical since ducklings of all species are highly dependent on protein-rich invertebrate food in early life. Furthermore, the mobility of young broods in search of food is more limited and, if overland, invites predation. All dabblers and at least one diver (the Lesser Scaup, *Aythya affinis*) are primarily upland nesters whereas other divers prefer to nest over water in emergent vegetation. (The term 'upland' refers to all dry vegetated sites suitable for nesting, such as hedgerows, fencelines, road allowances, dry slough margins, pastures, and even the actual crops.) While nesting cover preferences are species-specific, undisturbed stands of grasses, forbs, bushes and aquatic emergents are usually chosen. One species, the Northern Pintail (*Anas acuta*) is unusual in that it nests in low or sparse vegetation.

Both the aquatic and undisturbed upland habitats are in short supply in heavily cultivated areas such as the prairies. As a result, birds are forced to nest in close association with agriculture, often in the crops themselves. The sloughs that are so critical for successful breeding are often islands in seas of cropland. The quality of those sloughs is necessarily a reflection of the land management practices occurring around them. Waterfowl, by virtue of their ecological requirements, are likely to bear the brunt of any environmentally damaging practice. This also makes them a valuable monitoring tool.

QUANTIFYING THE OVERLAP BETWEEN WATERFOWL AND AGRICULTURE

A major goal of this exercise was to use available information to estimate the actual physical overlap between nesting ducks and a number of primary prairie crops. Without this information, it is difficult to estimate the impact of a given agricultural practice or a given pesticide on the duck population as a whole. The procedure proved complex and fraught with problems but, until the critical information is obtained, this is the only way available. The reader is referred to Chapter 3 of Sheehan *et al.* (1987) for details. Basically the following sources of information were used:

1. The Canada Land Inventory (CLI), a mapping and land classification exercise begun in 1963, which assesses among other things the waterfowl and the agricultural potential of surveyed lands. These two resources are assigned a potential, ranging from 1 for the best lands to 6 for the poorest.
2. The annual waterfowl surveys conducted jointly by the United States Fish and Wildlife Service and the Canadian Wildlife Service.
3. A national agricultural census conducted every five years by Statistics Canada to collect crop information.
4. Research on duck nesting preferences and densities in various habitat types in both pristine and heavily cultivated areas.

Table 2: Number of breeding ducks (in thousands) and percentage of total estimated prairie population (in brackets) within designated waterfowl classes which overlap with agriculture Classes 1–3.

Waterfowl	Alberta	S.W. Saskatchewan	S.E. Saskatchewan	Manitoba	Prairie Total
1–2	1,083 (6.5%)	473 (2.8%)	1,231 (7.4%)	377 (2.3%)	3,163 (18.9%)
3	607 (3.6%)	576 (3.4%)	265 (1.6%)	245 (1.5%)	1,694 (10.1%)
4–5	958 (5.7%)	2,082 (12.5%)	966 (5.8%)	427 (2.6%)	4,433 (26.5%)
1–5	2,648 (15.8%)	3,131 (18.7%)	2,462 (14.7%)	1,049 (6.3%)	9,290 (55.5%)

A critical step in this analysis was the assignment of actual duck breeding densities to the CLI classification system since the CLI deals with potential rather than realized value. For this, we relied heavily on the unpublished work of Patterson (1978). Fortunately, the breeding densities of all ducks combined matched the subjective assessment of the habitat potential. This allowed us (Sheehan *et al.* 1987) to estimate the amount of overlap between actual duck nesting and agriculture. It must be kept in mind that our estimates of overlap are affected by some agricultural development such as drainage. Overlap between the two resources is expected to increase to the point where the habitat becomes completely unsuitable for waterfowl, at which point nesting waterfowl are forced out and the overlap becomes negligible. Indeed, much of the good waterfowl land had already been eliminated before the CLI classification came into effect. The loss of wetlands is continuing at an alarming rate throughout the prairies and, therefore, the measure of overlap is constantly changing, but not necessarily in a predictable direction. A better estimate of the overlap between agriculture and waterfowl must await an up-to-date land inventory of the same scale as the 1963 effort.

Results from this analysis are presented in *Tables 2* and *3*. We believe that the current situation falls somewhat between the two sets of data presented. Agriculture CLI Classes 1–3 reflect the very best arable lands, the majority of which are currently in production. Most of the planned expansion of agriculture will take place in Class 4 lands and to a lesser extent in lands of lower quality. Lands of Class 5 or lower are seldom cropped but they may be used for pasture. On that basis, it can be seen that the overlap between nesting ducks and agricultural lands is very extensive. An estimated 55.5 to 75 percent of all ducks nest in association with lands that are currently cropped or have a good chance of being cropped in the near future.

These figures do not imply that this number of ducks use the crops themselves for nesting. Within the agricultural landscape, ducks nest preferentially in the vegetative margins left intact around sloughs or in suitable upland sites such as idle grassland, field edges and roadsides. Estimates of the non-crop area available to nesting ducks within prairie agricultural landscapes are in the range of ten percent

Table 3: Number of breeding ducks (in thousands) and percentage of total estimated prairie population (in brackets) within designated waterfowl classes which overlap with agriculture Classes 1–4.

Waterfowl	Alberta	S.W. Saskatchewan	S.E. Saskatchewan	Manitoba	Prairie Total
1–2	1,588 (9.5%)	575 (3.5%)	1,302 (7.8%)	385 (2.3%)	3,851 (23.1%)
3	877 (5.1%)	666 (4.0%)	943 (5.7%)	290 (1.7%)	2,757 (16.5%)
4–5	1,462 (8.8%)	2,667 (16.0%)	1,083 (6.5%)	629 (3.8%)	5,840 (35.0%)
1–5	3,907 (23.4%)	3,909 (23.4%)	3,328 (19.9%)	1,305 (7.8%)	12,449 (75.0%)

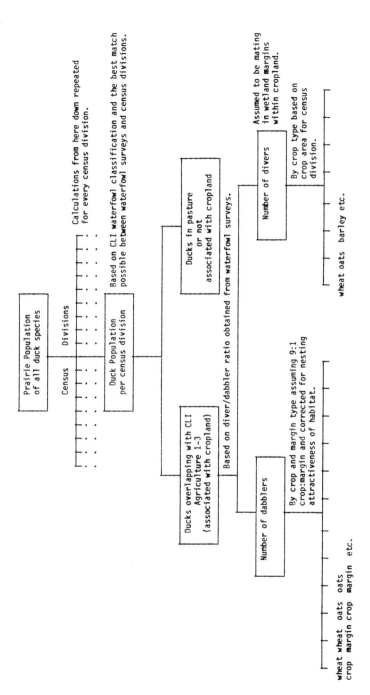

Figure 1: Flow chart of calculations used to apportion ducks to specific crop types.

(Higgins 1977; Sugden & Beyersbergen 1984). What the overlap estimates of *Tables 2* and *3* do show is the intimate relationship between nesting ducks and agricultural activities. We argue that birds nesting in association with cropland are most at risk from the point of view of any agricultural practice such as pesticide use. The impacts of pesticides may be at several levels, including disruption of aquatic food sources which may be within cropped areas even though the nesting areas are sufficiently distant from the fields. It is important to note that a limited amount of nesting by dabbling ducks takes place in the crops proper, depending on crop type and phenology. Tame hay (mostly alfalfa), for example, attracts high densities of upland-nesting ducks. The success of these birds depends on the cropping practices and the breeding phenology of the nesting pairs.

Taking this analysis one step further, we assigned ducks to crop types based on nesting preferences and crop distribution information. *Figure 1* describes this process. The assumptions are somewhat different for the dabbler and diver species. We assume that the latter nest exclusively in association with wetlands, and therefore their association with the various crop types is proportional to the predominance of each crop type in any census division. (The prairie region under consideration comprises 43 census divisions.) We further assume independence between crop type and nesting density. Dabblers on the other hand are assigned following an estimated 9:1 crop to 'margin' ratio and nesting densities obtained from the literature for both crop and non-crop areas.

The analysis was carried out at the level of each census division but only the summary is presented in *Table 4*. Not surprisingly, ducks nesting in association with wheat (especially in the upland non-crop areas (the 'margins') in proximity to wheat fields) represent the largest proportion of ducks associated with any cropland (35 percent). Given the marked preference by upland-nesting ducks for forage crops or tame hay (Duebbert & Kantrud 1974), this crop type assumes an importance totally out of proportion to the crop area. This should alert us to the need to closely monitor pesticide use in these crops. Forage (tame hay) and canola (low erucic acid varieties of rapeseed) hold the highest densities of dabblers and divers respectively. In the case of the latter crop type, this is explained by the co-correlation between the crop distribution and the best diving duck producing areas—the northern prairies known as the parklands.

PESTICIDE USE IN THE PRAIRIES

There are several sources of information on pesticide use but unfortunately none that are sufficiently detailed for environmental planning or impact assessment. The best data are either confidential business information, pooled by several active ingredients (the pesticidal components of the numerous pesticide formulations), or geographically very limited. Furthermore, the extreme volatility of some markets, e.g. insecticides used on major pest outbreaks, is such that extrapolations from one year to the next cannot be made with any degree of confidence.

Currently, the prevalent insecticide in the Canadian prairies is carbofuran (see Appendix 1 for chemical names). For control of grasshoppers, the major prairie pest problem, it is the most widely used, followed by deltamethrin and carbaryl. In 1985, those three insecticides accounted for most of the grasshopper control in roughly a 2:1:1 ratio. Dimethoate had for a number of years been the insecticide used almost exclusively for grasshopper control. Its replacement by the aforementioned three is an important factor in our hazard assessment. Whereas

Table 4: Major crop areas in the grassland-parkland regions of the prairie provinces and estimated numbers of dabbling and diving ducks nesting within or in association with these crops (expressed as thousands of ducks and proportion of the totals nesting within these particular crop types).

	WHEAT Crop	WHEAT Margin	OATS Crop	OATS Margin	BARLEY Crop	BARLEY Margin	RYE Crop	RYE Margin	FLAX Crop	FLAX Margin	CANOLA Crop	CANOLA Margin	TAME HAY Crop	TAME HAY Margin	SUMMER FALLOW Crop	SUMMER FALLOW Margin
Dabblers (×1000)																
Alberta	270	300	42.4	47.1	162	180	11.7	13.0	3.30	3.67	46.7	51.9	702	78.0	67.5	225
Saskatchewan	1070	1190	67.0	74.5	221	245	28.1	31.3	22.2	24.6	83.3	92.5	1010	113	301	1000
Manitoba	86.2	95.7	13.4	14.9	51.1	56.8	4.39	4.88	15.3	17.0	13.0	14.5	228	25.3	12.6	41.9
TOTAL	1430	1590	123	136	434	482	44.2	49.1	40.8	45.3	143	159	1940	216	381	1270
Divers (×1000)																
Alberta	115		25.5		97.3		4.24		1.25		28.6		43.1		79.3	
Saskatchewan	317		23.1		85.4		8.25		6.98		39.0		35.9		26.3	
Manitoba	53.3		8.74		33.2		2.78		8.08		8.41		18.2		27.9	
TOTAL	485		57.3		216		15.3		16.3		76.0		97.2		370	
Crop Area in grassland-parkland region (km²)	116,194		10,223		42,090		3,898		4,486		11,410		19,718		90,445	
% contribution to area in these major crops	38.9%		3.43%		14.1%		1.31%		1.50%		3.82%		6.61%		30.3%	
Dabblers—proportion associated with crop type	35.5%		3.05%		10.8%		1.10%		1.01%		3.56%		25.47%		19.5%	
Divers—proportion associated with crop type	36.4%		4.30%		16.2%		1.15%		1.22%		5.70%		7.29%		27.8%	

dimethoate was only moderately toxic to either vertebrates or aquatic invertebrates, its replacements are acutely toxic either to vertebrates (carbofuran) or to aquatic invertebrates (deltamethrin).

Based on data from the last two decades, we (Sheehan *et al.* 1987—section 4.2) estimate that approximately two million hectares are sprayed for grasshoppers during a moderate–severe outbreak. The extended spray area (including reapplication) in the recent 1985 outbreak (a record one) was estimated to have been between 3.7 and 4.7 million hectares. Spray areas would have been substantially higher had better growing conditions prevailed that summer. In contrast, the worst non-grasshopper pest outbreaks have been in the range of 0.4–0.5 million hectares and the estimated average baseline insecticide use (the yearly use of insecticides not related to a particular outbreak) is around 1.0–1.5 million hectares. In 1985, the total insecticide spray area was equivalent to an estimated 21–23 percent of the best cropland (CLI Classes 1–3). Temporally, all of these spray programmes overlap with the duck breeding season. It is difficult to estimate the extent of aerial application but for some crops, for example canola, it is almost 100 percent. 'Educated guesses' by provincial agricultural officials place the aerial component of grasshopper control programmes between 10 and 25 percent of total insecticide use (Sheehan *et al.* op. cit.). A weighted average by province would place the proportion of aerial spraying for grasshoppers at 13 percent or less. Given that aerial application is an important factor in defining pesticide impacts (see below), it is imperative that these estimates of aerial use be improved.

It is our contention that a direct overspray with insecticides of both the nesting and aquatic feeding habitat is probable at least where aerial application is used (Sheehan *et al.* 1987—Chapter 5). Drift and other sources of non-target contamination are a potential problem in the remaining areas. Depending on meteorological and topographical conditions, off-target sites contiguous to the spray areas can receive equal or higher rates of application than the target area.

Herbicide use is easier to quantify than insecticide use since it tends to be more static both in time and space. We estimate that approximately 13–15 million hectares are sprayed yearly with grassy or broadleaf herbicides or both (Sheehan *et al.* 1987—section 4.3). Some crops are sprayed very extensively indeed. For example, an estimated 80 percent of the wheat crop is sprayed with broadleaf herbicides and 91.5 percent of the canola crop is sprayed with grass herbicides. King (1978) etimated that nine percent of total herbicide delivery was aerial.

LIKELY IMPACTS OF PESTICIDES ON WATERFOWL

Toxic impact

The acute or chronic toxicity of modern pesticides to wildlife in general (Grue *et al.* 1983) and waterfowl in particular (Grue *et al.* 1986) have been reviewed extensively. Generally speaking, insecticides are more toxic to vertebrates than herbicides by several orders of magnitude. Of the available prairie insecticides, carbofuran is reportedly the most toxic to waterfowl. The LD_{50} (measured as the amount of toxicant in mg per kg of test animal necessary to kill 50 percent of the test population) of carbofuran to three-month-old mallards is 0.397 with a 95 percent confidence interval of 0.315–0.500 (Hudson *et al.* 1984). This is one full order of magnitude more toxic than the next most toxic insecticides: diazinon and demeton. Yet, the survival of duck broods exposed to a direct spray of carbofuran has not been investigated. Exposure of both young and adult birds is likely to be through a variety of routes, including ingestion of contaminated invertebrate prey or vegetation, preening, dermal uptake and inhalation.

Since 1972, at least fourteen incidents of bird kills have been attributed to the use of carbofuran flowable in the United States and Canada (Flickinger *et al.* 1980; Hill & Fleming 1982; NRCC 1979; University of Saskatchewan 1986; United States Environmental Protection Agency (U.S. EPA) 1979; California Fish and Game 1976, 1978, 1986; Virginia Polytechnic Institute 1986). Over 6000 birds were reported to have died in these incidents. Cases where liquid carbofuran was used to deliberately poison wildlife are excluded from this total. In all but three instances, waterfowl were the primary non-target casualties. Ten of the eleven waterfowl kills were related to alfalfa spraying. The four worst incidents reported involved 2500, 1100+, 750–1000 and 500 adult ducks or geese. Alfalfa is the principal forage (tame hay) crop being grown on the prairies.

Over approximately the same period, 48 incidents of bird mortality were documented following the use of a granular formulation of carbofuran (CWS files unpubl.). A full review of this problem is beyond the scope of this paper but the situation is worrisome since granular carbofuran is used extensively on the prairies as a prophylactic treatment for fleabeetle in canola.

Furthermore, we are of the opinion that only a very small proportion of kills are ever discovered and reported. Dead birds are notoriously hard to find and subject to rapid removal by scavengers (Balcomb 1986). The exact number of birds exposed to toxic insecticides is a matter of debate. Using the best estimates available and what we believe is a very conservative scenario, we estimate that 0.93 million breeding dabblers and 0.13 million breeding divers were within the grasshopper spray area in 1985 (Sheehan *et al.* 1987—Chapter 8). This represents between six and seven percent of the Canadian prairie populations for these two groups. Half of these birds and their broods (provided hatch had already occurred before spray) were potentially exposed to carbofuran, since this product was used to treat half of the total area.

The number of birds directly at risk from other pest control programmes, including non-outbreak insect pest control, is smaller. During this 'baseline' insecticide use, an additional 2.3 percent of the Canadian prairie dabbler population and 3.4 percent of the diver population are estimated to be within a spray zone. The most important non-grasshopper outbreaks are of pests of canola. Pesticide use against a major outbreak in this crop is thought to impact more on diving ducks since the spraying operations tend to be later and thus coincide with diver nesting. A further two percent of that population is expected to be in the spray zone during such a major outbreak. In 1985, all three insecticide use scenarios occurred together. Grasshopper levels were at a record high, and there was an outbreak of Diamond-backed Moth over an estimated 0.5 million hectares of canola. It can therefore be estimated that approximately 9 percent of the breeding dabblers and 12 percent of the breeding divers were located within the insecticide treatment area in that year.

Although pesticide-induced mortality is a direct impact, other more subtle toxic effects also can occur. For example, organisms exposed to cholinesterase-inhibiting insecticides (the majority of registered products) frequently become anorexic and lose weight. Other possible consequences are lowered production, retardation of growth in the young, disruption of normal behavioural patterns—including food acquisition, breeding and predator avoidance, lowered resistance to environmental stresses such as temperature extremes etc. . . . (see Grue *et al.* 1983 for review).

Indirect impact
Pesticides may impact on duck populations through more than their direct toxic action. Because large parts of the waterfowl breeding habitat are directly over-

sprayed in the course of insect control programmes, we have been quite concerned by the potential impact that these insecticides might have on the food resource. As mentioned above, an abundant aquatic invertebrate food source is critical to waterfowl reproduction. In Sheehan *et al.* (1987—Chapter 6), we made use of computer simulation models to determine both the magnitude of pesticide concentrations and their persistence in ponds, and compared these values with levels known to be toxic to aquatic invertebrates. On the basis of a short exposure to the pesticide, we determined that the synthetic pyrethroids, azinphos methyl, chlorpyrifos, malathion and methoxychlor were highly hazardous to the aquatic invertebrate fauna of prairie sloughs. Depending on specific environmental conditions, such as pH, a chronic hazard may develop in the case of the above compounds, as well as for carbofuran. The latter is one of the most poorly studied insecticides in aquatic environments, a serious oversight in view of its wide use.

We further modelled duckling growth in order to predict the consequences of a depletion of the aquatic invertebrate standing crop. We used two 'benchmark' insecticides: the synthetic pyrethroid permethrin, and carbaryl, representing the high and moderate risk categories respectively. We concluded that, following an overspray, compounds calculated to have a high relative hazard equivalent to permethrin can deplete macroinvertebrate standing stocks by more than 90 percent. This level of biomass removal is predicted to allow only for marginal growth in a single Mallard or Lesser Scaup duckling. These conditions are considered to be totally inadequate for a normal sized brood of one week of age in a pond of average size. Efforts are currently under way to verify the conclusions of this model with one of the most hazardous insecticides to aquatic life: the synthetic pyrethroid deltamethrin.

The number of birds likely to be affected through such a process of food elimination is difficult to predict. Most at risk are the birds that nest in association with sloughs surrounded by canola in the parklands. Since almost all insecticide applications are aerial, the chance of direct overspray is high. Furthermore, diving ducks have a longer strict dependency on aquatic invertebrates and, for reasons of timing outlined above, they are most at risk from these operations. As mentioned earlier, our estimates are that approximately two percent of the Canadian prairie diver population will be within the spray zone during a heavy infestation of a canola pest. The amount of breeding habitat at risk through grasshopper spraying programmes and through baseline insecticide use may be lower given that most of the insecticides used are applied by ground equipment. The impact in this case will be dictated by how well buffer zones are followed and by the choice of the insecticide. Clearly, regulators are faced with a difficult choice since some of the safest insecticides from a vertebrate toxicity point of view (e.g. the synthetic pyrethroids) are the most hazardous to the breeding habitat of waterfowl species.

On average, the use of herbicides tends to be far greater than the use of insecticides. Some herbicides, notably 2,4-D, atrazine, simazine, and trifluralin can pose a moderate hazard to the major invertebrate taxa contributing substantially to duckling feeding. However, impacts are more likely due to a reduction in slough macrophyte density and diversity which results in a lowered biomass of macroinvertebrates. Any reduction in macrophyte abundance may also affect herbivorous feeding fowl directly. Unfortunately, there are few data on the effect of herbicides on pond vegetation at levels expected from off-target contamination (Sheehan *et al.* 1987 – Chapter 7).

Impingement of herbicides on upland vegetation can have an impact on waterfowl through reductions in plant food as well as nesting cover. Habitats which still provide good nesting cover consist principally of roadsides, slough margins, rights-of-ways and idle land. While the effects of herbicides on weed populations in cultivated fields are relatively well known, their impact on 'natural' plant communities has not been investigated. In the only study of its type, a 2,4-D application to prime nesting habitat on an island in Alberta resulted in a 75 percent decline in nest density (Dwernychuck & Boag 1973). One would have expected this sort of result to spark a flurry of research activity, but to date this has not happened. In Sheehan (1987—Chapter 8), we used these research results, along with data on herbicide use and duck nesting, to try to predict the maximum impact possible from herbicide use. We assumed that impact resulted only from drift and aerial overspray of field edges—in other words, proper, on-target use of herbicides was defined as the most desirable (baseline) situation. As a result of cover reduction, birds were forced to relocate within the remaining habitat. Using the density reduction obtained by Dwernichuk & Boag (op. cit.), a decline in total duck production of 7.3–18.0 percent was predicted using our rather simplistic model. If cover reduction also leads to reduced nesting success, possibly as a result of increased nest predation, potential production losses as high as 30 percent are predicted for complete nest failures in impacted margins. We fully acknowledge that the situation studied by Dwernychuk & Boag (op. cit.) may not have been typical and thus results of this analysis should be viewed with caution. However, the results clearly point to the need to investigate these effects further.

It may not be sufficient, to ensure the well-being of waterfowl populations, to leave an adequate supply of upland nesting areas and sufficient waterbodies. The quality of both requirements will have to be closely monitored.

CONCLUSION

We conclude that there are indeed some legitimate concerns with respect to the well-being of waterfowl populations and the use of pesticides in the Canadian prairies. A corollary of this is that waterfowl could be used with good success to look at the viability of the remaining natural (and not so natural) habitat in the prairies, specifically wetlands and sheltered upland habitat. A number of non-waterfowl species also have requirements for one or the other of these habitat types.

Of great concern is the paucity of good information needed to carry out a more accurate evaluation than the one presented here. Some of these gaps were outlined above. We found it very difficult to relate the laboratory data on pesticide toxicity and behaviour to the waterfowl and pesticide census data because of the different spatial and temporal scales involved. Collection of data that is both *useful* and *realistic* is badly needed. In our experience, this can only mean a field research programme on the impacts of pesticide use (and possibly other agricultural disturbances) on waterfowl. A possible model for such a study is the 'Cereals and Game Birds Research Project' under way since 1983 in northeast Hampshire, England. This project was 'set up to quantify the effects of pesticides on farmland wildlife, including game birds, and to seek practical methods of conserving wildlife that are compatible with modern farming . . .' (Rands & Sotherton 1985). This project, principally funded by land-owners, arose from a concern over the decline of the Grey Partridge and other wildlife residents of farmland. A study of similar scale (50–100 km^2), or better yet, several such study areas selected to reflect the varied agricultural landscape of the prairies, would go a long way in solving some of the questions raised in this paper. In view of changing agricultural practices, including the constant introduction of new pesticides, these study areas should be selected with long-term monitoring in mind. With the current level of concern over diminishing waterfowl resources on the North American continent, funding for such a study should be readily elicited. The co-operation on such a study of ecologists, hydrologists, pedologists, toxicologists, chemists, agronomists, economists and last but not least, farmers, would allow us to tackle the pressing problems of soil, water and habitat conservation in the context of the pervasive effects of chemical contamination.

ACKNOWLEDGEMENTS

We would like to thank D. K. Smith, W. K. Marshall and all the individuals who have provided guidance and data in the writing of the report (Sheehan *et al.* 1987) on which this discussion is based. We also wish to thank A. Harfenist, J. A. Keith, K. M. Lloyd and W. K. Marshall for their constructive comments on an earlier version of this paper.

APPENDIX

Common and (IUPAC) chemical names [and CAS#] of pesticides mentioned in the text.

atrazine	6-chloro-N-ethyl-N'-isopropyl-1,3,5-triazinediyl-1-2,4-diamine; 2-chloro-4-ethylamino-6-isopropylamino-1,3,5-triazine; [1912–24-9].
azinphos-methyl	S-(3,4-dihydro-4-oxobenzo[d][1,2,3]triazin-3-ylmethyl) 0,0-dimethyl phosphorodithioate; [86-50-0].
carbaryl	1-naphtyl methylcarbamate(I); [63-25-2].
carbofuran	2,3-dihydro-2,2-dimethyl benzofuran-7-yl methylcarbamate; [1563-66-2].
chlorpyrifos	0,0-diethyl 0-3,5,6-trichloro-2-pyridyl phosphorothioate; [2921-88-2].
2,4-D (acid)	(2,4-dichlorophenoxy)acetic acid(I); [94-75-7].
deltamethrin	(S)-α-cyano-3-phenoxybenzyl(1R,3R)-3-(2,2-dibromovinyl-2, 2-dimethylcyclopropanecarboxylate; (S)--cyano-3-phenoxybenzyl(1R)-cis-3-(2,2-dibromovinyl)-2,2-dimethylcyclopropanecarboxylate; [52918-63-5].
demeton	(i) 0,0-diethyl 0-2-ethylthioethyl phosphorothioate and (ii) 0,0-diethyl S-2-ethylthioethyl phosphorothioate; [126-75-0] and [8065-48-3].
diazinon	0,0-diethyl 0-2-isopropyl-6-methylpyrimidin-4-yl phosphorothioate; [333-41-5].
dimethoate	0,0-dimethyl S-methylcarbamoylmethyl phosphorodithioate; [60-51-5].
malathion	diethyl(dimethoxythiophosphorylthio)succinate; S-1,2-bis-(ethoxycarbonyl)ethyl 0,0-dimethyl phosphorodithioate; [121-75-5].
methoxychlor	1,1,1-trichloro-2,2-bis(4-methoxyphenyl)ethane; 1,1,1-trichloro-2,2-di(4-methoxyphenyl)ethane; [72-43-5].
permethrin	3-phenoxybenzyl(1RS,3RS; 1RS, 3SR)-3-(2,2-dichlorovinyl)-2, 2-dimethyl cyclopropanecarboxylate; 3-phenoxybenzyl(1RS)-cis-trans-3-(2,2-dichlorovinyl)-2,2-dimethylcyclopropanecarboxylate; [52645-53-1].
simazine	6-chloro-N,N'-diethyl-1,3,5-triazine-2,4-diyldiamine; 2-chloro-4,6-bis(ethylamino)-1,3,5-triazine; [122-34-9].
trifluralin	α,α,α-trifluoro-2,6-dinitro-N,N-dipropyl-p-toluidine(I); 2,6-dinitro-N,N-dipropyl-4-trifluoromethylaniline; [1582-09-8].

REFERENCES

BALCOMB, R. 1986. Songbird carcasses disappear rapidly from agricultural fields. *Auk* **103**, 817–20.

BELLROSE, F. C. 1979. Species distribution, habitats and characteristics of breeding dabbling ducks in North America. *In: Waterfowl and Wetlands, an Intergrated Review.* Proceedings of a symposium held at the 39th Midwest Fish and Wildlife Conference, Madison, Wisconsin.

CALIFORNIA DEPARTMENT OF FISH AND GAME. 1976. Investigation of pesticide-caused fish and wildlife losses. July 1, 1975–June 30, 1976.

CALIFORNIA DEPARTMENT OF FISH AND GAME. 1978. Investigation of pesticide-caused fish and wildlife losses. FW-1-R-15.

CALIFORNIA DEPARTMENT OF FISH AND GAME. 1986. Pesticide Laboratory Report. E.P. No. P-971.

COOCH, F. G. 1981. A continental duck population balance for North America. Unpublished Report. Canadian Wildlife Service. Environment Canada.

DUEBBERT, H. F. & KANTRUD, H. A. 1974. Upland duck nesting related to land use and predator reduction. *J. Wildl. Manage.* **38**, 257–65.

DWERNYCHUK, L. W. & BOAG, D. A. 1973. Effect of herbicide-induced changes in vegetation on nesting ducks. *Can. Field-Nat.* **87**, 155–65.

FLICKINGER, E. L., KING, K. A., STOUTARD W. F. & MOHN, M. M. 1980. Wildlife hazards from furadan 3G applications to rice in Texas. *J. Wildl. Manage.* **44(1)**, 190–97.

FLICKINGER, E. L., MITCHELL, C., WHITE, D. & KOLBE, E. 1986. Bird poisonings from misuse of the Carbamate Furadan in a Texas rice field. *Wildl. Tox. Bull.* **14**, 59–62.

GRUE, C. E., FLEMING, W. J., BUSBY D. G. & HILL, E. F. 1983. Assessing hazards of organophosphate pesticides to wildlife. *Trans. N. Am. Wildl. Nat. Res. Conf.* **48**, 200–20.

GRUE, C. E., DE WEESE, L. R., MINEAU, P., SWANSON, G. A., FOSTER, J. R., ARNOLD, P. M., HUCKINS, J. N., SHEEHAN, P. J., MARSHALL, W. K. & LUDDEN, A. P. 1986. Potential impacts of agricultural chemicals on waterfowl and other wildlife inhabiting prairie wetlands: an evaluation of research needs and approaches. *Trans. 51st N. Am. Wildl. Nat. Res. Conf.* Pp. 357–383.

HIGGINS, K. F. 1977. Duck nesting in intensively farmed areas of North Dakota. *J. Wildl. Manage.* **41(2)**, 232–42.

HILL, E. F. & FLEMING, W. J. 1982. Anticholinesterase poisoning of birds: field monitoring and diagnosis of acute poisoning. *Environ. Toxicol. Chem.* **1**, 27–38.

HUDSON, R. H., RICHARD, K. T. & HAEGELE, M. A. 1984. *Handbook of Toxicity of Pesticides to Wildlife.* U.S. Dept. of the Interior, Fish and Wildlife Service.

KING, G. J. 1978. Rural aircraft utilization in Canada 1976. Agriculture Canada publication no. 78/11. 71 p.

MINEAU, P. & PEAKALL, D. B. In Press. An evaluation of avian impact assessment techniques following broadscale forest insecticide sprays. Environmental Toxicology and Chemistry.

NATIONAL RESEARCH COUNCIL OF CANADA (NRCC). 1979. Carbofuran: Criteria for Interpreting the Effects of its Use on Environmental Quality. NRCC No. 16740.

PATTERSON, J. H. 1978. Canadian Waterfowl Management Plan. Unpublished Report. Canadian Wildlife Service. Environment Canada. 88 p.

RANDS, M. & SOTHERTON, N. 1985. Pesticides threaten British wildlife. *New Scientist,* 4th July: pp. 32.

SHEEHAN, P. K., BARIL, A., MINEAU, P., SMITH, D. K., HARFENIST, A. & MARSHALL, W. K. 1987. The impact of pesticides on the ecology of prairie-nesting ducks. Canadian Wildlife Service. Canadian Wildlife Service Technical Report Series No. 19.

SUGDEN, L. G. & BEYERSBERGEN, G. W. 1984. Farming intensity on waterfowl breeding grounds in Saskatchewan parklands. *Wildl. Soc. Bull.* **12(1)**; 22–6.

UNIVERSITY OF SASKATCHEWAN. 1986. Western College of Veterinary Medicine. Pathology Report # N86–3919.

U.S. ENVIRONMENTAL PROTECTION AGENCY. 1979. Summary of reported pesticide incidents involving carbofuran. PIMS Report No. 231.

U.S.N.R.C. 1982. *Impacts of emerging agricultural trends on fish and wildlife habitat.* National Academy Press. Washington D.C. 303 p.

VIRGINIA POLYTECHNIC INSTITUTE. 1986. Virginia-Maryland Regional College of Veterinary Medicine. Necropsy Report # 86–1236.

WATERFOWL AS INDICATORS OF WETLAND ACIDIFICATION IN ONTARIO

D. K. McNicol, P. J. Blancher & B. E. Bendell

Canadian Wildlife Service, Ontario Region, 1725 Woodward Drive, Ottawa, Canada K1A 0H3

ABSTRACT

This paper summarizes current information on waterfowl-acid rain relationships in Ontario, identifies the advantages of using breeding waterfowl as indicators of wetland acidification, and provides recommendations for the development of a biomonitoring protocol using waterfowl. The effects on waterfowl of ecological changes associated with lake acidification were studied in an acid-stressed (Wanapitei) and an unstressed (Ranger Lake) area of northeastern Ontario. The availability of food for some species has been influenced by acidification. In the stressed area, acid-sensitive organisms, such as certain fish, Ephemeroptera and Gastropoda, occurred infrequently in lakes where pH was below 5.5. Acid-tolerant organisms, including certain Odonata and nekton (Notonectidae, Corixidae and Dytiscidae), were common at low pH. Nekton was most abundant in the absence of fish. Diets among non-piscivores (Common Goldeneye, Hooded Merganser, Ring-necked Duck and Black Duck) were more similar in acidic (pH < 5.5) compared to non-acidic habitats, due to a reliance on a few abundant insect taxa, particularly libellulid dragonflies. Piscivores (Common Loon and Common Merganser) produced fewer broods relative to the number of indicated nesting pairs observed in the stressed area. Because the Common Loon relies on a healthy fish population, the breeding success of this species is a good indicator of the effects of acidification on fish at moderately high pHs (pH > 5.5). Non-piscivores integrate the combined effects of fish predation and acidity on major invertebrate prey under more stressful conditions (pH < 5.5). In view of their economic and symbolic importance in North America and their value as bio-indicators of acid stress, we conclude that studies of the reproductive success of Common Loons and selected duck species should be an integral part of a long-term biomonitoring programme.

INTRODUCTION

Acid precipitation has become a serious environmental threat to aquatic and terrestrial ecosystems in North America and Europe (Memorandum of Intent 1983). Changes in water quality arising from acid precipitation have been linked to lethal and sub-lethal effects resulting in changes in the composition, distribution and abundance of biota at several levels of the aquatic food-chain. Current and possibly increased levels of acid deposition will continue in most regions of eastern North America for the foreseeable future, with no guarantees that the emission reduction standards (target sulphate loadings of 20kg/ha/yr) proposed for the mid-1990s will curtail further degradation of the aquatic environment. Due to the lack of long-term monitoring, the rates of acidification and changes in water quality over time in eastern Canada cannot be assessed adequately at present. It is necessary, therefore, to develop long-term atmospheric, chemical and biological monitoring programmes that will reliably measure these changes. The effectiveness of the biomonitoring programme will depend largely on the reliability of the indicator species selected. Bio-indicators must link changes in the biological parameters of the species to water quality and thereby to atmospheric deposition rates and the adequacy of emission reduction standards.

There is general agreement within the scientific community that biomonitoring should include higher trophic levels, most notably fish and waterfowl, which rely on the integrity of various components of the food-chain (Aquatic Effects Task Group 1984). Due to their dependence on the immediate aquatic environment for nest sites, brood protection and food, waterfowl may be seriously affected by acid precipitation (Haines & Hunter 1982; Eriksson 1984). The availability of prey during the brood-rearing period,and the long-term impact of low-level exposure to heavy metals on survival and reproduction, are of particular importance for biomonitoring purposes. The selection of an appropriate indicator species must be based on an understanding of the mechanisms by which individual species respond to chemical and biological changes in their habitat. All waterfowl may not be equally at risk from the long-term effects of acidification, and may differ in their suitability as bio-indicators of acid stress.

This paper summarizes current information on waterfowl-acid rain relationships in Ontario, identifies the advantages of using breeding waterfowl as indicators of wetland acidification and provides recommendations for the development of a biomonitoring protocol using waterfowl.

METHODS

From 1983 to 1985, studies of waterfowl habitat selection and aquatic food-chains were conducted on small headwater lakes in two areas of northeastern Ontario receiving different acid-loading levels (*Figure 1*). The Ranger Lake area, northeast of Sault Ste. Marie, Ontario, receives moderate levels of wet sulphate deposition (20–30kg/ha/yr) (Thompson & Hutton 1985), and represents a largely unaffected but sensitive area. The Wanapitei area, northeast of Sudbury, Ontario, receives high acid-loading levels (> 30kg/ha/yr) and represents a heavily stressed area which has undergone considerable lake acidification (Pitblado *et al.* 1980) and loss of aquatic biota (Yan & Miller 1984), as a result of nickel smelting operations near Sudbury.

In 1984 and 1985, food habits of ducklings of several species were examined on both acidic (pH < 5.5) and non-acidic (pH > 5.5) lakes in the two study areas. Foraging birds were collected using a 12-gauge shotgun. The numbers of food items of each major type were estimated from the combined contents of the oesophagus, proventriculus and gizzard of each duckling. At the same time, the availability and abundance of major prey taxa were determined using several sampling techniques. Benthic macroinvertebrates were examined in 20 lakes at Wanapitei (pH range 4.2 to 7.5) using random, one-half-metre benthic drags with

Figure 1: Maps of Ontario showing location of Ranger Lake (R) and Wanapitei (W) study areas in relation to:
  A — Precipitation amount—weighted mean annual pH in 1980 (from MOI 1983).
  B — Mean annual wet sulphate deposition (kg/ha/yr) (from MOI 1983), showing outline of Precambrian Shield and sensitive surface waters.

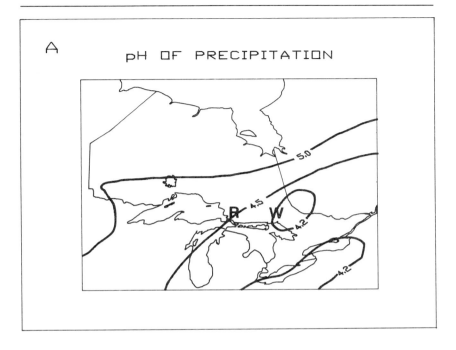

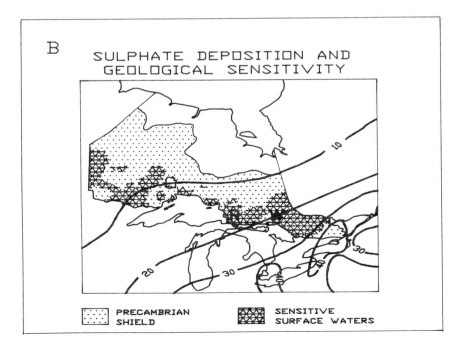

a sweep net. Free-swimming (nektonic) invertebrates were examined using a water column sampler on 15 lakes at Wanapitei, including those with and without fish, and across a range of pH (Bendell & McNicol 1987a, 1987b). In 1983, small, non-game fish species were sampled with wire minnow traps in 124 lakes in the two study areas (Bendell & McNicol 1987c).

On a broader scale, a systematic survey, using 2km × 2km plots located at 20km intervals in standard 100km per side blocks, was instituted throughout much of northeastern and central Ontario, following the procedure described by Ross (1985). The location and number of pairs of waterfowl nesting in each plot was determined using helicopter surveys conducted during the nest-initiation period in May. Surveys of individual wetlands were also conducted at Ranger Lake and Wanapitei. Results are expressed in numbers of 'indicated pairs' per species which for dimorphic waterfowl is derived from observation of the number of lone males, pairs, and males of flocks of five males and less (as in Dzubin 1969). The sex of the Black Duck could not usually be determined in the field and so 'indicated pair' estimates were generated using the known sex ratios of the closely related Mallard (*A. platyrhynchos*) as in Dennis (1974). The Common Loon is also effectively monomorphic. Because these birds are very strongly territorial, indicated pairs were determined from the presence of either a single bird or a pair in close proximity. Procedures used to generate 'indicated pair' estimates are described in McNicol et al. (1987). In 1983, two ground surveys were conducted in June and July respectively to assess habitat use by adults and broods, along with data on water quality and lake morphometry (McNicol et al. 1987).

RESULTS

An estimate of the number of breeding waterfowl and loons potentially at risk from the effects of acid precipitation was obtained from aerial surveys. Approximately 105,000 pairs of waterfowl nest in sensitive terrain, covering roughly 97,500km^2 of northeastern and central Ontario, that is currently receiving wet sulphate deposition in excess of 10kg/ha/yr (*Figure 1b*). A substantial waterfowl resource is, therefore, threatened by acid precipitation; however, overall breeding densities were relatively low (*ca.* one indicated pair per km^2), and no significant trends in population levels have been noted since 1980 (McNicol et al. 1987). Based on co-occurrences of species within aerial survey plots, broad ecological associations were noted (*Figure 2*). Boreal-lake species, including Common Goldeneye (*Bucephala clangula*), Hooded Merganser (*Lophodytes cucullatus*), Ring-necked Duck (*Aythya colaris*) and Black Duck (*Anas rubripes*), comprise nearly 47 percent of the waterfowl resource and commonly breed on small lakes and wetlands (< 4.0ha) (McNicol et al. 1987). Piscivores, including Common Merganser (*Mergus merganser*) and Common Loon (*Gavia immer*), use larger lakes (> 4.0ha) and rivers. The Wood Duck (*Aix sponsa*), Blue-winged Teal (*Anas discors*) and Mallard (*Anas platyrhynchos*) use well-buffered aquatic habitat associated with agricultural land, while Green-winged Teal (*Anas crecca carolinensis*) and Bufflehead (*Bucephala albeola*) nest infrequently in the region.

Comparisons between Ranger Lake and Wanapitei showed major differences in water quality, including significantly higher lake acidity at Wanapitei (*Figure 3*) (McNicol et al. 1987). While a broad range of lake pH was found in both areas, 66 percent of the study lakes at Wanapitei were acidic (pH < 5.5), compared to only 9 percent at Ranger Lake.

Lake acidity was correlated with a reduction in fish populations and a simplifica-

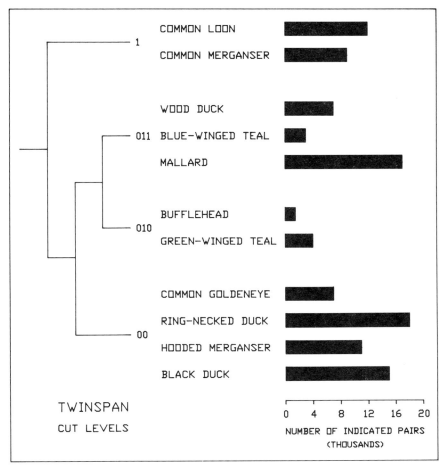

Figure 2:   The numbers of indicated breeding pairs in acid-sensitive areas of northeastern and central Ontario and the dendrogramme produced by the TWINSPAN reciprocal averaging ordination technique (Hill 1979) to show associations of major waterfowl species from aerial surveys.

tion of fish communities. Below pH 5.5, lakes without fish were common (*Figure 4*). Of the 30 acidic lakes (pH < 5.5) sampled at Wanapitei, 20 were without fish. At Ranger Lake, the occurrence of eight fishless lakes was unrelated to lake pH, and was likely a result of winter anoxia or biogeographic isolation, which have been found to restrict fish faunas in other shallow headwater lakes (Rahel 1986).

Despite these differences, no significant difference in the proportion of lakes occupied by indicated nesting pairs was observed between the two study areas in spring aerial surveys, (McNicol *et al.* 1987). On average, slightly fewer lakes were occupied by waterfowl at Ranger Lake (59 percent) than at Wanapitei (76 percent) during the nest-initiation period. However, the percentage of lakes occupied by adults and broods, in relation to those occupied by indicated breeding

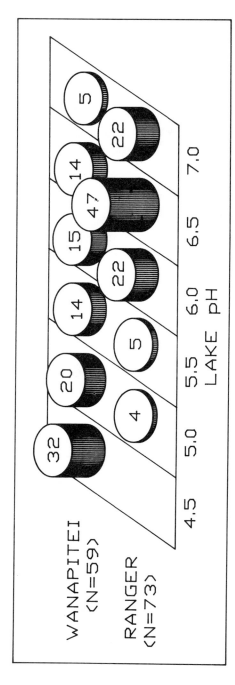

Figure 3: Comparison between lake pH distributions (expressed as percent occurrence in pH classes) in the Ranger Lake and Wanapitei study areas.

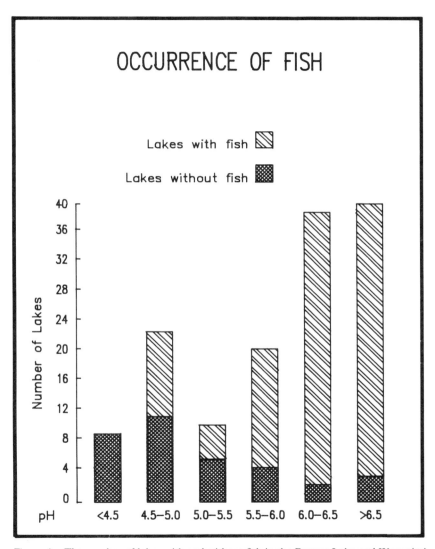

Figure 4:   The number of lakes with and without fish in the Ranger Lake and Wanapitei study areas, in relation to lake pH.

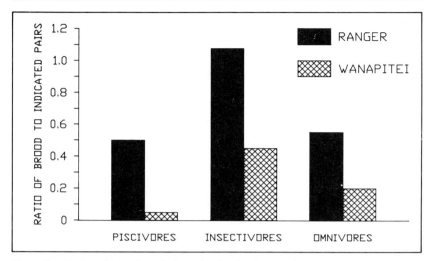

Figure 5:   Ratios of broods to indicated pairs for three major waterfowl groups (pisci-vores = Common Loon + Common Merganser; insectivores = Common Goldeneye + Hooded Merganser; and omnivores = Ring-necked Duck + Black Duck + Mallard) in the two study areas.

pairs in the spring, differed between the two study areas (*Figure 5*). At Ranger Lake, the brood versus indicated breeding pair ratios were nearly 1:2 for piscivores (Common Loon and Common Merganser combined) and omnivores (Ring-necked Duck, Black Duck and Mallard combined) and nearly 1:1 for insectivores (Common Goldeneye and Hooded Merganser combined). At Wanapitei, the ratio was lower for all groups, and particularly for piscivores (1:17).

Ground surveys conducted during the brood-rearing period revealed that fish-eating species, including both Common Merganser and Common Loon, preferred lakes with fish (*Figure 6*). Not unexpectedly, an examination of the gut contents of Common Merganser ducklings, collected primarily on non-acidic (pH > 5.5) lakes, also revealed a reliance on fish, although aquatic insects were taken from the nekton, neuston and benthos (*Figure 7*).

Conversely, adults and broods of Common Goldeneye and Hooded Merganser were observed more frequently on fishless lakes compared to lakes containing fish (*Figure 6*), while more generalized feeders, including Ring-necked Duck and Black Duck, showed little preference for either condition. The use of fishless lakes by insectivores, including Common Goldeneye and to a lesser extent Hooded Merganser, during the brood-rearing period suggests that fish may act as competitors for the insect prey of these ducklings. Insect assemblages from fishless lakes in both areas, along with lakes containing only a few fish, regardless of lake pH, shared many more taxa in common than with lakes containing large numbers of fish (Bendell & McNicol 1987a). These differences in insect commun-ity structure were largely explained by the increased occurrence and abundance of large, free-swimming organisms, including backswimmers (Notonectidae) and water boatmen (Corixidae) (*Figure 8*), and the diving beetle (*Graphoderus liberus*) and the phantom midge larvae (*Chaoborus americanus*). These nektonic

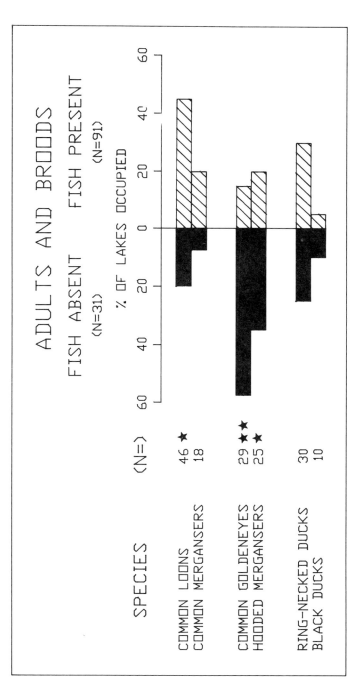

Figure 6: Summary of waterfowl survey results for adults and broods observed during the brood-rearing period, in relation to the presence or absence of fish (Fisher Exact Test, * p < 0.01, ** p < 0.0001).

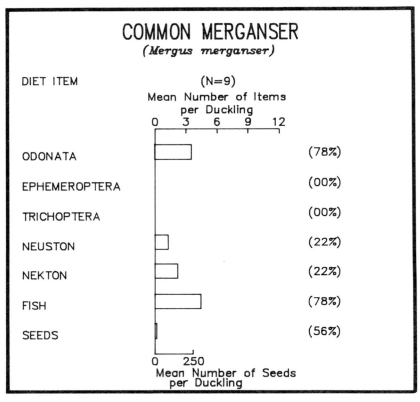

Figure 7: Use of major aquatic insect prey, fish and seeds (expressed as mean number of items per duckling) by Common Merganser ducklings (N = 9, 1 from an acidic lake) collected in 1984 and 1985. Percent occurrence of diet items is expressed in parentheses.

taxa are abundant in the absence of fish, regardless of pH, and replace fish as top predators in the food-chain as lakes acidify, as also found by Eriksson *et al.* (1980).

However, drag-net samples from lakes in the Wanapitei area revealed that fewer benthic species tolerated acidic compared to non-acidic conditions. Certain crustaceans (amphipoda) and molluscs occurred infrequently below pH 5, while other acid-sensitive organisms, in particular Ephemeropterans, were absent below pH 5.6 (*Figure 9b*). Other benthic organisms, such as Odonata, showed a pronounced shift in species composition in relation to lake pH. Anisoptera were more abundant but less diverse on acidic lakes, because of the extreme abundance of a Libellulid species, *Leucorrhinia glacialis* (*Figure 9a*).

From an examination of the gut contents of ducklings collected in both acidic and non-acidic lakes (*Figure 10*), it was found that the feeding habits of non-pis-civorous species differed between acidic and non-acidic conditions. In non-acidic situations, both Common Goldeneye and Hooded Merganser took large numbers of nektonic prey, primarily notonectids, corixids and dytiscids, (*Figures 10a and 10b*). Both species increased this consumption under acidic conditions, presuma-bly in response to the increased availability of these organisms. While adept at

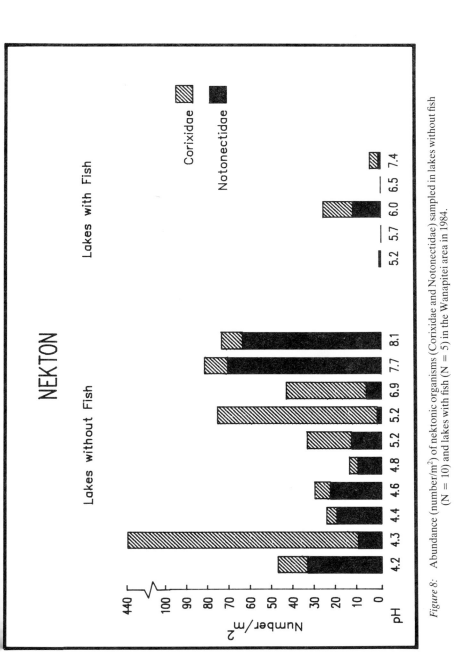

Figure 8: Abundance (number/m²) of nektonic organisms (Corixidae and Notonectidae) sampled in lakes without fish (N = 10) and lakes with fish (N = 5) in the Wanapitei area in 1984.

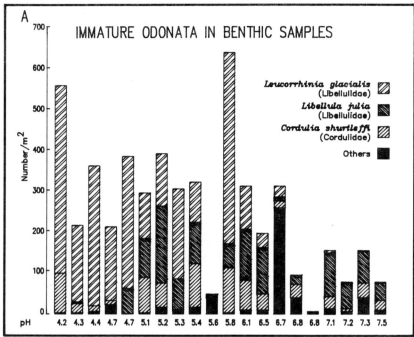

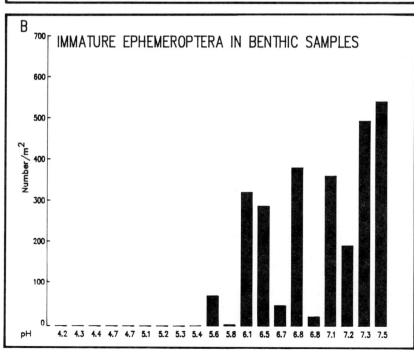

diving, Common Goldeneyes take more benthic material, especially immature libellulids and Trichoptera, than Hooded Mergansers, which exploit large numbers of the climbing Aeshnid dragonfly larvae (Merritt & Cummins 1978), often found attached to submerged ericaceous shrubs or woody detritus.

More generalized feeders, Ring-neck ducklings, took noticeably more surface insects (neuston) on non-acidic lakes, especially waterstriders (Gerridae), which are often associated with emergent and floating-leaved vegetation (*Figure 10c*). The Black Duck, a surface feeder, took large numbers of emerging insects (teneral forms), particularly Odonata on acidic lakes, and Ephemeroptera on non-acidic lakes, while also using seeds (*Figure 10d*).

All four non-piscivores modified their feeding habits between acidic and non-acidic conditions. On acidic lakes, the consumption of Odonata, particularly the immature Libellulid dragonfly *Leucorrhinia glacialis*, increased (*Figure 10*). On acidic lakes, consumption of Trichoptera, especially by Common Goldeneyes, declined, while Ring-neck ducklings used fewer surface organisms. On acidic lakes, both Common Goldeneyes and Hooded Mergansers increased their consumption of nektonic prey, while Ephemeroptera, primarily used by Black Duck ducklings, were no longer consumed. As a result, the diets of non-piscivorous species converged on acidic lakes due to a reliance on a few abundant insect prey, such as immature Libellulid dragonflies and nektonic insects.

DISCUSSION AND CONCLUSIONS

Waterfowl represent an important socio-economic resource in North America, and provide substantial recreation and hunting opportunities for residents of both Canada and the United States. A large segment of this resource is produced in the boreal forest region of eastern Canada, and may be at risk from the effects of acid precipitation. In northeastern and central Ontario alone, more than 105,000 pairs of ducks and loons nest in wetlands threatened by acid precipitation. Beyond their value as a natural resource, certain waterfowl species and loons may be useful indicators of lake acidification by fulfilling several essential requirements of a reliable bio-indicator organism. Most species are widely distributed, and are common inhabitants of wetlands throughout the Precambrian Shield in eastern Canada, in areas receiving different levels of acid deposition. Due to the longevity of waterfowl and the fidelity of females to natal nesting areas (Bellrose 1976), long-term studies of reproductive success could provide the necessary data to assess recruitment trends.

Comparisons of waterfowl breeding success, food-chain relationships and food habits between two areas of northeastern Ontario receiving differing inputs of acid deposition revealed that food availability may be a limiting factor in the distribution and reproductive success of some species. Our results revealed that the reproductive performance of most species, as measured by the proportion of broods produced in relation to the number of indicated nesting pairs (nesting potential), was lower in the acid-stressed study area (Wanapitei) compared to the largely unaffected area (Ranger Lake). Piscivores, particularly Common Loons, suffered very poor reproductive success at Wanapitei relative to indicated breeding potential; a likely function of the considerable damage to the fish populations caused by pH declines in the area (Keller *et al.* 1980). The poor performance of

Figure 9:   Abundance (number/m^2) of immature Odonata (A) and immature Ephemeroptera (B) collected in benthic drag samples from 20 lakes in the Wanapitei area in 1985.

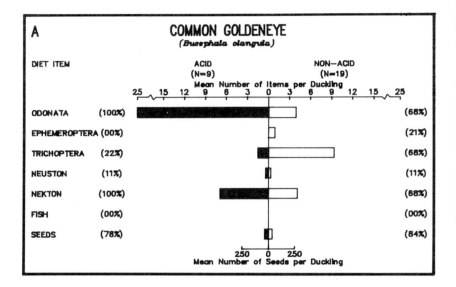

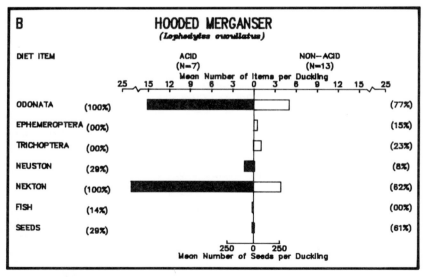

Figure 10:   Comparative use of major aquatic insect prey, fish and seeds (expressed as mean number of items per duckling) by Common Goldeneye (A), Hooded Merganser (B), Ring-necked Duck (C) and Black Duck (D) collected in acidic (pH < 5.5) and non-acidic (pH > 5.5) lakes in 1984 and 1985. Percent occurrence of diet items is expressed in parentheses.

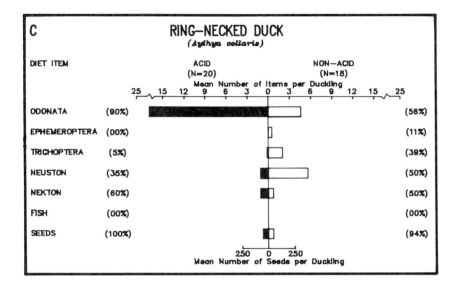

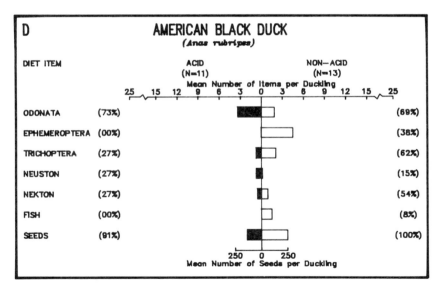

Common Loons on acidic lakes was corroborated by Alvo (1985) who examined the breeding success of Common Loons in relation to the buffering capacity of lakes in the Sudbury area from 1982 to 1984. He found a strong positive relationship between breeding success and alkalinity, primarily due to a high level of brood mortalities on acidic lakes which he attributed to food (fish) limitation. Other studies (Barr 1973, 1986) have linked the poor reproductive success of loons in northwestern Ontario to elevated levels of mercury. These results suggest that both the scarcity of fish and their potential contamination by heavy metals, as a result of increased lake acidity, may impair the reproductive success of Common Loons at moderately high pHs (pH 5 to 6).

The relationship between non-piscivorous waterfowl and lake acidification is complicated by altered trophic relationships, specialized feeding habits and considerations involved in the selection of nesting and brood-rearing sites. Hunter *et al.* (1986) suggested that ducklings of several species of dabbling and diving ducks, most notably pursuit divers such as Common Goldeneyes, that feed largely on invertebrate prey, may derive some short-term benefits from breeding in acidic and fishless conditions, as a result of reduced competition with fish for common insect prey. Eriksson (1979) and Eadie & Keast (1982) argued that competition between fish and Common Goldeneyes affected the selection of feeding localities and brood-rearing sites. Our results suggest that certain nektonic insects are more abundant under fishless conditions, regardless of lake pH, and are used by ducklings of several non-piscivorous species, most notably Common Goldeneyes and Hooded Mergansers. In situations where acid-sensitive fish and invertebrates are eliminated, in most cases below pH 5.5, ducklings of several species must rely on the few aquatic insects that tolerate these conditions and which are abundant in the absence of fish. As a result, diets converge among duck species due to a reliance on a few abundant insect prey items, such as immature Libellulid dragonflies and nektonic insects. While the amount of available insect prey may not be lower under acid-fishless conditions, the composition and variety of food does differ from more circum-neutral situations. Such a restricted resource base may influence duckling survival and ultimately the long-term reproductive performance of several species, including Common Goldeneye, Hooded Merganser, Ring-necked Duck and Black Duck.

However, circumstances leading to the elimination of fish in headwater lakes on the Precambrian Shield may not occur regularly. While lakes may continue to acidify and become less productive, they may also continue to support impoverished fish populations. For example, in the acid-stressed Wanapitei area, 14 of the 31 lakes with fish contained Yellow Perch (*Perca flavescens*), and were characterized by an average pH of 5.5 (range 4.9 to 6.1). This species can tolerate a wide pH range (Ryan & Harvey 1980), and is a particularly effective insectivore (Eriksson 1979; Post & Cucin 1984). As pH declines, traditional brood-rearing sites may become less suitable for waterfowl as they are forced to compete for insect prey with the remaining, acid-tolerant fish populations. In east-central Maine, McAuley (1986) found that the brood survival of Ring-necked Ducks, particularly older ducklings, breeding on wetlands containing fish, was lower on low pH areas (pH < 6.0) than on high pH wetlands (pH > 6.0), and concluded that survival on more acidic sites could be lowered if ducklings were forced to feed on either more mobile (nekton) or less palatable species, or if numbers of invertebrate foods were reduced. Experimental studies, using imprinted Black Duck ducklings in Quebec (DesGranges & Rodrigue 1986) and Maryland (Haramis & Chu, this volume), have also shown impaired growth and reduced survival of ducklings on acidified wetlands. Therefore, under moderately acidic conditions (pH 5 to 6), the combined effects of lake acidity and fish predation may limit the abundance, availability and quality of invertebrate prey leading to an alteration in feeding habits (dietary convergence) and measurable declines in duckling growth and survival.

SUMMARY

In view of their economic and symbolic importance in North America, and their value as indicators of biological response to lake acidification, long-term reproductive studies of Common Loons and selected duck species should be an integral part of a biological monitoring programme. The breeding success of the Common Loon might be a good early indicator of the effects of acidification on fish populations at moderately high pHs (pH > 5.5). Other non-piscivorous waterfowl, for example the Black Duck and Common Goldeneye, integrate the combined effects of fish predation and acid-tolerance on major invertebrate prey taxa under more stressful conditions (pH < 5.5). We recommend that a biomonitoring protocol which will measure the long-term impact of acidic inputs on the reproductive success of waterfowl indicator species must also include monitoring of some aspects of the food-chain, given the significant role that fish and aquatic invertebrates play in determining the quality of habitat suited for rearing ducklings.

ACKNOWLEDGEMENTS

We wish to acknowledge the contributions made by the Ontario Ministry of Natural Resources and the Great Lakes Forestry Research Centre. For field, laboratory and computer assistance, we are indebted to many summer students, contract assistants and term employees. Don Fillman, Kim Adams and Sharon Bradford helped with the preparation of figures and typing. Helpful guidance in the preparation of the manuscript was provided by Dan Welsh, Ken Ross and Hugh Boyd. This work was funded by the federal Long-Range Transport of Airborne Pollutants (LRTAP) programme.

REFERENCES

ALVO, R. 1985. The breeding success of Common Loons (*Gavia immer*) in relation to lake acidity. M.Sc. thesis, Trent University, Peterborough, Ontario. 122 p.

AQUATIC EFFECTS TASK GROUP. 1984. Sampling and analysis protocol for long-term chemical monitoring of lakes and streams relative to effects of acidic deposition. U.S. Interagency Task Force on Acid Precipitation. 16 p.

BARR, J. F. 1973. Feeding biology of the Common Loon (*Gavia immer*) in oligotrophic lakes of the Canadian Shield. Ph.D. thesis, Univ. of Guelph, Guelph, Ontario.

BARR, J. F. 1986. Population dynamics of the Common Loon (*Gavia immer*) associated with mercury-contaminated waters in northwestern Ontario. Canadian Wildlife Service Occasional Paper No. 56, 25 p.

BELLROSE, F. C. 1976. *Ducks, Geese and Swans of North America*. Stackpole Books, Harrisburg, Pa. 540 p.

BENDELL, B. E. & McNICOL, D. K. 1987a. Fish predation, lake acidity and the composition of aquatic insect assemblages. *Hydrobiologia* 150, 193–202.

BENDELL, B. E. & McNICOL, D. K. 1987b. Estimation of nektonic insect populations. *Freshwater Biology* 18.

BENDELL, B. E. & McNICOL, D. K. 1987c. Cyprinid assemblages, and the physical and chemical characteristics of small northern Ontario lakes. *Environ. Biol. of Fishes* **19**, 229–34.

DENNIS, D. G. 1974. Waterfowl observations during the nesting season in Precambrian and clay belt areas of north-central Ontario. *In:* Boyd, H. (ed.) *Waterfowl studies in eastern Canada, 1969–73.* Can. Wildl. Serv. Rep. Ser. No. 29, 105 p.

DESGRANGES, J.-L. & RODRIGUE, J. 1986. Influence of acidity and competition with fish on the development of ducklings in Québec. *Water, Air and Soil Pollut.* **30**, 743–50.

DZUBIN, A. 1969. Assessing breeding populations of ducks by ground counts. *In: Saskatoon wetlands seminar.* Can. Wildl. Serv. Rep. Ser. No. 6, 262 p.

EADIE, J. M. & KEAST, A. 1982. Do goldeneye and perch compete for food? *Oecologia* **55**, 225–30.

ERIKSSON, M. O. G. 1979. Competition between freshwater fish and Goldeneyes (*Bucephala clangula*) for common prey. *Oecologia* **41**, 99–107.

ERIKSSON, M. O. G. 1984. Acidification of lakes: effects on waterbirds in Sweden. *Ambio* **13**, 260–2.

ERIKSSON, M. O. G., HENRIKSON, L., NILSSON, B. L. NYMAN, G., OSCARSON, H. G., STENSON, A. E. & LARSSON, K. 1980. Predator-prey relations important for the biotic changes in acidified lakes. *Ambio* **9**, 248–9.

HAINES, T. A. & HUNTER, M. L. 1982. Waterfowl and their habitat: threatened by acid rain? *In: Fourth International Waterfowl Symposium:* Ducks Unlimited. New Orleans, La. 265 p.

HILL, M. O. 1979. TWINSPAN—A FORTRAN program for arranging multivariate data in an ordered two-way table by classification of the individuals and attributes. Ecology and Systematics, Cornell University, Ithaca, New York.

HUNTER, M. L., JONES, J. J., GIBBS, K. E. & MORNING, J. R. 1986. Duckling responses to lake acidification: do black ducks and fish compete? *Oikos* **47**, 26–32.

KELLER, W., GUNN, J. M. & CONROY, N. I. 1980. Impacts in lakes in Sudbury, Ontario, Canada. *In:* Drablos, D. & Tollan, A. (eds.) *Proc. Int. Conf. Ecological Impact of Acid Precipitation.* Sandefjord, Norway. 383 p.

MCAULEY, D. G. 1986. Ring-necked Duck productivity in relation to wetland acidity: nest success, duckling diet and survival. M.Sc. thesis, University of Maine at Orono, Maine. 71 p.

MCNICOL, D. K., BENDELL, B. E. & ROSS, R. K. 1987. Studies of the effects of acidification on aquatic wildlife in Canada: waterfowl and trophic relationships in small lakes in northern Ontario. Can. Wildl. Serv. Occas. Pap. No. 62.

MEMORANDUM OF INTENT (MOI). 1983. Memorandum of Intent on Transboundary Air Pollution. Final Report. January 1983.

MERRITT, R. W. & CUMMINS, K. W. 1978. *An Introduction to the Aquatic Insects of North America.* Kendall/Hunt Publ. Co., Dubuque, Iowa. 441 p.

PITBLADO, J. R., KELLAR, W. & CONROY, N. I. 1980. A classification and description of some northeastern Ontario lakes influenced by acid precipitation. *Journal of Great Lakes Res.* **6**, 247–57.

POST, J. R. & CUCIN, D. 1984. Changes in the benthic community of a small precambrian lake following the introduction of yellow perch, *Perca flavescens. Can. J. Fish. Aquat. Sci.* **41**, 1496–1501.

RAHEL, F. J. 1986. Biogeographic influences on fish species composition of northern Wisconsin lakes with applications for lake acidification studies. *Can. J. Fish. Aquat. Sci.* **43**, 124–34.

ROSS, R. K. 1985. Helicopter versus ground surveys of waterfowl in the boreal forest. *Wildl. Soc. Bull.* **13**, 153–7.

RYAN, P. M. & HARVEY, H. H. 1980. Growth responses of yellow perch, *Perca flavescens,* to lake acidification in the La Cloche Mountain Lakes of Ontario. *Environ. Biol. of Fishes* **5**, 97–108.

THOMPSON, M. E. & HUTTON, M. B. 1985. Sulphate in lakes of eastern Canada: calculated yields with measured wet and dry deposition. *Water, Air and Soil Pollut.* **24**, 77–83.

YAN, N. D. & MILLER, G. E. 1984. Effects of deposition of acids and metals on chemistry and biology of lakes near Sudbury, Ontario. *In:* Nriagu, J. O. (ed.), *Environmental Impacts of Smelters.* John Wiley and Sons, Toronto, Ontario. 608 p.

WATERFOWL AS BIO-INDICATORS

E. Rutschke

University of Education, Department of Zoology, 1500-Potsdam-Sanssouci, Villa Liegnitz, GDR

INTRODUCTION

The concept of bio-indication is based on the assumption that an organism can, simply by its presence or absence, provide information about the condition of, and alterations in, the environment.

Animals and plants can substitute for technological measuring devices if they fulfil certain criteria. Essential in using the concept of biological indicators is whether or not the environmental conditions can be related to the presence or absence of the organism studied. Very often this premise is not taken into account. Birds react to alterations in the environment very sensitively. They are qualified as bio-indicators for the following reasons:

1. Homoiothermy, high metabolic rate, and the complexity of their behaviour involve a strong dependence of bird populations on certain factors in the environment.

2. The position of most bird species in ecosystems is well defined. Consequently, changes in bird stocks or in the diversity of species allow conclusions to be drawn about the condition of the environment.

3. It is relatively easy to find, identify and count birds. Therefore, changes in the size of populations or in diversity can be used to analyse the condition of a landscape. Waterfowl are particularly useful as bio-indicators because of their wide distribution; relative ease of identification and counting in autumn and in winter; different trophic positions between primary and end consumers; and significance as structural parts of aquatic ecosystems.

Essentially, waterfowl can indicate the trophic, structural and toxic conditions of aquatic ecosystems. Because of their specific adaptations, they react in distribution, frequency and behaviour very sensitively and in well-defined ways. Therefore, in many cases it is possible to correlate the changes in the environment and the reaction of waterfowl. As indicators, waterfowl are parts of the whole system, and are functionally connected with many processes and functions in the ecosystem. Waterfowl reflect dynamic changes in the system as a whole but do not indicate them very precisely. Consequently, it is not possible to recognize or define the 'ecological condition' of a water-body by means of waterfowl, because the term 'ecological condition' includes all parameters and functions within the system, including the flux of substances and energy. It is virtually impossible to comprehend that very complex condition by considering just one component. Consequently, bio-indication can be valid only for parts of a system.

Confusion can arise from the term 'waterfowl', too. Waterfowl are adapted to aquatic habitats to varying degrees. Consequently, single species are suitable for bio-indication only to a limited extent, especially because their positions in food chains and their distribution in space and time vary.

Breeding birds have different values from those of resting (staging) or wintering birds. Species that have specialized in a limited range of food have different values from omnivorous or ubiquitous species. For example, if one looks at breeding species one must take into consideration the structure of the shore. During the reproductive period the shore vegetation is a key factor limiting the size of the breeding population. The situation is completely different in winter. Wintering birds concentrate on the open water and the most important factor influencing the size of concentrations in winter is the food supply.

These differences resulting from the biology of waterfowl species affect the approach used. It is easier to obtain data from wintering birds (counts of individuals, species composition, food and food supply). Consequently, most papers on problems of bio-indication by waterfowl concern wintering birds.

Birds can be used at three levels as bio-indicators: at the level of the individual, of the population and as a structural part of ecosystems.

WATERFOWL AS INDICATORS OF AQUATIC ECOSYSTEMS

Waterfowl depend on the condition of their habitats during their whole life span. Consequently, they will react very sensitively, but in different ways, to certain types of habitat change.

A term that is often used but not well defined in discussions about bio-indication is the term 'quality of environment'. It will be interpreted depending on the point of view of the author. Ornithology has made a substantial contribution to the understanding of this term by relating a high quality of the environment to the variety of species and individuals. The principal method used to define the presence of waterfowl in a quantitative way is the estimation of the index of diversity using the Shannon-Weaver formula:

$$d = -\sum_{i=i}^{s} \left(\frac{N_i}{N} \cdot \log \frac{N_i}{N} \right)$$

Changes in the index of diversity of an aquatic biotope provide evidence of changes of the environment. The index indicates alterations of the biotope or landscape, independent of knowledge about the causes. Examples using the Shannon-Weaver formula to determine the connections between waterfowl and their habitats were given by Bezzel & Reichholf (1974). In practice, there are many difficulties in applying this procedure, and these have been discussed by Hummitsch (1985). Reichholf (1982) found well-defined relations between parameters of water quality in lakes in southern Bavaria (FRG) and the waterfowl present, measured both by the number of individuals (biomass) and by number of species. The deterioration of the water quality (= increase in eutrophication in that case) caused an increase in the number of individuals (biomass of waterfowl), but a drastic reduction in the number of species (*Figure 1*). The result is a dominance of unspecialized (omnivore) species such as Mallard (*Anas platyrhynchos*) and Coot (*Fulica atra*).

Hölzinger (1977) investigated the influence of sewage containing sulfite, cellulose and heavy metals on breeding and resting waterfowl in artificial ponds along the Danube, a wetland of international importance. Waterfowl were shown to be indicators of the trophic and toxic condition of the water. The connection between

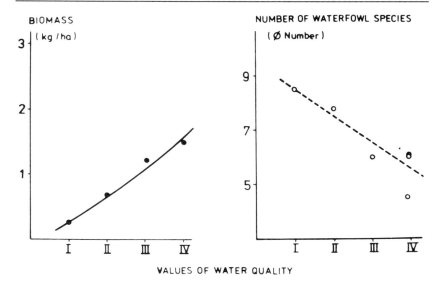

Figure 1: *Left* Correlation between water quality and waterfowl biomass, and *Right* Correlation between water quality and average species richness for aquatic birds. Data from lakes in Upper Bavaria; from Utschick (1976). I–IV = values of water quality according to the system of Liebmann 1969 (*After:* Reichholf 1982).

P-content and number of individuals (= biomass) and number of species is shown in *Figure 1*.

A problem in using the index of diversity is the amount of work connected with the gathering of the ornithological data. Kalbe (1985) tried to avoid these difficulties by using the rate of species deficiency as a criterion for determining changes in ecosystems. He used a simple formula based on Jaccard's index:

$$A = \frac{A_1 - A_x}{A_1} \cdot 100 \ (\%)$$

A_1 = number of species before the change,
A_x = number of species after the change.

The rate of species deficiency is used in limnology to characterize the load of running water ecosystems (Kothe 1962). According to this approach an isolated ecosystem contains a well-defined natural species composition. The rate of species diversity considers only species which will be absent after a change in the ecosystem, independent of the immigration of new species.

Since the species of a bird community are not all equally suitable for bio-indication, Kalbe (1985) proposed an indication value (i) for each species of the community. For example, the indication value of the Ruff (*Philomachus pugnax*) in inundated areas (lowlands) in Central Europe is higher than the indication value of the Mallard in the same area. In the following formula, the indication value of species is taken into account:

$$A_i = \frac{A_1 \, \Sigma \, (a_1 \cdot i) - A_x \, \Sigma \, (a_x \cdot i)}{A_1 \, \Sigma \, (a_1 \cdot i)} \cdot 100 \ (\%)$$

Where A_i is the species deficiency corrected for indication values, a_1 and a_x are the numbers of species before and after the change, and i is the indication value of species a.

In this way it is possible to ascertain the ecological relationships between species deficiency and environmental changes more clearly.

Independent of the methods used, information about the numbers and species composition of waterfowl gives clues to the condition of a body of water that cannot be obtained simply by summing physically and chemically measured data. However, it is difficult to move from clues to valid evidence.

Utschick (1981) tested whether or not waterfowl are bio-indicators for the 'ecological stability' of river reservoirs in southern Bavaria using very detailed investigations of the distribution of all waterfowl species in space and time. In order to characterize ecological stability in different ways, 20 parameters were established from the waterfowl investigations. These parameters were applied to correlations of 20 different environmental factors by stepwise multiple regression analysis. With an eight-year data set, significant multiple correlation-coefficients between stability-parameters and some environmental factors were found.

WATERFOWL POPULATIONS AS BIO-INDICATORS

Changes in single waterfowl populations can also be used to study aspects of changes in ecosystems. In investigations of limnological and ornithological changes in lakes in southern Sweden, Nilsson (1978) found a good correlation between the size of certain bird populations and the condition of the water. The number of individuals increased in connection with the P- and N-content of the lakes. Fuchs (1978) found similar results in formerly oligotrophic lakes in Switzerland.

An increase in the population of Great Crested Grebes (*Podiceps cristatus*) indicates the increasing eutrophication of the lake, a problem studied in more detail by Utschick (1981), who found that the density of populations of the Great Crested Grebe depended on the water quality (*Figure 2*). In comparison with other piscivorous birds, the Great Crested Grebe prefers water quality between class II and III (after Liebmann 1969) in water reservoirs. If the water is more eutrophic the density decreases again. In studies of the frequency of the Great Crested Grebe in natural lakes northwest of Berlin (GDR) we had obtained the same result. The highest density for the species is in lakes of medium-level eutrophication, probably due to the abundance of small fish species (in Lake Constance, Cyprinidae).

Some of the best-documented examples of the connection between water quality, and density and distribution of waterfowl in central Europe, are the recent changes in the distribution of the Tufted Duck (*Aythya fuligula*) on inland lakes. In the late fifties 5000–7000 Tufted Ducks wintered regularly on the lakes near Potsdam, with a maximum of 8300 in the winter of 1960/61 (Rutschke 1983). The main food of the ducks was the Zebra Mussel (*Dreissena polymorpha*). (The water quality changed from a more or less mesotrophic condition to increasing eutrophication.) As a consequence of increased eutrophication of the water the stock of *Dreissena polymorpha* was almost completely exterminated. In recent years a lot of work has been done by the authorities responsible for the quality of open waters. As a consequence, the winter stock of the Tufted Duck is increasing again (although the present abundance of *Dreissena polymorpha* has not been investigated).

In principle, on the basis of the same cause-effect chain we can understand the enormous increase of diving ducks in the late sixties on the western part of Lake

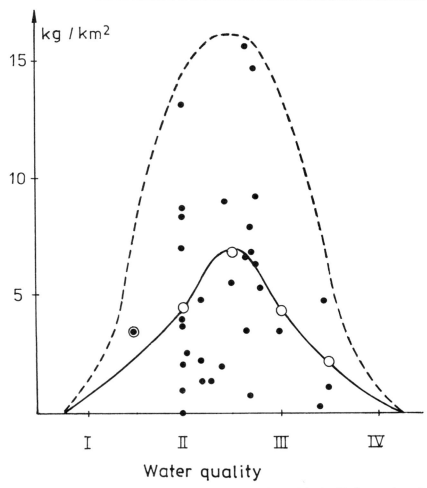

Figure 2: Dependence on water quality of the Great Crested Grebe (*Podiceps cristatus*). Compared with other piscivores, the Great Crested Grebe prefers heavily polluted reservoirs as long as the wastes are non-toxic. I–IV = values of water quality according to the system of Liebmann 1969 (*After:* Utschick 1981).

Constance (German-Swiss border) and other Swiss lakes (Suter 1982), which started soon after *Dreissena polymorpha* had colonized the lakes. It is not quite clear whether a change of the water quality enabled the mollusc to spread and establish itself. However, there is no doubt of the beginning of eutrophication in the formerly oligotrophic Swiss lakes in the sixties.

Strictly speaking, in the cited cases a change in a waterfowl population primarily indicated a change of food supply. The connection between the size of waterfowl populations and the water quality is only inferred indirectly. In the same way we can understand the increase in the stock of Black-headed Gull (*Larus ridibundus*) and Greylag Goose (*Anser anser*) as a consequence of better food supply, resulting from the increasing eutrophication of the whole landscape. The number of breeding pairs of the Black-headed gull in GDR nearly tripled from 1963 (*ca.* 38,000 breeding pairs) to 1983 (99,900) (Litzbarski 1982; Naacke, in press a). The stock of the Greylag Goose in GDR increase from 2300 breeding pairs in 1977 to nearly 3800 breeding pairs in 1985 (Naacke 1982, in press b).

CONCLUDING REMARKS

The use of waterfowl as bio-indicators is limited by the demands for an obvious connection between cause (alteration of the environment) and effect (change in the biological system or organism). However, many of the questions to be answered should be solved in the near future. Investigations should be aimed at qualitative bio-indication, characterized by decisions about the presence or absence of a single species (population) or a whole set of species. Bio-indication at a quantitative level requires more work because numerous statistically reliable data have to be evaluated.

REFERENCES

BEZZEL, E. & REICHHOLF, J. 1974. Die Diversität als Kriterium zur Bewertung der Reichhaltigkeit von Wasservögel-Lebensräumen. *J. Orn.* **115**, 50–61.

FUCHS, E. 1978. Bestand und Verbreitung des Haubentauchers *Podiceps cristatus* in der Schweiz. *Orn. Beob.* **75**, 19–32.

HÖLZINGER, J. 1977. Der Einfluss von Sulfitzellstoff-Abwässern und Schwermetallen auf das Ökosystem des Opfinger Donaustausees. *J. Orn.* **118**, 330–415.

HUMMITSCH, P. 1985. Probleme des Feuchtgebietsschutzes im Zschornaer Teichgebiet. *Beitr. Vogelkd.* **31**, 55–72.

KALBE, L. 1985. Der Artenfehlbetrag in der Ornithökologie. *Acta ornithoecol.*, Jena 1, 1, 47–56.

KOTHE, P. 1962. Der 'Artenfehlbetrag', ein einfaches Gütekriterium und seine Anwendung bei biologischen Vorflutuntersuchungen. *Dtsch. Gewässerkd. Mitt.* **6**, 60–5.

LIEBMANN, H. 1969. *Der Wässerguteatlas. Methodik und Anwendung.* Oldenburg, Munchen.

LITZBARSKI, H. 1982. Der Brutbestand der Lachmöwe in der DDR—Bestandserfassung 1978. *Falke* **29**, 234–41.

NAACKE, J. 1982. Effects of various factors on the size of breeding and resting stock of the Greylag Goose, *Anser anser* L., in the German Democratic Republic. *Aquila* **89**, 57–66.

NAACKE, J. (in press a). Der Brutbestand der Lachmöwe, *Larus ridibundus*, in der DDR—Bestandserfassung 1983.

NAACKE, J. (in press b). Der Brutbestand der Graugans, *Anser anser,* in der DDR—Bestandserfassung 1985.

NILSSON, L. 1978. Breeding waterfowl in eutrophicated lakes in South Sweden. *Wildfowl* **29**, 101–10.

NÜMANN, W. 1961. Gewässerzustand und Bodenseefischerei. *Österr. Wasserwirtsch.* **13**, 230–31.

REICHHOLF, J. 1982. Wasservögel als Indikatoren des Gewässerzustandes. *Decheniana-Beih.* **26**, 138–44.

RUTSCHKE, E. (ED.) 1983. *Avifauna der Deutschen Demokratischen Republik, Bd. 2, Die Vogelwelt Brandenburgs.* Jena.

SUTER, W. 1982. Der Einfluss von Wasservögeln auf Populationen der Wandermuschel (Dreissena polymorpha Pall.) am Untersee/Hochrhein (Bodensee). *Schweiz. Z. Hydrol.* **44**, 149–61.

UTSCHICK, H. 1981. Wasservögel als Indikatoren fur die ökologische Stabilität süd-bayerischer Stauseen. *Verh. Orn. Ges. Bayern* **23**, 273–345.

ACID RAIN EFFECTS ON WATERFOWL: USE OF BLACK DUCK BROODS TO ASSESS FOOD RESOURCES OF EXPERIMENTALLY ACIDIFIED WETLANDS

G. M. HARAMIS & D. S. CHU

U.S. Fish & Wildlife Service, Patuxent Wildlife Research Center, Laurel, MD 20708, USA

ABSTRACT

A long-term decline in population levels of American Black Ducks (*Anas rubripes*) has led waterfowl managers to suspect acid deposition as one of several possible contributing factors. Acidification of wetlands may reduce food availability for Black Ducks and other waterfowl, and therefore may adversely affect the breeding performance of adults, as well as the growth and survival of ducklings. Herein, we describe the experimental use of pen-reared Black Duck broods and man-made emergent wetlands to assess the effects of acidification on Black Duck productivity. We exposed 18 broods (females with four 10-day-old ducklings) for 10-day trial periods on acidified (pH 5.0) and control (pH 6.8) wetlands. Impaired growth and reduced survival of ducklings was evident on acidified wetlands.

INTRODUCTION

The status of the American Black Duck (*Anas rubripes*) is cause for concern. Once an abundant game-bird in eastern freshwater and coastal habitats, the Black Duck has declined significantly during the past 30 years. Estimates of bird numbers from the mid-winter waterfowl inventory, a nationwide aerial waterfowl census conducted jointly each January by the U.S. Fish and Wildlife Service and the states, have indicated a 60 percent decline in Black Ducks in the Atlantic Flyway since 1955 (Steiner 1984). This decline has prompted close scrutiny of Black Duck management by the Fish and Wildlife Service, heated debates in public forums, and even court action by private groups aimed at curtailment of the Black Duck hunting season (Grandy 1983; Feierbend 1984). More restrictive harvest regulations have resulted, but causes for the decline remain controversial.

Many factors have been identified as contributing to the decline of the Black Duck (U.S. Dept. Interior 1982). Most prominent are overhunting (Grandy 1983), hybridization and possible competition with increasing numbers of Mallards (*Anas platyrhynchos*) within the Black Duck's range (Johnsgard 1967; Heusmann 1974; Johnsgard & DiSilvestro 1976), direct loss of habitat associated with human population growth, particularly in the mid-Atlantic region, and the effects of environmental contaminants. In controlled experiments, DDT was shown to reduce the hatchability of Black Duck eggs through eggshell thinning (Longcore *et al.* 1971; Longcore & Samson 1973; Longcore & Stendell 1983), and may have been instrumental in the decline of this species in the 1950s and 1960s, a period in which this pesticide was widely used in marshes for mosquito control and in northern breeding areas for spruce budworm control. In 1972, DDT was banned from use in the United States. The plight of the Black Duck is also deeply immersed in the lead shot-steel shot controversy, and in some areas lead toxicity from ingestion of spent lead shot (Bellrose 1959, 1975) remains a significant cause of mortality in Black Ducks (Longcore *et al.* 1982).

Recently, the potential effects of acid rain on aquatic environments have also been implicated in the Black Duck decline (Haines & Hunter 1981). The efficacy of this relationship lies in three important observations: (1) the Black duck breeds over much of eastern Canada and the northeastern United States where soil and water are low in alkalinity and therefore sensitive to acidification from acid rain; (2) acidification of surface waters is probably disruptive to aquatic food chains and may reduce food availability to waterfowl (Haines & Hunter 1981); (3) the Black Duck decline has coincided with the intensification of acid rain as measured by a progressive decline in the pH of precipitation over the past 30 years (Cogbill 1976).

Although there has been much research over the past decade focused on the effects of acid rain on aquatic invertebrates (e.g. Drablos & Tollan 1980; Singer 1980; Johnson 1980), there have been few field studies and no experimental studies conducted to investigate the effects of acidification on waterfowl. Recently, field studies have been completed in Sweden (Eriksson 1984), in Maine (Hunter *et al.* 1985, 1986) and in Quebec (DesGranges 1985; DesGranges & Darveau 1985; DesGranges & Rodrigue 1987). Our objective was to investigate the possible link between acid rain, degradation of aquatic habitat, and Black Duck productivity.

RESEARCH STRATEGY

If acid rain has been insidiously reducing the quality of Black Duck breeding habitats and productivity, how would such a limitation be likely to operate? Although primarily herbivorous during the non-breeding period, dabbling ducks (*Anatini*) depend on an abundance of animal foods to provide the protein requirement for reproduction. This requirement is particularly critical at two points during the breeding season: (1) for females before and during the laying cycle when large amounts of protein are needed for egg production (Swanson & Meyer 1973; Swanson *et al.* 1974; Krapu 1974, 1979, 1981; Drobney & Fredrickson 1979, 1985) and (2), for ducklings during their development when a high-protein diet is vital to tissue synthesis for rapid growth (Scott *et al.* 1959; Chura 1961; Perret 1962; Sugden 1973; Reinecke 1979; Street 1978). These invertebrate foods must be available at different times during the season and may be supplied from different habitat types. In general, ephemeral and seasonal wetlands have been identified as being particularly important in supplying the protein nutrition of breeding adults during spring, while more permanent wetlands, particularly marshes, are more important as brood foraging areas during late spring and summer.

Because of the need to establish a cause-and-effect relationship between wetland acidity and Black Duck productivity, we selected an experimental approach. This design required construction of a number of similar wetlands that would serve as experimental units and would permit isolation of wetland acidity as a treatment effect. Because of construction expense, these wetlands were small, limited in number, and permanent. Such wetlands simulated brood habitat. We maximized invertebrate abundance by maintaining our wetlands fish-free, a condition common to many temporary and seasonal wetlands in nature, and one highly attractive to waterfowl. A captive colony of Black Ducks at the Patuxent Wildlife Research Center provided a source of females with broods for our study. Growth and survival of ducklings placed on the wetlands for trial periods were the primary criterion for wetland quality. Such a design allowed ducklings to develop normally in the presence of a female and for an extended period. Ducklings were permitted full diurnal and nocturnal foraging opportunities, an important aspect in a thorough evaluation of avilable food resources of the wetlands. This approach also provided opportunities for study of the effects of acidification on various components of the aquatic ecosystem. Measurements of primary and secondary production, epiphytic growth, invertebrate populations and water chemistry were vital in evaluating ecosystem effects and their relationship to waterfowl productivity.

METHODS

Wetland construction and acidification

The selected construction site was a well-drained upland field that had lain fallow for at least 15 years. The soils were only slightly acid (pH 6.8) and graded from silty to sandy loam. We blocked the wetlands in pairs along this soil gradient. A total of six wetlands (three blocks) was built. Each wetland was circular, 15m in diameter (0.02ha), and was laid out on a 23m × 23m (0.05ha) plot to provide adequate upland fringe. Each wetland was deep enough (0.8m) to inhibit complete coverage by emergent vegetation. Because there was limited water at the site, we reduced demands on our water supply by using polyvinylchloride (PVC) plastic to line our wetlands. These liners served to maximize water retention as well as isolate individual wetlands.

Wetland construction began by removing topsoil from the site and excavating the wetland basins. An underground gravity-flow drainage system of 10cm PVC plumbing was installed; drains were anchored in concrete at the centre of each wetland where a vertical 10cm diameter standpipe was used to regulate water level. The standpipe was set inside a 30cm diameter PVC collar that was used for attachment of the PVC liners.

The PVC liners measured 20m × 20m and were 0.76mm (0.03in) thick. Before installation, we spread a 2cm layer of sand in each basin to protect liners from puncture by stones. Once set in place, a smooth circular hole about 15cm in diameter was cut in each liner directly over each drain; this hole was stretched over the 30cm PVC collar and cemented to it to ensure a watertight seal.

We buried each liner under about 20cm of topsoil and spread about 20 bales of wheat straw as a mulch. This mulch helped prevent soil erosion before the wetlands could be filled with water, but also served as an organic substrate for rapid colonization by invertebrates (Street 1980). To accelerate growth of emergent plants within the wetlands, we spread seeds of Burreed (*Sparganium* sp.) and planted plants of Burreed and Rice Cutgrass (*Leersia oryzoides*) along the fringes of each wetland as they were being filled. The wetlands were filled on 1 August 1983 and the water level was allowed to fluctuate naturally over the late summer and fall season.

Each wetland was enclosed with 2m-high chain-link fence that was skirted at ground level with a 61cm-wide, 1.3cm-mesh hardware cloth. About 15cm of the hardware cloth was buried in the ground to confine ducklings. The entire wetland facility was bordered by a second 2m-high perimeter fence that was buried and electrified to exclude burrowing and climbing predators. Each wetland was additionally covered with 5cm-mesh overhead netting to protect broods from avian predators. Finally, we erected a 3m-high observation tower in the middle of the facility for making brood observations. Total cost of materials for the complex was about $11,000.

We acidified the treatment wetlands by addition of reagent-grade sulphuric acid from early spring (1 April) until after the hatching season (early July). This was accomplished in two ways. While filling each wetland, weak acid was added to the water line by use of an inexpensive venturi device. Once the wetlands were filled, further addition of acid was accomplished by cycling water to and from an open 200l tank where acid was added at a controlled rate with the use of a petcock. To minimize the mechanical effect of pumping, low pressure electric pumps were used. These pumps cycled water at a rate of 15-20l/min and a typical pumping schedule recycled water for 3–6 hrs/day and acidified up to 20 percent of the wetland volume. Because the treated volume was only a fraction of total wetland volume (40,000l), the effluent pH was necessarily lower (range between 3 and 4) to achieve the target pH value of 5.0. The effluent was added to the centre surface water of the wetland where pH values were monitored. Because wetland pH varies on a daily cycle with the balance of carbon dioxide (between photosynthesis and respiration), pH was measured in the early morning to record minimum values. An arbitrary target pH of 5.0 was selected as representative of acidified surface waters over much of the Black Duck breeding range in eastern Canada; it is a conservative value for the mean pH of precipitation over much of this region (Haines & Hunter 1981: Figure 1). A pH of 5.0 essentially marks the end of bicarbonate buffering and the loss of calcium carbonate from the water column, an essential substance to many aquatic organisms. The wetlands required little acid to depress pH in early spring, but with rising water temperature and increased biological activity, more lengthy and regular acidification was necessary. Approximately eight litres of concentrated sulphuric acid were used to acidify each wetland during each three-month (April to July) study period.

Experimental use of captive Black Ducks

Black Ducks at the Patuxent colony were hatched from eggs collected from the wild in the maritime provinces of Canada. Successful maintenance of the colony required adequate provision of space, water, food, hygiene, protection from predators, and severe weather, and proper breeding. Ducks were housed in pens measuring 5m × 9m × 2m, each provided with a water trough measuring 0.7m × 3.0m. The ducks were fed a maintenance diet during the non-breeding period, but were placed on a high-protein breeding diet in early February. Best breeding performance was achieved by pairing and visually isolating birds beginning in the fall. Pairs were selected on the basis of genealogical record; no ducks were paired for breeding unless neither had shared common parentage for at least two generations (i.e. neither bird shared a common parent or grandparent). Nest boxes were placed in the pens in early spring and egg laying usually began by mid-March.

Our objective was to manipulate the breeding of Black Ducks such that six newly hatched broods (three pairs) could be placed simultaneously on our wetlands at a minimum of two different dates (two trial periods) during the breeding season. Because the length of the nesting period varies with several factors (e.g., the number of eggs laid, nest attentiveness, and incubation period), matching nests by date of first egg was not satisfactory in matching hatching dates.

We therefore devised a procedure that matched the hatching date for pairs of nests. This was compatible with our experimental design because synchronously hatched pairs of broods could be assigned to blocked pairs of wetlands. We first identified closely synchronized pairs of nests. In one nest, we substituted hard-boiled, brown chicken eggs, one at a time, for the newly laid duck eggs. Accepting these eggs, this female would remain in incubation for up to 7–10 days or more beyond the normal incubation period. Duck eggs removed from this nest were then used to increase the clutch size of the second nest up to 14–16 eggs. When the second nest began to hatch (pip), half of the eggs would be removed and substituted for the chicken eggs under the first female. This female readily accepted her new-found young.

We first placed day-old ducklings on our wetlands, but recorded high mortality after four days of cold, rainy weather. We next reared our broods on a diet of starter mash until they were nominally 10 days of age (about 100g in weight). This provided a distinct advantage for it allowed us to select only the more robust individuals for experimental use. In this way, paired broods of ducklings, matched exactly by age and as closely as possible by weight, were placed on each block (pair) of wetlands during the study.

Data collection
Limnological measurements.   Various limnological measurements were made during the course of the study. Water depth and pH were monitored daily; alkalinity, conductivity, water temperature and colour were measured bi-weekly; chlorophyll 'a' and major ions were monitored monthly. Macro-invertebrates were sampled with sweep nets before and following brood trials; zooplankton samples were taken bi-weekly.

Duckling growth, behaviour and survival.   Weight, tarsus and culmen measurements were made on ducklings before and after the trial periods. Duckling survival was monitored daily. We monitored duckling behaviour during each trial, (1) to ensure that broods behaved 'normally' and (2) to collect time-activity data to examine foraging and resting time and, in particular, to determine the location of foraging (i.e. aquatic or terrestrial). Broods on each pair of wetlands were observed for one hour, alternating every five minutes between treatment and control; behaviour was recorded every 15 seconds. The unit of observation was the randomly selected duckling, although for the most part this was synonymous with brood because ducklings of this age acted as a group and did not behave independently. Ducklings were observed for six hours (from sunrise to about noon) for nine days of each ten-day trial. A total of about 54 hours of observations were recorded per trial.

PRELIMINARY RESULTS

Results of three 10-day brood trials, conducted over a two year period (1984–85), revealed impaired growth and survival of ducklings on acidified wetlands (*Table 1*). Of 36 ducklings exposed on acid wetlands, only 2 (6 percent) gained more than 5 percent of their original body weight, while 18 (50 percent) died. On control wetlands, 23 ducklings (64 percent) gained more than 5 percent of their original weight, while only 5 (14 percent) died. The results were consistent for all pairs of wetlands over all trials. Analysis of variance of behavioural data revealed that in Trial 1, ducklings on acid wetlands spent less time foraging ($P < 0.02$) than those on control wetlands (*Table 2*). This finding was not repeated in subsequent trials.

Table 1:   Growth performance (weight gain or loss) and survival of ducklings exposed for three 10-day trial periods on experimentally acidified (pH 5.0) and control (pH 6.8) wetlands in 1984 and 1985.

	Number of ducklings		
	Acid wetlands	Control wetlands	Row χ^1
Gained weight[a]	2	23	17.6
Maintained weight[b]	8	6	0.2
Lost weight[c]	8	2	3.6
Died	18	5	7.4
Total ducklings	36	36	28.8[d]

Notes: a Gained more than 5% of weight at beginning of trial.
b Maintained within plus or minus 5% of weight at beginning of trial.
c Lost more than 5% of weight at beginning of trial.
d Chi-square test for homogeneity, $P < 0.001$.

Table 2:   Average percentage time spent in three activities for ducklings reared during three 10-day trials on acid versus control wetlands, 1984/85; results of analysis of variance.

	Trial/wetland					
	1		2		3	
Activity	Acid	Control	Acid	Control	Acid	Control
Foraging	62.7**	73.8	67.5	70.8	77.5	77.1
Resting	22.0	20.4	14.7	21.8	18.4	20.0
Other	15.3***	5.7	17.7***	7.4	4.1*	2.9

Note: $*P < 0.10$; $**P < 0.02$; $***P < 0.01$.

Table 3:   Average percentage time spent foraging in aquatic habitat by ducklings reared during three 10-day trials on acid versus control wetlands, 1984/85; results of analysis of variance.

	Wetland	
Trial	Acid	Control
1	43.9**	78.1
2	77.4*	86.8
3	54.0	58.8

Note: $*P < 0.05$; $**P < 0.01$.

We found a more consistent result in that treatment ducklings spent more time on 'other' behaviour (walking, walking the fence, swimming, alert) than did controls. This difference was significant in Trials 1 and 2 and nearly so in Trial 3 ($P < 0.10$). Of particular interest was *where* the ducklings were spending their foraging time. Analysis of variance revealed that in all three trials, ducklings on treatment wetlands spent consistently less time foraging in aquatic habitat. This difference was significant in two of three trials (*Table 3*).

Although analyses of limnological data remain to be completed, it was evident that acidification produced major physical and biological changes in the aquatic system. For instance, acidification suppressed phytoplankton growth and produced clear water; epiphytic growth was reduced, and submerged plants grew more rapidly because of the better light. In contrast, control wetlands were darkly stained and productive of phytoplankton; epiphytic growth coated submerged plants and slowed their growth. Control wetlands developed extensive mats of surface algae and *Lemna* sp., while acid wetlands remained relatively free from such growth. Preliminary analyses indicate that control wetlands had greater invertebrate biomass than acidified wetlands.

DISCUSSION AND CONCLUSIONS

The results of our duckling trials provide experimental evidence of the potential deleterious effect of wetland acidification on the productivity of free-ranging Black Ducks and possibly other populations of waterfowl inhabiting regions affected by acid deposition. Although we did not make a direct study of foods eaten by ducklings, we suggest that reduced invertebrate abundance is primarily responsible for the poor growth and survival of ducklings reared on acidified wetlands. Results of our behaviour study reveal that 'other' (*i.e.* non-feeding) behaviours were responsible for the major differences. Ducklings reared on acid wetlands were more distressed, probably due to food deprivation, and spent more time walking the fence and in alert posture. Time spent on 'other' behaviours subtracted from that which might have been spent foraging or resting. Although duckling behaviour was highly variable, a general observation was that ducklings on acid wetlands were less cohesive as broods and exhibited less of a general pattern of daily behaviour than control ducklings. In nature, such distress behaviour may attract predators and so reduce duckling survival. In addition, ducklings on treatment wetlands spent consistently less time foraging aquatically than did control ducklings (*Table 3*). Broods that are forced to spend more time food-seeking in terrestrial habitats, or travelling overland, might also be at greater risk to predation.

While our study clearly demonstrated that deleterious effects on duckling growth, behaviour and survival were associated with acidification, these results are not free from qualification. Our wetlands were newly established and were only representative of a variety of those soils, water, and aquatic life available to free-ranging Black Ducks. Although nearby ponds and marshes were similar in pH to our treatment wetlands, we cannot be sure that acid-tolerant aquatic colonists were as available at our study site as in the Black Duck breeding range in eastern Canada. Presence of such colonists may increase food availability to waterfowl in acidified waters. In addition, our study did not address the question of whether the loss of fish in moderately acidified waters provides a degree of compensatory food availability for Black Ducks. This relationship has been demonstrated for the Common Goldeneye (*Bucephala clangula*), a diving duck of lacustrine habitats that competes closely with fish for food (Eriksson 1979; Eadie

& Keast 1982; Eriksson 1984). Some evidence (Hunter *et al.* 1986; DesGranges & Rodrigue 1987) suggests that this mechanism may also exist, at least in certain lake and pond habitats, for young Black Ducks. However, these habitats contrast sharply to those highly selected emergent and herbaceous marshy habitats preferred by Black Duck broods in Maine (Ringelman & Longcore 1982). It seems likely that Black Duck broods do benefit from reduced competition with fish for food in certain habitats; however, until this mechanism has been examined in preferred brood foraging habitats, its overall importance for Black Ducks remains unclear.

Finally, we wish to emphasize the value of proper experimental design when studying such complex entities as acid rain, wetland ecosystems and waterfowl behaviour. Carefully controlled studies are vital in establishing a scientific basis of cause and effect. We have demonstrated that emergent wetlands can be constructed as experimental units and that Black Duck broods can be used as indicators of wetland quality. Our experimental approach has potential for assessing the effects of a variety of environmental impacts on waterfowl and aquatic systems.

REFERENCES

BELLROSE, F. C. 1959. Lead poisoning as a mortality factor in waterfowl populations. *Ill. Nat. Hist. Surv. Bull.* **27**, 235–88.

BELLROSE, F. C. 1975. Impact of ingested lead pellets on waterfowl. *Int. Waterfowl Symp.* **1**, 163–7.

CHURA, N. J. 1961. Food availability and preferences of juvenile Mallards. *Trans. N. Am. Wildl. Nat. Resour. Conf.* **26**, 121–34.

COGBILL, C. 1976. The history and character of acid precipitation in eastern North America. U.S. Forest Serv. Gen. Tech. Rep. NE-23.363–370.

DESGRANGES, J.-L. 1985. L'acidite des lacs et les canards: premiere etape. Rapport technique prepare dans le cadre du programme 'Environment 2000' par Canards Illimites et le Service canadien de la faune. xii + 152 p.

DESGRANGES, J.-L. & DARVEAU, M. 1985. Effect of lake acidity and morphometry on the distribution of aquatic birds in southern Quebec. *Holarctic Ecology* **8**, 181–90.

DESGRANGES, J.-L. & RODRIGUE, J. 1986. Influence of acidity and competition with fish on the development of ducklings in Quebec. *Water, Air and Soil Pollution* **30**, 743–50.

DRABLOS, D. & TOLLAN, A. (EDS.). 1980. *Proceedings of the international conference on the ecological impact of acid precipitation. Acid precipitation effects on forest and fish project.* Aas, Norway. 383 pp.

DROBNEY, R. D. & FREDRICKSON, L. H. 1979. Food selection by Wood Ducks in relation to breeding status. *J. Wildl. Manage.* **43**, 109–20.

DROBNEY, R. D. & FREDRICKSON, L. H. 1985. Protein acquisition: a possible proximate factor limiting clutch size in Wood Ducks. *Wildfowl* **36**, 122–8.

EADIE, J. M. & KEAST, A. 1982. Do Goldeneye and perch compete for food? *Oecologia* **55**, 225–30.

ERIKSSON, M. O. G. 1979. Competition between freshwater fish and Goldeneyes (*Bucephala clangula*) for common prey. *Oecologia* **41**, 99–107.

ERIKSSON, M. O. G. 1984. Acidification of lakes. Effects on waterbirds in Sweden. *Ambio* **13**, 260–2.

FEIERBEND, J. C. 1984. The Black Duck: an international resource on trial in the United States. *Wildl. Soc. Bull.* **12**, 128–34.

GRANDY, J. W. 1983. The North American Black Duck (*Anas rubripes*): a case study of 28 years of failure in American wildlife management. *Int. J. Study An. Problems. Suppl. Vol.* **4**, 35 pp.

HAINES, T. A. & HUNTER, M. L., JR. 1981. Waterfowl and their habitat: threatened by acid rain? *Int. Waterfowl Symp.* **4**, 177–90.

HEUSMANN, H. W. 1974. Mallard-Black Duck relationships in the Northeast. *Wildl. Soc. Bull.* **2**, 171–7.

HUNTER, M. L., JR., JONES, J. J., GIBBS, K. E., MORING, J. R. & BRETT, M. 1985. Interactions among waterfowl, fishes, invertebrates, and macrophytes in four Maine lakes of different acidity. U.S. Fish Wildl. Serv., Biol. Rep. 80(40.20). 80 pp.

HUNTER, M. L., JR., JONES, J. J., GIBBS, K. E. & MORING, J. R. 1986. Duckling responses to lake acidification: do Black Ducks and fish compete? *Oikos* **47**, 26–32.

JOHNSGARD, P. A. 1967. Sympatry changes and hybridization incidence in Mallards and Black Ducks. *Am. Midl. Nat.* **77**, 51–63.

JOHNSGARD, P. A. & DISILVESTRO, R. 1976. Seventy-five years of changes in Mallard-Black Duck ratios in eastern North America. *Am. Birds* **30**, 904–8.

JOHNSON, R. E. (ED.). 1980. Acid rain/fisheries—proceedings of an international symposium on acidic precipitation and fishing impacts in northeastern North America. Am. Fisheries Society. 357 pp.

KRAPU, G. L. 1974. Feeding ecology of Pintail hens during reproduction. *Auk* **91**, 278–90.

KRAPU, G. L. 1979. Nutrition of female dabbling ducks during reproduction. Pp. 59–70 *In:* Bookout, T. A. (ed.). *Waterfowl and wetlands—an integrated review.* North Central Sect. Wildl. Soc.

KRAPU, G. L. 1981. The role of nutrient reserves in Mallard reproduction. *Auk* **98**, 29–38.

LONGCORE, J. R., SAMSON, F. B. & WHITTENDALE, T. W., JR. 1971. DDE thins eggshells and lowers reproductive success of captive Black Ducks. *Bull. Environ. Contam. Toxicol.* **6**, 485–90.

LONGCORE, J. R. & SAMSON, F. B. 1973. Eggshell breakage by incubating Black Ducks fed DDE. *J. Wildl. Manage.* **37**, 390–4.

LONGCORE, J. R. & STENDELL, R. C. 1983. Black Ducks and DDE: review and status. *Trans. N.E. Fish Wildl. Conf.* **39**, 68–75.

LONGCORE, J. R., CORR, P. O. & SPENCER, H. E., JR. 1982. Lead shot incidence in sediments and waterfowl gizzards from Merrymeeting Bay, Maine. *Wildl. Soc. Bull.* **10**, 3–10.

PERRET, N. G. 1962. The spring and summer foods of the common Mallard (*Anas platyrhynchos* L.) in south central Manitoba. M.S. Thesis, Univ. British Columbia, Vancouver. 82 pp.

REINECKE, K. J. 1979. Feeding ecology and development of juvenile Black Ducks in Maine. *Auk* **96**, 737–45.

RINGELMAN, J. K. & LONGCORE, J. R. 1982. Movements and wetland selection by brood-rearing Black Ducks. *J. Wildl. Manage.* **46**, 615–21.

SCOTT, M. L., HILL, F. W., PARSONS, E. H., JR., BRUCKNER, J. H. & DOUGHERTY, E. 1959. Studies on duck nutrition 7. Effects of dietary energy protein relationships upon growth, feed utilization and carcass composition in market ducklings. *Poult. Sci.* **38**, 497–507.

SINGER, R. (ED.). 1980. Effects of acidic precipitation on benthos—proceedings of a symposium. U.S. EPA/North Carolina State Acid Rain Program/North Am. Benthol. Society. 154 pp.

STEINER, A. J. 1984. Mid-winter waterfowl inventory—Atlantic Flyway 1954–1984 trend analysis. U.S. Fish Wildl. Serv., Newton Corner, MA 02158. 284 pp.

STREET, M. 1978. The role of insects in the diet of Mallard ducklings—an experimental approach. *Wildfowl* **29**, 93–100.

STREET, M. 1980. The importance of invertebrates and straw. *The Game Conservancy Annual Review* **11**, 34–8.

SUGDEN, L. G. 1973. Feeding ecology of Pintail, Gadwall, American Widgeon and Lesser Scaup ducklings. Canadian Wildl. Serv. Rept. Ser. 24. 43 pp.

SWANSON, G. A. & MEYER, M. I. 1973. The role of invertebrates in the feeding ecology of Anatinae during the breeding season. Pp. 143–77 *In: Waterfowl Habitat Management Symposium,* Moncton, New Brunswick. 306 pp.

SWANSON, G. A., MEYER, M. I. & SERIE, J. R. 1974. Feeding ecology of breeding Blue-winged Teals. *J. Wildl. Manage.* **38**, 396–407.

U.S. DEPT. INTERIOR. 1982. Black Duck management plan for North America 1980–2000. Part I—operational plans and progress. The Black Duck Comm., H. Spencer, Chairman, U.S. Dept. Int., Fish Wildl. Serv., Wash., D.C. 20240. 35 pp.

SOME EFFECTS OF FRESHWATER
ACIDIFICATION ON BIRDS IN SWEDEN

Mats O. G. Eriksson

University of Göteborg, Department of Zoology, P.O. Box 25059,
S-400 31 Göteborg, Sweden

ABSTRACT

In Sweden, research on the effects of acid precipitation on freshwater ecosystems has followed the approach of separating abiotic effects, such as reduced reproduction and increased mortality of some organisms, especially fish, from biotic changes following the decline in fish density.

The abiotic effects discussed are exposure to aluminium among passerines feeding on insects emerging from acid lakes, and contamination by heavy metals, for example mercury, originating from airborne pollutants which dissolve more easily in acid water. Hitherto, there have been insufficient data supporting the assumption that these mechanisms are of quantitative importance.

The biotic changes connected with the decline in density of fish include the increased abundance of pelagic insects and an increase in water transparency. Non-piscivorous ducks may benefit from the increased availability of pelagic insects. For an understanding of the effects on fish-eating birds, knowledge of their foraging behaviour is essential to judge whether the increase in water transparency may compensate for the decreased availability of prey fish.

The effects on birds of the liming of acidified lakes has been little investigated, but preliminary results indicate no harmful effects.

For the monitoring of freshwater acidification in Sweden, I think that birds can complement the use of other indicator organisms and more traditional methods such as analyses of water chemistry.

INTRODUCTION

In the research on the effects of acid precipitation on freshwater ecosystems in Sweden, a general approach has been to distinguish between abiotic effects, such as reduced reproduction or increased mortality of some organisms, especially fish, molluscs, crustaceans and aquatic insects, and biotic changes following the decline in fish density (e.g. Eriksson *et al.* 1980; Nilssen *et al.* 1984). This approach has also been used for the interpretation of the effects on birds (Eriksson 1984).

ABIOTIC EFFECTS OF EXPOSURE TO METALS

These effects are connected with the increased exposure to metals through the intake of food items from acid lakes. There are two kinds of metal sources; (1)

airborne metal pollutants which dissolve more easily in water with low pH (e.g. Johansson 1980; Björklund et al. 1984), and (2) aluminium leaching from soil percolated with acid precipitation (e.g. Dickson 1978). Increased concentrations of heavy metals, such as mercury, have been detected in fish and aquatic insects from acid lakes (e.g. Johansson 1980; Björklund et al. 1984), and as the birds often occupy a high level in the food chains of lake ecosystems, the risk of contamination may be high.

Hitherto, most work in Scandinavia has been concentrated on the effects of aluminium. Damage to bone tissue and eggshells, and impaired reproductive success, have been reported among passerines, and the damage has been ascribed to exposure to aluminium through feeding on emerging insects with aquatic larval stages (Nyholm & Myhrberg 1977; Nyholm 1981). These effects are more apparent in northern Sweden than farther south, probably because of a lower availability of alternative food items, without any aquatic larval stage, to birds with a northerly located breeding site (E. Nyholm, pers. comm.). Attempts to demonstrate effects on the reproduction or growth of captive birds fed on dietary aluminium have been unsuccessful, however, but the reasons for this discrepancy between experimental results and field data may be ascribed to differences between species in their response to aluminium or to higher concentrations of phosphorus and calcium in the experimental diet than in the natural food organisms (Carrière et al. 1986).

The importance of other metals has been little investigated so far. Preliminary results from the first year of a two-year study of the amounts of metals in livers of Goldeneye (*Bucephala clangula*) ducklings do not exclude the possibility of higher concentrations of cadmium, copper and rubidium in samples from acid lakes, but sample sizes are small and trends are not statistically significant (Eriksson & Henrikson 1986). Black-throated Diver (*Gavia arctica*) eggs collected in southwest Sweden have high mercury contents, but here also sample sizes are too small to allow any definitive conclusions (Ahlgren et al. 1986) to be made. Furthermore, present results are to some extent contradictory: Eriksson (1983a, *Table 1*) found no differences in the amounts of mercury in Goldeneye eggs from two areas, with and without acidified lakes respectively, in southwest Sweden.

In summary: from the general knowledge of the spread of metals in acid lakes, it can be concluded that birds foraging in such lakes run the risk of exposure. There are still few data to indicate whether this mechanism is of any quantitative importance, but the risk of damage to presumably susceptible species, such as some fish-eating birds, or to passerines such as Grey Wagtails (*Motacilla cinerea*) and Dippers (*Cinclus cinclus*) with breeding distributions restricted to aquatic habitats, needs further investigation.

CHANGES FOLLOWING THE DECLINE IN FISH DENSITY

During recent decades, the importance of fish as a key group influencing the chemical, physical and biological conditions in fresh waters has received increased attention, and many of the biological changes in acidified lakes are not primary effects of low pH in itself but effects of the decline in the density of fish (e.g. Eriksson et al. 1980; Nilssen et al. 1984). Research on the importance of fish for the chemical and physical conditions in Scandinavian lakes has been carried out, for example, by Andersson et al. (1978), Stenson et al. (1978) and Henrikson et al. (1980), and studies on the effects of predation by fish on the structure of the invertebrate community by, for example, Stenson (1972, 1979) and Eriksson

(1979). Many of the present ideas concerning the effects of acidification on waterbirds is based on this general knowledge of the interactions between fish, invertebrates and the abiotic environment. Two effects have been recognized as important for birds: (1) increased abundance of some aquatic insects due to the reduced predation pressure from fish (e.g. Macan 1977; Stenson 1979; Eriksson 1979; Andersson 1981; Nilssen *et al.* 1984) and (2) the increase in water transparency due to the changed productivity and nutritional status in lakes where the predation by fish on zooplankton has decreased (e.g. Henrikson *et al.* 1980). In lakes with low pH, precipitation of humic substances by aluminium makes an additional contribution to the increase in water clarity (e.g. Almer *et al.* 1978; Effler *et al.* 1985).

Non-piscivorous birds

From studies on Long-tailed Duck (*Clangula hyemalis*) (Pehrsson 1974), Goldeneye (Eriksson 1979; Eadie & Keast 1982) and Mallard (*Anas platyrhynchos*) (Pehrsson 1979, 1984) there is evidence of competition between non-piscivorous ducks and freshwater fish for common prey such as aquatic insects. The connection between acidity, decreased abundance of fish, and increased abundance of food organisms to some species of ducks has also been discussed in North American studies by, for example, DesGranges & Darveau (1985), DesGranges & Rodrigue (1986), Hunter *et al.* (1986), and McNicol *et al.* (this volume).

But many aquatic invertebrates are adversely affected by acidity, and the biotic changes in acidified lakes include a shift in the benthic community towards an increased proportion of pelagic species which can expand due to the reduced predation from fish (e.g. Henrikson & Oscarson 1981; Nilssen *et al.* 1984; Dermott 1985). Hitherto, much research in Scandinavia has been focused on positive effects, such as the possibilities for ducks to exploit the increased abundance of pelagic insects, and little attention has been paid to the possible negative effects of reduced abundance of other aquatic invertebrates. Some diving ducks, such as Pochard (*Aythya ferina*) and Tufted Duck (*Aythya fuligula*) are poorly adapted to exploit the increased stocks of highly mobile aquatic insects because of their bill morphology and feeding behaviour (Suter 1982). Tufted Duck, for example, feed to a large extent on molluscs, whose abundance often declines in acidified lakes (e.g. Økland & Økland 1986).

In Sweden, little research has been done on the effects on birds of biotic changes in running water. The risk of adverse effects on Dippers (*Cinclus cinclus*) similar to those reported in Wales (e.g. Ormerod *et al.* 1985) and Germany (Kaiser 1985) cannot be excluded as decreased abundance of benthic insects in streams with low pH has been reported (Økland & Økland 1986, and references therein). A study of Grey Wagtail (*Motacilla cinerea*) indicates only moderate effects on the availability of food and breeding performance of acidity in streams (Johansson 1986), similar to those reported in Wales (Ormerod & Tyler, this volume).

Fish-eating birds

During the last few years, fish-eating birds have received increased attention in the research into the effects on birds of freshwater acidification. There is a combination of reasons for this. For some fish-eating birds, such as Black-throated Diver and Osprey (*Pandion haliaetus*) a considerable proportion of the total European population is found in Scandinavia (Österlöf 1973; Nilsson & Pettersson 1978; Nilsson 1981), and thus there are risks that adverse effects of freshwater acidification may influence large parts of the breeding populations in this part of the world. Furthermore, effects such as increased abundance of aquatic insects or increased water transparency may for some species counterbalance the negative effects of decreased fish density. To understand the effects on fish-eating birds, knowledge of their feeding techniques and, in particular, whether each species concerned can make use of the improved visibility in acidified lakes, is essential (Eriksson 1985).

The Black-throated Diver is a good example of the complexity of this subject. Adult birds feed almost exclusively on fish, but the young are fed also on aquatic insects—at least during the very first period after hatching (e.g. Lehtonen 1970). In breeding lakes devoid of fish they can feed almost entirely on insects until they fledge (Bergman & Derksen 1977). In addition, Pike (*Esox lucius*) have been identified as important predators on non-fledged young (Lehtonen 1970). A study of 24 oligotrophic lakes in southwest Sweden revealed a higher production of young in lakes with low densities of fish (Eriksson 1986a). Thus, the selection of lakes for rearing young includes a compromise between the conditions necessary for foraging by adult birds and the demands for rearing young. Studies on the selection of lakes by adult birds during the breeding season indicate not only density of fish but also water transparency as important factors. Black-throated Divers search for fish while swimming with their eyes below the water surface for short periods, and they can exploit depths below the transparency generally recorded in acid lakes in Sweden. Thus, they can profit from a high water transparency as compensation for a low density of prey fish, as a larger volume of water can be searched per unit of time spent in foraging (Eriksson 1985).

The Osprey is a fish-eating raptor with a very different foraging technique; it flies or hovers over the water surface, and it has a low diving depth of at most one metre (Cramp & Simmons 1979). Thus, it cannot profit from the increased transparency in acid lakes, and I have hypothesized that fish-eating birds with this kind of feeding behaviour are more susceptible to a reduced density of fish than birds using a foraging technique similar to that of the Black-throated Diver (Eriksson 1985). During the 1970s, no overall decrease in the reproductive success of Osprey could be detected in Sweden, but a negative trend in the production of young occurred among pairs breeding in areas with many acidified lakes (Eriksson et al. 1983). Studies in North America indicate that Ospreys do not adjust their clutch size and initial brood size to the expected foraging success during the nestling period (e.g. Stinson 1978; Poole 1982; Jamieson et al. 1983) and that a reduced rate of fish delivery to the nests increases the risk of nestling mortality (Poole 1982; Van Daele & Van Daele 1982; Jamieson et al. 1983; Kushlan & Bass 1983). An investigation of Osprey nests in southwest Sweden supports the conclusion of a relationship between low food delivery rate and nestling mortality (Eriksson 1986b). In addition, in southwest Sweden distances between occupied nests have been shown to be shorter where large areas of non-acidified lakes surround the nests, which indicates that a decrease in the density of occupied nests can be expected if damage due to acidification turns out to be more widespread (Eriksson 1986b).

LIMING OF LAKES

Lime treatment has proved effective in restoring fish stocks in acidified lakes (e.g. Bengtsson et al. 1980; F. Eriksson et al. 1983; Nyberg 1984; Nyberg et al. 1986; Eriksson & Tengelin 1987) and the technique is now frequently used in Sweden. For non-piscivorous ducks, increased competition with fish for common prey may be disadvantageous, while the situation for fish-eating birds is more complicated to analyse as the benefit of an increased density of fish may be counteracted by a decrease in water transparency. A comparison of bird densities, gill-net catches of fish, and water transparency in 14 lakes in 1983, before liming, and again in 1985, after liming of eight of the lakes during summer-autumn 1983, did not indicate any change in bird densities that can be ascribed to the liming: the trends recorded were the same in limed lakes and control lakes. The bird species included were Black-throated Diver, Mallard, Teal (*Anas crecca*), Goldeneye and Goosander (*Mergus merganser*). Average fish density increased and water transparency decreased significantly in the limed lakes, but remained unchanged in the control lakes (Eriksson 1987a). For Black-throated Diver, a comparison of the production of young before and after liming of another 13 lakes in southwest Sweden did not indicate any significant change in the average production per pair per lake (Eriksson 1987b). So far, no harmful effects to waterbirds due to liming of lakes have been reported.

BIRDS AS INDICATORS OF FRESHWATER ACIDIFICATION

Because of the complex pattern of changes occurring during the process of acidification of a lake, I find it difficult to suggest any good indicator species.

The use of birds as a means of monitoring the spread of metals in acidified lake ecosystems may look attractive as birds often occupy high levels in the food-chains. Furthermore, birds as well as birds' eggs are easy to handle during field work; the organs to be analysed are well protected inside the skin or shell, and there is no risk of contamination of samples due to inaccurate field procedures during collection. Nevertheless, the use of birds does have some methodological problems. Collection of eggs is an effective method, once the nests have been located, and it is also an easy procedure if the collection is concentrated on a species, such as Goldeneye, that breeds in nest-boxes. On the other hand, it is often difficult to judge whether the metal content measured in eggs genuinely reflects the exposure at the sampling site, or whether the results are influenced by exposure through the food intake during the winter and on migration. Furthermore, the birds often forage in lakes other than the breeding lake during the egg-laying period; in fact the breeding lakes can sometimes be ice-covered when egg-laying starts. The alternative of collecting young in order to analyse the metal content of some of their organs may give a better indication of the situation at the site where the young have been foraging (or fed by their parents). On the other hand, this method includes more time spent on field work in relation to each sample obtained, and for some species a large-scale killing and collection of non-fledged young is unwarranted for conservation reasons. Thus, the use of birds as indicators of the metal contamination of acidified freshwater ecosystems involves methodological and ethical problems concerning the collection of samples. We hope that some of these difficulties can be evaluated by our current work on metal contamination in Goldeneye ducklings.

As an indicator of biotic changes in acid lakes, a fish-eating bird species may at first look attractive. The decline in the production of young by Ospreys in areas with many acidified lakes in southwest Sweden during the 1970s (see above) may support the argument for the use of this bird for monitoring, but in large parts of Sweden the density of breeding pairs is too low to allow the meaningful use of this species for monitoring. Alternative species, such as Black-throated Diver, are affected by acidification in too complicated a way. An alternative approach is to use a non-piscivorous species as an indicator of increased abundance of pelagic invertebrates in the absence of fish. Density of Goldeneye is negatively correlated with density of fish (Eriksson 1983b), but scarcity of nest sites (tree holes) is another important limiting factor (e.g. Fredga 1962; Leidgren 1967; Rajala & Ormio 1971; Eriksson 1982). Thus, monitoring of a Goldeneye population should be restricted to areas with a surplus of suitable nest-boxes.

In Sweden, birds can be a valuable complement to other organisms, such as fish and aquatic invertebrates, used as indicators of freshwater acidification. However, the complex pattern behind the fluctuations in density and reproductive success, in combination with the complications following habitat rehabilitation programmes, including liming of lakes and fish stocking, makes it difficult to work with birds only. The situation is probably different in eastern North America, where the history and nature of the acid rain problem, combined with the life history strategies of the major waterbird species, supports the contention that useful bio-indicator species are available for long-term monitoring studies of acidified freshwater ecosystems (McNicol, this volume).

REFERENCES

AHLGREN, C.-G., JOHANSSON, J., KARLSSON, G. & KONGBÄCK, H. 1986. Projekt storlom— en presentation av undersökningsåret 1985. *Gavia* 12, 16–24.

ALMER, B., DICKSON, C., EKSTRÖM, C. & HÖRNSTRÖM, E. 1978. Sulphur pollution and the aquatic ecosystem. *In:* Nriagu, J. O. (ed.) *Sulphur in the environment: Part II, ecological impacts* 271–311. John Wiley & Sons, New York.

ANDERSSON, G. 1981. Influence of fish on waterfowl and lakes. *Anser* 20, 21–34 (Swedish, English summary).

ANDERSSON, G., BERGGREN, H., CRONBERG, G. & GELIN, C. 1978. Effects of planktivorous and benthivorous fish on organisms and water chemistry in eutrophic lakes. *Hydrobiologia* 59, 9–15.

BENGTSSON, B., DICKSON, W. & NYBERG, P. 1980. Liming acid lakes in Sweden. *Ambio* 9, 34–6.

BERGMAN, R. D. & DERKSEN, D. V. 1977. Observations on Arctic and Red-throated Loons at Storkersen Point, Alaska. *Arctic* 30, 41–51.

BJÖRKLUND, I., BORG, H. & JOHANSSON, K. 1984. Mercury in Swedish lakes—its regional distribution and causes. *Ambio* 13, 118–21.

CARRIÈRE, D., FISCHER, K. L., PEAKALL, D. B. & ANGHERN, P. 1986. Effects of dietary aluminium sulphate on reproductive success and growth of Ringed Turtle-Doves (*Streptopelia risoria*). *Can. J. Zool.* 64, 1500–05.

CRAMP, S. & SIMMONS, K. E. L. (EDS.) 1979. *The birds of the Western Palearctic, Vol. II.* Oxford University Press, Oxford.

DERMOTT, R. M. 1985. Benthic fauna in a series of lakes displaying a gradient of pH. *Hydrobiologia* 128; 31–8.

DESGRANGES, J.-L. & DARVEAU, M. 1985. Effect of lake acidity and morphometry on the distribution of aquatic birds in southern Quebec. *Holarct. Ecol.* 8, 181–90.

DESGRANGES, J.-L. & RODRIGUE, J. 1986. Influence of acidity and competition with fish on the development of ducklings in Quebec. *Water, Air and Soil Pollution* 30, 743–50.

DICKSON, W. 1978. Some effects of acidification of Swedish lakes. *Verh. Internat. Verein. Limnol.* 20, 851–6.

EADIE, J. McA. & KEAST, A. 1982. Do Goldeneye and Perch compete for food? *Oecologia (Berl.)* 55, 225–30.

EFFLER, S. W., SCHAFRAN, G. C. & DRISCOLL, C. T. 1985. Partitioning light attenuation in an acidic lake. *Can. J. Fish. Aquat. Sci.* 42, 1707–11.

ERIKSSON, F., HÖRNSTRÖM, E., MOSSBERG, P. & NYBERG, P. 1983. Ecological effects of lime treatment of acidified lakes and rivers in Sweden. *Hydrobiologia* 101, 145–64

ERIKSSON, M. O. G. 1979. Competition between freshwater fish and Goldeneyes *Bucephala clangula* (L.) for common prey. *Oecologia (Berl.)* 41, 99–107.

ERIKSSON, M. O. G. 1982. Differences between old and newly established Goldeneye *Bucephala clangula* populations. *Ornis Fennica* 59, 13–9.

ERIKSSON, M. O. G. 1983a. (Effects of lake acidification on bird populations.) *Statens Naturvårdsverk PM* 1658 (Swedish, English summary).

ERIKSSON, M. O. G. 1983b. The role of fish in the selection of lakes by nonpiscivorous ducks: Mallard, Teal and Goldeneye. *Wildfowl* **34**, 27–32.

ERIKSSON, M. O. G. 1984. Acidification of lakes: effects on waterbirds in Sweden. *Ambio* **13**, 260–2.

ERIKSSON, M. O. G. 1985. Prey detectability for fish-eating birds in relation to fish density and water transparency. *Ornis Scand.* **16**, 1–7.

ERIKSSON, M. O. G. 1986a. Reproduction of Black-throated Diver *Gavia arctica* in relation to fish density in oligotrophic lakes in southwestern Sweden. *Ornis Scand.* **17**, 245–8.

ERIKSSON, M. O. G. 1986b. Fish delivery, production of young, and nest density of Osprey (*Pandion haliaetus*) in South-west Sweden. *Can. J. Zool.* **64**, 1961–5.

ERIKSSON, M. O. G. 1987a. Liming of acidified lakes in southwestern Sweden: short-term effects on waterbird densities. *Wildfowl* **38** (in press).

ERIKSSON, M. O. G. 1987b. (The production of young in Black-throated Diver, *Gavia arctica*, in South-west Sweden.) *Vår Fågelvärld* **45**, 172–86. (Swedish, English summary).

ERIKSSON, M. O. G. & HENRIKSON, L. 1986. Försurningsinducerad metallbelastning på knipa. Preliminary report for 1985, appendix enclosed to a research proposal to The National Swedish Environment Protection Board.

ERIKSSON, M. O. G., HENRIKSON, L., NILSSON, B.-I., NYMAN, H. G., OSCARSON, H. G., STENSON, J. A. E. & LARSSON, P. K. 1980. Predator-prey relations important for the biotic changes in acidified lakes. *Ambio* **9**, 248–9.

ERIKSSON, M. O. G., HENRIKSON, L. & OSCARSON, H. G. 1983. (Acid rain—a future danger for the Osprey, *Pandion haliaetus*) *Vår Fågelvärld* **42**, 293–300 (Swedish, English summary).

ERIKSSON, M. O. G. & TENGELIN, B. 1987. Short-term effects of liming on perch *Perca fluviatilis* populations in acidified lakes in South-west Sweden. *Hydrobiologia* **146**, 187–91.

FREDGA, S. 1962. Sätt upp knipholkar—det lönar sig. *Svensk Jakt* **100**, 70–1.

HENRIKSON, L., NYMAN, H. G., OSCARSON, H. G. & STENSON, J. A. E. 1980. Trophic changes, without changes in the external nutrient loading. *Hydrobiologia* **68**, 257–63.

HENRIKSON, L. & OSCARSON, H. G. 1981. Corixids (Hemiptera-Heteroptera), the new top predators in acidified lakes. *Verh. Internat. Verein. Limnol.* **21**, 1616–20.

HUNTER, M. L., JR., JONES, J. J., GIBBS, K. E. & MORING, J. R. 1986. Duckling responses to lake acidification: do black ducks and fish compete? *Oikos* **47**, 26–32.

JAMIESON, I., SEYMOUR, N., BANCROFT, R. P. & SULLIVAN, R. 1983. Sibling aggression in nesting ospreys in Nova Scotia. *Can. J. Zool.* **61**, 466–9.

JOHANSSON, K. 1980.(Heavy metals in acid woodland lakes.) *Statens Naturvårdsverk PM* 1359 (Swedish, English summary).

JOHANSSON, O. 1986. Forsärlans *Motacilla cinerea* reproduktion och födounderlag i försurade och icke försurade vattendrag i sydvästra Sverige. *Honours Thesis, University of Göteborg, Dept. Zoology, Göteborg.*

KAISER, A. 1985. Zur Verbreitung und Bestandssituation des Wasseramsel (*Cinclus c. aquaricus*) in Rheinhessen, Rheingau und östlichen Hunsrück. *Ökol. Vögel* **7**, 185–96.

KUSHLAN, J. A. & BASS, O. L. 1983. Decrease in the southern Florida Osprey population, a possible result of food stress. *In:* Bird, D. (ed.). *Biology and management of Bald Eagles and Ospreys:* 187–200. Harpell Press, Ste. Anne de Bellevue.

LEHTONEN, L. 1970. Zur Biologie des Prachttauchers, *Gavia a. arctica* (L.). *Ann. Zool. Fennici* **7**, 25–60.

LEIDGREN, A. 1967. Knipan som häckfågel i Linaälvsdalen. *Norrbottens Natur* **34**, 30–40.

MACAN, T. T. 1977. The influence of predation on the composition of freshwater communities. *Biol. Rev.* **52**, 45–70.

NILSSEN, J. P., ØSTDAHL, T. & POTTS, W. T. W. 1984. Species replacements in acidified lakes: physiology, predation or competition? *Rep. Inst. Freshw. Res. Drottningholm* **61**, 148–53.

NILSSON, S. G. 1981. (The size of the breeding populations of diurnal raptors in Sweden.) *Vår Fågelvärld* **40**, 249–62 (Swedish, English summary).

NILSSON, S. G. & PETTERSSON, Å. 1978. (An estimate of the population size of the

Black-throated diver *Gavia arctica* in Sweden.) *Vår Fågelvärld* **37**, 251–3 (Swedish, English summary).

NYBERG, P. 1984. Effects of liming on fisheries. *Phil. Trans. R. Soc. Lond. B* **305**, 549–60.

NYBERG, P., APPELBERG, M. & DEGERMAN, E. (1986), Effects of liming on crayfish and fish in Sweden. *Water, air and soil pollution* **31**, 669–87.

NYHOLM, N. E. I. 1981. Evidence of involvement of aluminium in causation of defective formation of eggshells and impaired breeding in wild passerine birds. *Environmental Research* **26**, 363–71.

NYHOLM, N. E. I. & MYHRBERG, H. E. 1977. Severe eggshell defects and impaired reproductive capacity in small passerines in Swedish Lapland. *Oikos* **29**, 336–41.

ØKLAND, J. & ØKLAND, K. A. 1986. The effects of acid deposition on benthic animals in lakes and streams. *Experientia* **42**, 471–86.

ORMEROD, S. J. & TYLER, S. J. 1985. The distribution of Grey Wagtails in relation to stream acidity in upland Wales: a preliminary survey. *Unpublished report, ICBP Wales Office, Newtown.*

ORMEROD, S. J., TYLER, S. J. & LEWIS, J. M. S. 1985. Is the breeding distribution of Dippers influenced by stream acidity? *Bird Study* **32**, 32–9.

ÖSTERLÖF, S. 1973. (The Osprey *Pandion haliaetus* in Sweden in 1971.) *Vår Fågelvärld* **32**, 100–6 (Swedish, English summary).

PEHRSSON, O. 1974. Nutrition of small ducklings regulating breeding area and reproductive output in the Long-tailed Duck, *Clangula hyemalis*. *Proc. Int. Congr. Game Biol.* **11**, 259–64.

PEHRSSON, O. 1979. Feeding behaviour, feeding habitat utilization, and feeding efficiency of Mallard ducklings (*Anas platyrhynchos*) as guided by a domestic duck. *Swedish Wildlife Research* **10**, 191–218.

PEHRSSON, O. 1984. Relationships of food to spatial and temporal breeding strategies of Mallards in Sweden. *J. Wildl. Manage.* **48**, 322–39.

POOLE, A. 1982. Brood reduction in temperate and sub-tropical Ospreys. *Oecologia (Berl.)* **53**, 111–19.

RAJALA, P. & ORMIO, T. 1971. On the nesting of the Goldeneye, *Bucephala clangula* (L.), in the Meltaus Game Research Area in Northern Finland, 1959–1966. *Finn. Game Res.* **31**, 3–9.

STENSON, J. A. E. 1972. Fish predation effects on the species composition of the zooplankton community in eight small forest lakes. *Rep. Inst. Freshw. Res. Drottningholm* **52**, 132–148.

STENSON, J. A. E. 1979. Predator-prey relations between fish and invertebrate prey in some forest lakes. *Rep. Inst. Freshw. Res. Drottningholm* **58**, 166–83.

STENSON, J. A. E., BOHLIN, T., HENRIKSON, L., NILSSON, B.-I., NYMAN, H. G., OSCARSON, H. G. & LARSSON, P. K. 1978. Effects of fish removal from a small lake. *Verh. Internat. Verein. Limnol.* **20**, 794–801.

STINSON, C. H. 1978. The influence of environmental conditions on aspects of the time budgets of breeding Ospreys. *Oecologia (Ber.)* **36**, 127–39.

SUTER, W. 1982. Vergleichende Nahrungsökologi von überwinternden Tauchenten (*Bucephala, Aythya*) und Blässhuhn (*Fulica atra*) am Untersee-Ende/Hochrhein (Bodensee). *Der Ornithologische Beobachter* **79**, 225–54.

VAN DAELE, L. J. & VAN DAELE, H. A. 1982. Factors affecting the productivity of Ospreys nesting in West-central Idaho. *Condor* **84**, 292–9.

ICBP Technical Publication No. 6, 1987

DIPPERS (*CINCLUS CINCLUS*) AND GREY WAGTAILS (*MOTACILLA CINEREA*) AS INDICATORS OF STREAM ACIDITY IN UPLAND WALES

S. J. Ormerod[1] & Stephanie J. Tyler[2]

1 *Dept. of Applied Biology, University of Wales Institute of Science and Technology, King Edward VII Avenue, Cardiff CF1 3XF, UK*
2 *Royal Society for the Protection of Birds, Wales Office, Bryn Aderyn, Newtown, Powys SY16 2AB, UK*

ABSTRACT

Dippers (*Cinclus cinclus*) and Grey Wagtails (*Motacilla cinerea*) are passerines closely associated with lotic ecosystems. In Britain, the ranges of both species include upland areas that are underlain by base-poor rocks and that are subject to the acidifying influences of atmospheric deposition and conifer afforestation. Consequently in Wales, where there is evidence of surface-water acidification, both species have recently been the subject of intensive autecological studies.

During the breeding season, Dippers occupy linear territories along rivers and feed almost exclusively from the river benthos. Breeding abundances (pairs/10km) showed highly significant correlations ($r = 0.6$–0.8; $P < 0.001$) with the abundances of two invertebrate groups—may-fly nymphs and caddis larvae. Several families amongst these taxa are influenced by acid-related factors, and Dippers were scarcest along streams with low pH (<5.7–6.0) and elevated concentrations of aluminium (>0.08–$0.10g/m^3$). One river for which historical data were available showed a decline in measured pH of 1.7 units between the 1960s and 1984, and the Dipper population fell concomitantly by 70 to 80 percent.

Dietary studies subsequently revealed the importance of may-fly nymphs and caddis larvae, particularly when Dippers were feeding nestlings.

Delayed clutch initiation, and significantly smaller clutch and brood sizes, were recorded in Dippers breeding along acidic streams by comparison with those breeding elsewhere. Food provisioning to nestlings on acidic streams may also be impaired.

Grey Wagtails are less closely associated with rivers than Dippers, and outside the breeding season they sometimes forage in other habitats. Nevertheless, 95 percent of nests are near flowing water, where the species feeds when breeding.

The abundance of Grey Wagtails correlated weakly (although significantly) with stream total hardness ($r = 0.41$; $P < 0.01$) and with the abundance of some invertebrates. However, at 74 sites in upland Wales, Grey Wagtails preferred rivers with adequate riffle and tree-lining, irrespective of hardness and acidity. Preliminary dietary studies indicate the importance of Diptera, in some cases of non-riverine origin. There is no evidence of impaired breeding at low stream pH or elevated aluminium concentration ($>0.5g\ Al/m^3$).

We concluded that Dippers provide a more suitable indicator of stream acidity than Grey Wagtails, although further data are required on the latter species.

INTRODUCTION

Although the acidification of surface-waters can occur through a variety of natural (Pennington 1984) and man-induced mechanisms (e.g. acid mine-drainage, Greenfield & Ireland 1978, Scullion & Edwards 1980; impoundment, Brooker 1981), concern has been expressed recently in North America and Europe over acidification resulting from atmospheric deposition (Overrein, Seip & Tollan 1980; Haines 1981; Altshuller & Linthurst 1984). Further exacerbation in Britain has been ascribed to the widespread establishment of non-native conifer forests (Harriman & Morrison 1981; Stoner, Gee & Wade 1984; Ormerod & Edwards 1985).

Because acidic waterways in temperate areas support relatively impoverished fish and invertebrate faunas (Sutcliffe & Carrick 1973; Zeimann 1975; Hall et al. 1980; Townsend, Hildrew & Francis 1983; Stoner et al. 1984), some authors have drawn attention to the possible influences of acidification on animals that are not totally aquatic, but which depend on lakes and rivers for food (Eriksson 1984; Ormerod, Tyler & Lewis 1985; Ormerod et al. 1986). For example, Dippers (*Cinclus cinclus*) and Grey Wagtails (*Motacilla cinerea*) are passerines closely associated with running waters along which they feed and breed; their ranges in Britain and mainland Europe include upland areas that are underlain by base-poor rocks or soils, and that are subject to acidifying effects from atmospheric deposition and conifer afforestation (Britain: Sharrock 1976; Fowler et al. 1982; Sutcliffe et al. 1982; Cape et al. 1984; Stoner et al. 1984; Ormerod & Edwards 1985. Europe: Granat 1978; Overrein et al. 1980; Ottar 1983; Beilke 1983; Kallend et al. 1983; Paces 1985). Moreover, influences by acidity on their distributions have already been described in Britain and Germany (Tyler 1970; Ormerod et al. 1985a, 1986; Kaiser 1985).

As birds typical of clean hillstreams, Dippers have been viewed traditionally as indicators of water quality in rivers receiving industrial or domestic pollution. Dipper and Grey Wagtail eggs have also been used to monitor levels of heavy metals and chlorinated hydrocarbons in German rivers (Lachenmayer, Kunze & Holzinger 1985; Monig 1985). We believe that these species might also have value as indicators of stream acidity or acidification: historical records of their distribution are sometimes available and, unlike other biological indicators of acidity such as invertebrates or diatoms (Stoner et al. 1984; Engblom & Lingdell 1984; Charles 1985), they are easy to census and identify.

In this paper, we examine influences by acidity on the ecology of Dippers and Grey Wagtails in upland Wales. We focus on breeding distribution, diet and breeding performance.

DIPPERS

General ecology

Dippers are unique amongst passerines in their close association with lotic ecosystems, and they are anatomically and physiologically adapted to such environments (Goodge 1959; Murrish 1970a, 1970b). They feed almost exclusively from the river benthos by swimming underwater or by foraging in shallow riffles and at the river margins (Jost 1975; Bryant, Hails & Prys-Jones 1985; Ormerod 1985a, 1985b; Spitznagel 1985).

Because of the nature of their habitat, Dippers occupy linear territories (Bakus 1959; Balat 1962). Consequently, they are easily censused, and nests are easily located to permit straightforward monitoring of breeding performance (Price &

Bock 1983; Tyler & Ormerod 1985). Their habitat requirements are also well known. Typical abundance values are 2–16 pairs per 10km, and spatial patterns in distribution have been related to habitat physiography, stream chemistry and food availability (Price & Bock 1983; Ormerod *et al.* 1985a, 1986; Ormerod, Boilstone & Tyler 1985b).

Relationships with stream acidity
Breeding distribution. The distribution of Dippers and stream acidity are closely related. Ormerod *et al.* (1985a) considered the abundance of breeding pairs over 220km of tributaries of the River Wye. When influences by stream slope were masked out by considering only the upper reaches (10km) of 17 tributaries, breeding abundance and mean pH were highly significantly correlated (*Figure 1*). Whilst the lowest mean pH values indicated only moderate acidity (pH 6.0), pH minima on rivers where Dippers were scarce were 4.5–5.0. Moreover, one river for which historical data were available showed a decline of 1.7 units in pH measured in winters between the 1960s and 1984; the dipper population fell from 9 pairs to 1–2 pairs per 10km (*Figure 2*).

However, the wide range of pH values investigated in the Wye catchment (6.0–8.0) clearly incorporated other chemical changes; breeding abundance also correlated with calcium and total hardness, both of which influence invertebrate abundance (*Figure 1*).

To assess the distribution of Dippers with respect to acidity over a restricted range of calcium and hardness concentrations, the Royal Society for the Protection of Birds conducted a subsequent survey on soft-water streams (7–25g $CaCo_3/m^3$) in mid and north Wales. Dippers were again scarce along such waterways, and breeding pairs were found at only 21 of 74 sites surveyed. Streams without Dippers had significantly lower mean pH and higher aluminium concentrations than those where Dippers were present, whilst total hardnesses were not different (*Table 1*); aluminium concentrations and pH were shown by multiple discriminant analysis to be particularly important variables discriminating between sites with and without breeding pairs (Ormerod *et al.* 1986).

Food availability. Changes in stream pH and the mobilization of aluminium are characteristics of acidified water-courses which detrimentally influence some fish and benthic invertebrates (Hall *et al.* 1980, 1985; Ormerod *et al.* 1987). Moreover, many invertebrate genera (e.g. *Baetis, Ecdyonurus, Hydropsyche, Gammarus*) and some fish are known to be infrequent in European rivers below pH 5.4–5.7 and at aluminium concentrations of over 1.0–1.5g/m³—values beyond which

Table 1: Parameters showing significant differences between sites with and without breeding Dippers on soft-water streams in mid and north Wales. The probability of a significant difference is shown according to appropriate tests (U or t test). (*After:* Ormerod *et al.* 1986.)

	Dippers present		Dippers absent		P
	x̄	S.D.	x̄	S.D.	
% Broad leaved lining	34.9	± 32.3	13.1	± 22.9	0.001
% Catchment afforested	8.4	± 14.8	36.3	± 39.1	0.001
Mean pH	6.37	± 0.37	5.97	± 0.51	0.001
Mean filterable aluminium (g/m³)	0.039	✕ 1.38	0.086	✕ 1.99	0.001
May-fly nymph abundance index	8.49	✕ 5.14	1.80	✕ 3.09	0.01
Caddis larvae abundance index	12.50	✕ 2.76	4.85	✕ 2.71	0.01

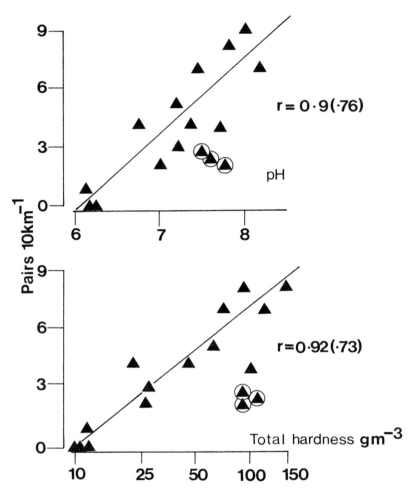

Figure 1: The breeding abundance of Dippers (pairs per 10km) on the upper reaches (nominally 10km) of 17 tributaries in or adjacent to the Wye catchment plotted against (*top*) mean pH and (*bottom*) mean total hardness. The correlation coefficients were calculated including (and excluding) the enclosed values which were from streams of low gradient (Ormerod *et al.* 1985a).

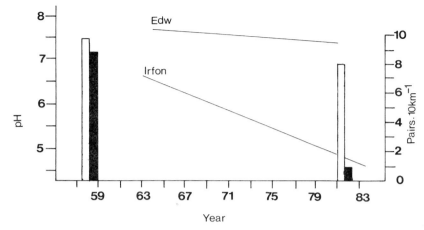

Figure 2:   The breeding abundance of Dippers along the Rivers Edw (open bars) and Irfon (shaded bars) in the mid 1950s and 1982. The regression lines show trends in spot-metred winter pH (Ormerod *et al.* 1985a).

Dippers are also scarce (Sutcliffe & Carrick 1973; Harriman & Morrison 1981; Townsend *et al.* 1983; Stoner *et al.* 1984; Ormerod *et al.* 1986). Consequently, the abundance of breeding Dippers could be related in the Welsh studies to the abundance of two invertebrate groups, may-fly nymphs and caddis larvae (*Figure 3, Table 1*). There were also low densities of salmonid and cottid fishes where birds were absent (Welsh Water Authority, unpubl.). Because both fish and invertebrates are frequently eaten by Dippers, it therefore seemed possible that elevated acidity and aluminium concentrations might have some influence through the food supply. As further evidence, Dippers breeding at low density (i.e. on acidic streams) defended longer territories than birds breeding elsewhere (*Figure 4*). Similar patterns in other species have been related to food availability (e.g. Newton *et al.* 1977, Enoksson & Nilsson 1983).

Dietary studies.   The diets of breeding Dippers and their nestlings were investigated in Wales, northern England, Ireland and southern Norway, and generally similar patterns were apparent in each area (Ormerod 1985a, 1985b; Ormerod & Perry 1985; Ormerod, Efteland & Gabrielsen, in press). In all these cases, the percentage frequency of occurrence of prey correlated closely with percentage contribution by number (see Ormerod 1985a; Ormerod & Tyler 1986), and data are presented here as numerical contributions (see Swanson *et al.* 1974). May-fly nymphs provided most of the items (40–77 percent) eaten by adults, whilst caddis larvae provided most of those eaten by nestlings (37–79 percent, *Table 2*); caddis larvae also dominated nestling diet by weight, although fish were important in two studies (*Table 2*). This pattern has been related to central-place foraging because caddis larvae are usually large items which permit an efficient capture and transfer of energy to the nest (Ormerod 1985b; *Figures 5* and *6*). However, young nestlings have a relatively small energy demand, and adults feed to them mostly small items amongst which the may-fly family Baetidae seems particularly important (*Figures 6* and *7*).

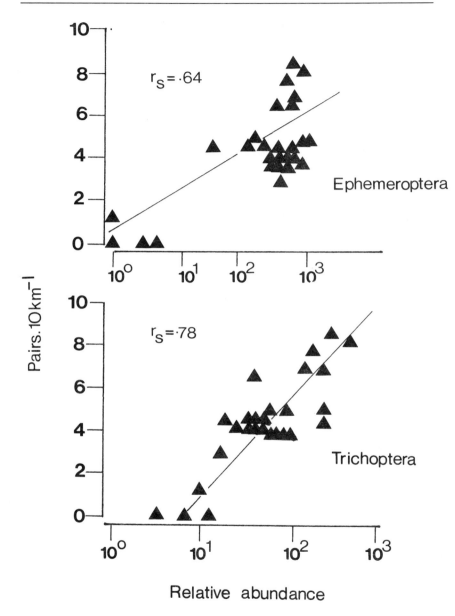

Figure 3:   Relationships between the breeding abundance of Dippers (pairs per 10km) in the Wye catchment and the abundances of (*top*) nymphal may-flies (*bottom*) larval caddis (number per 2 × 3 minute sample, log scale).

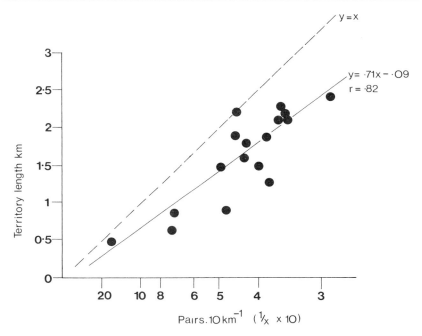

Figure 4: The mean lengths of territories held by 90 pairs of breeding Dippers plotted against abundance (shown as its reciprocal). The dotted line shows the maximum possible territory length at any abundance.

Overall it is apparent that some aquatic taxa which are scarce in acidic waters, and which show a strong relationship with the breeding distribution of Dippers (*Figure 3, Table 1*), are also of clear dietary importance during chick-rearing. Additionally, during winter and the moult, Dippers forage opportunistically on items which are not necessarily scarce in acidic streams (Ormerod & Tyler 1986; Smith & Ormerod 1986). Therefore, it seems likely that stream acidity and prey availability limit Dippers most strongly during the breeding season. Furthermore Dippers were unable to feed nestlings, at any age, as frequently on acidic streams as on circumneutral streams (*Figure 8*).

Breeding performance.   A study of the breeding performance of Dippers has been in progress in the southern catchment of the Welsh River Wye since 1977 (Tyler & Ormerod 1985). In 1985 it was expanded to include sites on acidic streams throughout mid Wales.

Irrespective of influences by altitude, clutch initiation was delayed on acidic streams and early clutches were absent below pH 6.0 (*Figure 9*). Additionally, both mean clutch-size and brood-size were significantly smaller below pH 6.0 than at pH 6.0–8.5 (*Table 3*). Probably because they started breeding later, Dippers on acidic streams seldom attempted second clutches following a successful first. Contrastingly, 19–24 percent of pairs on streams at pH > 6.0 successfully reared two broods per season (*Table 3*).

Table 2: The diets of breeding Dippers and their nestlings shown by studies in north-western Europe. The values are percentage contributions.

Prey-type	Wales[1]		N. England[2]		N. W. Ireland[3]		S.W. Norway[4]	
	Adults	Nestlings	Adults	Nestlings	Adults	Nestlings	Adults	Nestlings
(a) By number								
Ephemeroptera (May-flies)	59.4	34.7	77.0	10.7	61.1	24.3	40.1	44.2
Plecoptera (Stone-flies)	11.0	3.9	3.3	2.1	8.6	2.4	20.5	16.9
Trichoptera (Caddis-flies)	21.6	55.5	9.2	79.2	24.1	73.3	28.6	37.4
Others	6.8	4.6	10.5	3.7	6.4	0.0	10.8	0.8
Fish	1.2	1.3	0.0	4.3	0.0	0.0	0.0	0.0
Total items	814	775	393	140	510	246	652	827
(b) By weight								
Ephemeroptera (May-flies)	18.4	5.7	75.9	1.3	24.6	3.8	7.9	8.4
Plecoptera (Stone-flies)	4.5	0.9	3.4	2.2	10.0	0.9	7.2	6.3
Trichoptera (Caddis-flies)	31.8	68.9	16.2	62.5	63.2	95.3	84.1	85.2
Others	1.4	0.6	4.5	0.1	2.2	0.0	0.8	0.1
Fish	43.7	23.9	0.0	33.9	0.0	0.0	0.0	0.0

Notes: 1. Ormerod 1985a. 2. Ormerod 1985b.
3. Ormerod & Perry 1985. 4. Ormerod Efteland & Gabrielsen (in press).

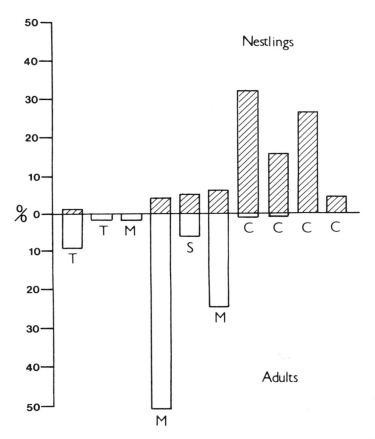

Figure 5:   The percentage contribution by invertebrates to the diets of nestling and adult Dippers at a nest site in northern England (families in increasing order of mean weight). Those marked C are caddis; M = May-flies; S = Stone flies; T = True flies.

Table 3:   The breeding performance of dippers on acidic and circumneutral Welsh streams. The values are means with standard deviation and sample size.

pH range	Clutch size	Brood size	% second clutches
4.5–6.0 (1985)	4.09 (0.83; 11)[a]	3.40 (1.07; 10)[a]	0.0
6.0–8.5 (1985)	4.86 (0.39; 52)[b]	4.16 (0.96; 49)[b]	23.2
7.5–8.5 (1978–85)	4.78 (0.61; 222)[b]	4.13 (1.04; 286)[b]	19.8

Note: Different superscripts (a, b) within clutch and brood size indicate significant differences (Mann-Whitney U-test, *P* < 0.02).

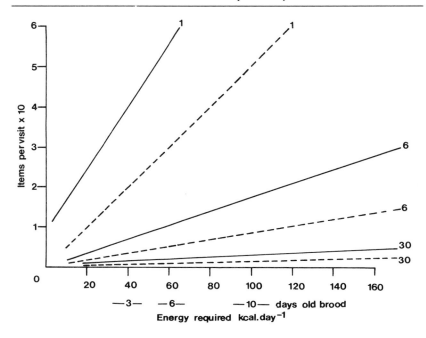

Figure 6: Theoretical values for the number of items required per visit to satisfy given energy requirement for a brood of five Dippers. Alternative models have been suggested for two visit regimes (broken line = 400 visits/day; solid line = 200 visits/day) and for three prey sizes (1, 6, 30mg dry weight).

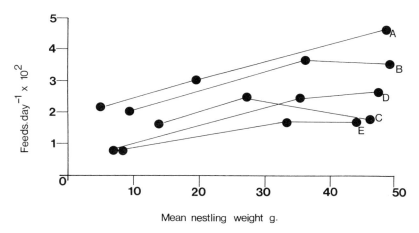

Figure 8: The number of feeds per day brought to Dipper nestlings at three age intervals at two sites on non-acidic streams (A, B) and three on acidic streams (C-E).

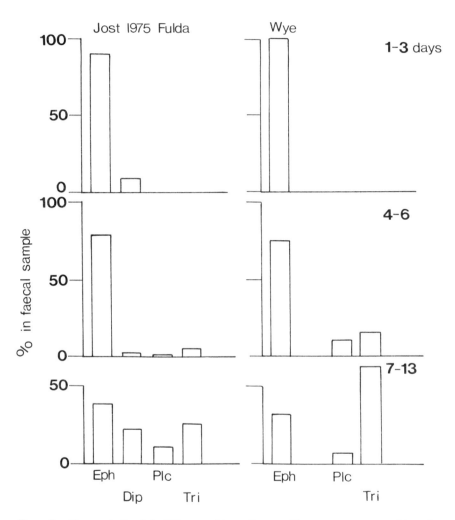

Figure 7: Changes in the diet of Dippers with nestling age. The percentage composition of the diet at each age interval is shown using data from (a) Central Germany (Jost 1975) and (b) Wales (Ormerod 1985a). Eph, May-flies; Plc, Stone flies; Dip, True flies; Tri, Caddis flies.

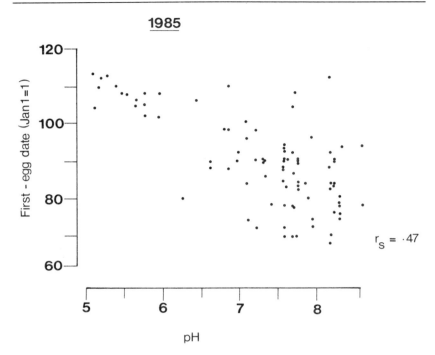

Figure 9:   First-egg dates for Welsh Dippers (excluding known re-lays and second clutches) in relation to mean pH (r = 0.468; *P* < 0.001).

The reasons for these patterns have yet to be described. Possibly, Dippers on acidic streams are limited by lack of food or specific minerals (e.g. Calcium) during egg formation (see Ormerod & Tyler 1986); further research on this aspect is now in progress.

GREY WAGTAILS

General ecology
Outside the breeding season, Grey Wagtails are more migratory than Dippers, with some British birds wintering on mainland Europe (Tyler 1979). A variety of wet habitats is used at this time, although many wintering birds remain alongside rivers (e.g. Tyler & Ormerod 1986).

Breeding Grey Wagtails are strongly associated with running waters, and 95 percent of nests are built along streams, where territories of 0.4km–2.0km are defended (Tyler 1972). Adults forage mostly around water-courses, but also in surrounding habitats, and prey taken include both benthic invertebrates and aerial insects (Schifferli 1972; Ormerod & Tyler, 1987).

Few data are available on factors influencing the abundance of Grey Wagtails. Stream physiography, characteristics of the surrounding habitat, and food availability all seem important (see refs. in Ormerod & Tyler, 1987).

Table 4: Paired comparisons of selected parameters between sites with and without breeding Grey Wagtails on soft-water streams in mid and north Wales. The probability of a significant difference is shown according to appropriate tests (U or t-test). (*After:* Ormerod & Tyler 1985.)

	Grey Wagtails present (45 sites)		Grey Wagtails absent (29 sites)		P
	x̄	S.D.	x̄	S.D.	
Width (m)	3.49 ×	1.69	2.27 ×	1.72	0.01
Riffle area (m²/km)	1059 ×	6.16	229 ×	16.21	0.01
Bank tree-lined (%)	23.6 ±	25.4	9.2 ±	20.5	0.001
Mean pH	6.14 ±	0.52	6.01 ±	0.49	N.S.
Mean filterable aluminium	0.066 ×	2.10	0.074 ×	1.88	N.S.
Invertebrate abundance index	76.21 ×	3.45	76.91 ×	2.97	N.S.

Relationships with stream acidity

Breeding distribution. Two studies in Wales have considered relationships between the distribution of breeding Grey Wagtails and stream chemistry. The RSPB surveyed their abundance on 55 plots (5–10km long) in the catchments of the River Wye and Teifi and found breeding pairs at 75 percent (Ormerod & Tyler, 1987). Although breeding abundance correlated positively with both total hardness and the abundances of some invertebrates, the resulting correlations were weak (*Figure 10*). In a further study, Ormerod & Tyler (1985) recorded Grey Wagtails at 45 percent of 74 survey plots on soft-water streams in mid and north Wales. Neither pH nor aluminium concentrations differed significantly between sites with and without breeding pairs, Grey Wagtails occasionally breeding at pH 4.5 and >0.5g Al/m³ (*Table 4*). Multiple discriminant analysis indicated that stream width, riffle area and the presence of bankside trees were the most important aspect of habitat selection.

Dietary studies. In Britain, dietary studies have been undertaken only in Wales. Preliminary data from the breeding season indicate a similar diet for adults and nestlings, with adult Diptera the most common prey (*Table 5*). The families taken include some of non-riverine origin (e.g. Syrphidae, Ephydridae, Bibionidae)

Table 5: The diets of adult and nestling Grey Wagtails at 16 sites in Wales as shown by faecal analysis. The values are percentage contributions by each order, separated where appropriate in aquatic and aerial stages.

	Adults		Nestlings	
	Aquatic	Aerial	Aquatic	Aerial
Diptera (True flies)	1.8	55.2	0.7	52.5
Plecoptera (Stone-flies)	8.5	7.3	5.9	9.5
Ephemeroptera (May-flies)	7.1	3.9	1.5	8.0
Trichoptera (Caddis-flies)	7.6	1.6	17.0	2.3
Coleoptera (Beetles)	6.2		1.8	
Arachnida (Spiders)	—		0.2	
Total items	384		388	

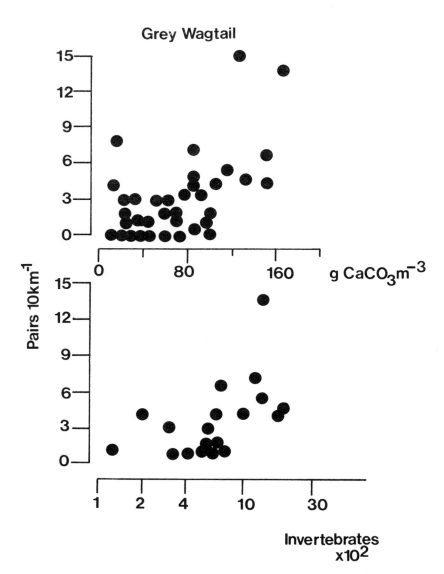

Figure 10:   The breeding abundance of Grey Wagtails in relation to (*top*) total hardness (r = 0.412; *P*, 0.01) (*bottom*) the combined abundances of Caddis larvae, may-fly and stone fly nymphs (r = 0.512; *P*, 0.05) at sites in the Wye and Teifi catchment, Wales.

and it is likely that Grey Wagtails are more flexible than Dippers in foraging away from the river benthos. Such flexibility would explain the limited influence by stream acidity on wagtails which so far seems apparent.

Breeding performance. A long-term study of the breeding biology of Grey Wagtails is currently in progress, and it was expanded in 1985 to include acidic streams (Ormerod & Tyler, 1987). Only altitude and spring temperatures appear to influence laying date, whilst clutch size depends on season (Ormerod & Tyler, 1987). Neither clutch nor brood-size differed between sites above and below pH 6.0 (*Table* 6).

Table 6: The breeding performance of Grey Wagtails on acidic and circumneutral Welsh streams. The values are means with standard deviation and sample size.

pH range	Clutch size	Brood size
4.5–6.0 (1985)	5.11 (0.33; 9)	4.50 (1.03; 16)
6.0–8.5 (1985)	5.04 (0.45; 25)	4.28 (1.34; 21)
7.5–8.5 (1978–85)	5.04 (0.53; 97)	4.48 (0.93; 119)

Because Grey Wagtails occur alongside streams with high aluminium concentrations ($>0.5g \ Al/m^3$) the species has been identified as one in which to examine Nyholm's (1981) hypothesis concerning aluminium and shell-thinning. Studies on this aspect are progressing, although no anomalies in eggs have been detected.

CONCLUSIONS

Dippers, because of their ecology, are highly suitable indicators of stream acidity or acidification. If habitat is suitable (slopes 10–150m/km; >25–30% riffle; >1m wide), their distribution is strongly related to acidity, aluminium concentration and the abundance of some fish and invertebrates. There is also evidence that population changes occur as a response to increasing acidity. Territory length is also indicative of breeding abundance and hence stream chemistry. Measures of breeding performance, including laying date, clutch-size, egg-shell thickness, brood-size and incidence of second clutches are also important potential indicators of effects by acidification.

By contrast, there is less evidence of an influence by acidity on the distribution or breeding performance of Grey Wagtails. Nevertheless, further work is in progress on this species, in particular to test hypotheses concerning influences by aluminium on shell-thickness in passerines.

ACKNOWLEDGEMENTS

We thank the Royal Society for the Protection of Birds, the Central Electricity Generating Board, Welsh Water Authority, the National Environmental Research Council and the University of Wales Institute of Science and Technology for funding various aspects of the work and providing facilities. We owe much to those who helped in the field. We are particularly indebted to the staff of the RSPB Wales Office for administrative help and for typing many manuscripts, including this one. SJO and SJT were respectively funded by the Royal Society and RSPB to attend this conference.

REFERENCES

ALTSHULLER, A. P. & LINTHURST, R. A. 1984. *The acid deposition phenomenon and its effects: critical assessment review papers* Vol. I & II. USEPA, Washington.

BAKUS, G. T. 1959. Territoriality, movements and population density of the Dipper in Montana. *Condor* **61**, 410–25.

BALAT, F. 1962. Distribution and movements of the Dippers (*Cinclus cinclus aquaticus*) Bechst. on a creek and their changes during the year. *Zool. Listy. II, 131–44.*

BEILKE, S. 1983. Origin, transport, conversion and deposition of air pollutants. *In:* Ott, H. & Stangl, H. (eds.) *Acid deposition, a challenge for Europe* pp. 303–20. Proceedings Symp. Karlsruhe, 19–21 September 1983. Commission of the European Communities Brussels.

BROOKER, M. P. 1981. The impact of impoundments on the downstream fisheries and general ecology of rivers. *Adv. Appl. Biol.* **6**, 91–157.

BRYANT, D. M., HAILS, C. J. & PRYS-JONES, R. 1985. Energy expenditure by free-living Dippers (*Cinclus cinclus*) in winter. *Condor* **87**, 177–86.

CAPE, J. N., FOWLER, D., KINNARD, J. W., PATERSON, I. S., LEITH, I. D. & NICHOLSON, I. A. 1984. Chemical composition of rainfall and wet deposition over northern Britain. *Atmos. Environ.* **18**, 1921–32.

CHARLES, D. F. 1985. Relationships between surface sediment diatom assemblage and lakewater characteristics in Adirondack Lakes. *Ecology* **66**, 994–1011.

ENGBLOM, E. & LINGDELL, P. 1984. The mapping of short-term acidification with the help of biological pH indicators. *Rep. Inst. Fresh. Res. Drottningholm* **61**, 60–8.

ENOKSSON, B. & NILSSON, S. G. 1983. Territory size and population density in relation to food supply in the Nuthatch (*Sitta europaea*) Aves. *J. Animal Ecology* **52**, 927–35.

ERIKSSON, M. O. G. 1984. Acidification of Lakes: effects on waterbirds in Sweden. *Ambio* **13**, 260–2.

FOWLER, D., CAPE, J. N., LEITH, I. E., PATTERSON, I. S., KINNAIRD, I. S. & NICHOLSON, I. A. 1982. Rainfall acidity in northern Britain. *Nature, Lond.* **18**, 1859–66.

GOODGE, W. R. 1959. Locomotion and other behaviour of the Dipper. *Condor* **61**, 4–17.

GOODGE, W. R. 1960. Adaptations for amphibious vision in the Dipper (*Cinclus mexicanus*) *J. Morphol.* **107**, 79–91.

GRANAT, L. 1978. Sulphate in precipitation as observed by the European air chemistry network. *Atmos. Environ.* **12**, 413–24.

GREENFIELD, J. P. & IRELAND, M. P. 1978. A survey of the macrofauna of a coal polluted Lancashire fluvial system. *Environ. Pollut.* (**Ser. A**) **16**, 105–22.

HAINES, T. A. 1981. Acid precipitation and its consequences for aquatic eco-systems: a review. *Trans. Am. Fish. Soc.* **110**, 609–707.

HALL, R. J., DRISCOLL, C. T., LIKENS, G. E. & PRATT, J. M. 1985. Physical, chemical and biological consequences of episodic aluminium additions to a stream. *Limnol. Oceanogr.* **30**, 212–20.

HALL, R. J., LIKENS, G. E., FIANCE, S. B. & HENDRY, G. R. 1980. Experimental acidification of a stream in the Hubbard Brook experimental forest, New Hampshire. *Ecology* **61**, 976–89.

HARRIMAN, R. & MORRISON, B. R. S. 1981. Ecology of streams draining forested and non-forested catchments of central Scotland subject to acid precipitation. *Hydrobiologia* **88**, 251–63.

JOST, O. 1975. *Zur okologie der Wasseramsel (Cinclus cinclus) mit besonderer berucksichtigung ernahrung.* Bonner Zoologische Monographien, Nr. 6. Zoologische Forchunginstitut und Museum Alexander Koenig, Bonn.

KAISER, A. 1985. Distribution and situation of the Dipper (*Cinclus cinclus aquaticus*) in Rheinhessen, Rheingau and Eastern Hunsruck. *Okol. Vogel* **7**, 185–96.

KALLEND, A. S., MARSH, A. R. W., PICKLES, J. H. & PROCTOR, M. V. 1983. Acidity of rain in Europe. *Atmos. Environ.* **17**, 127–37.

LACHENMAYER, E., KUNZE, P. & HOLZINGER, J. 1985. Heavy metals in food and eggs of the Dipper (*Cinclus cinclus*) and Grey Wagtail (*Motacilla cinerea*) in the area of Kirchheim, U.T. (SW-Germany). *Okol. Vogel* **7**, 327–51.

MONIG, R. 1985. Dipper's (*Cinclus c. aquaticus*) egg quality as a bio-indicator analysis of residues of chlorinated hydrocarbons (PCBs) in the eggs of birds living on running waters. *Okol. Vogel* **7**, 353–8.

MURRISH, D. E. 1970a. Responses to diving in the Dipper (*Cinclus mexicanus*). *Comp. Biochem. Physiol.* **34**, 853–8.

MURRISH, D. E. 1970b. Responses to temperature in the Dipper (*Cinclus mexicanus*). *Comp. Biochem. Physiol.* **34**, 859–69.

NEWTON, I., MARQUISS, M., WEIR, D. N. & MOSS, D. 1977. Spacing of Sparrowhawk nesting territories. *J. Anim. Ecol.* **46**, 425–41.

NYHOLM, N. E. I. 1981. Evidence of involvement of aluminium in causation of defective formation of eggshells and of impaired breeding in wild passering birds. *Env. Res.* **26**, 363–71.

ORMEROD, S. J. 1985a. The diets of breeding Dippers (*Cinclus cinclus*) and their nestlings in the catchment of the River Wye, mid Wales: a preliminary study by faecal analysis. *Ibis* **127**, 316–31.

ORMEROD, S. J. 1985b. Optimal foraging by breeding Dippers on a Lancashire hill-stream. *Naturalist* **101**, 99–103.

ORMEROD, S. J., ALLINSON, N., HUDSON, D. & TYLER, S. J. 1986. The distribution of breeding Dippers (*Cinclus cinclus* L., Aves) in relation to stream acidity in upland Wales. *Freshwat. Biol.* **16**, 501–9.

ORMEROD, S. J., BOOLE, P., McCAHON, P., WEATHERLEY, N. S., PASCOE, D. & EDWARDS, R. W. (1987). Short-term experimental acidification of a Welsh stream: comparing the biological effects of hydrogen ions and aluminium. *Freshwat. Biol.* **17**, 341–56.

ORMEROD, S. J., BOILSTONE, M. A. & TYLER, S. J. 1985b. Factors influencing the abundance of Dippers (*Cinclus cinclus*) in the catchment of the River Wye, mid Wales. *Ibis* **127**, 332–40.

ORMEROD, S. J. & EDWARDS, R. W. 1985. Stream acidity in some areas of Wales in relation to historical trends in afforestation and the usage of agricultural limestone. *J. Env. Mgmt.* **20**, 189–97.

ORMEROD, S. J., EFTELAND, S. & GABRIELSEN, L. (in press). The diets of breeding Dippers (*Cinclus cinclus*) and their nestlings in southern Norway. *Holarct. Ecol.*

ORMEROD, S. J. & PERRY, K. W. 1985. The diets of breeding Dippers and their nestlings in north-west Ireland. *Irish Birds* **3**, 90–5.

ORMEROD, S. J. & TYLER, S. J. 1985. The distribution of Grey Wagtails in relation to stream acidity in upland Wales: a preliminary survey. *Unpubl. Rept. RSPB Wales Office.*

ORMEROD, S. J. & TYLER, S. J. 1986. The diet of Dippers (*Cinclus cinclus*) wintering in the catchment of the River Wye, Wales. *Bird Study* **33**, 36–45.

ORMEROD, S. J. & TYLER, S. J. (1987). Aspects of the ecology of Welsh Grey Wagtails. *Bird Study,* **34**, 43–51.

ORMEROD, S. J., TYLER, S. J. & LEWIS, J. U. S. 1985a. Is the breeding distribution of Dippers influenced by stream acidity? *Bird Study* **32**, 33–9.

OTTAR, B. 1983. Air pollution, emission and ambient concentrations. *In:* Ott, H. & Stangl, H. (eds.) *Acid deposition, a challenge for Europe.* Proceedings SYMP. Karlsruhe, 19–21 September 1983. Commission of the European Communities, Brussels.

OVERREIN, L. N., SEIP, H. M. & TOLLAN, A. 1980. *Acid precipitation—effects on forests and fish.* SNSF project, final report. Oslo—As, Norway.

PACES, T. 1985. Sources of acidification in central Europe estimated from elemental budgets in small basins. *Nature Lond.* **315**, 31–6.

PENNINGTON, W. 1984. Long-term natural acidification of upland sites in Cumbria: evidence from post-glacial lake sediments. *Ann. Rep. Freshwat. Biol. Assn.* **52**, 28–46.

PRICE, F. E. & BOCK, C. C. 1983. *Population ecology of the Dipper (Cinclus mexicanus) in the Front Range of Colorado.* Studies in Avian Biology, 7, Cooper Ornithological Society, Kansas.

SCHIFFERLI, L. 1972. Futteringsfrequenz am nest der Bergstelze (*M. cinerea*) in Verschieden Biotopen und Brutmoraten. *Der. Orn. Beob.* **69**, 257–74.

SCULLION, J. & EDWARDS, R. W. 1980. The effect of coal industry pollutants on the macroinvertebrate fauna of a small river in the south Wales coalfield. *Freshwat. Biol.* **10**, 141–62.

SHARROCK, J. T. R. 1976. *The atlas of breeding birds of Britain and Ireland.* British Trust for Ornithology, Tring.

SMITH, R. P. & ORMEROD, S. J. 1986. The diet of moulting Dippers (*Cinclus cinclus*) in the catchment of the Welsh River Wye. *Bird Study* 33, 138–9.

SPITZNAGEL, A. 1985. Seasonal variation in food supply and food choice of the Dipper (*Cinclus c. aquaticus*). *Okol. Vogel* 7, 239–325.

STONER, J. H., GEE, A. S. & WADE, K. R. 1984. The effect of acidification on the ecology of streams in the upper Tywi catchment in west Wales. *Environ. Pollut. (Ser. A.)* 35, 125–57.

SUTCLIFFE, D. W. & CARRICK, T. R. 1973. Studies on mountain streams in the English Lake District. I. pH, calcium and the distribution of invertebrates in the River Duddon. *Freshwat. Biol.* 3, 437–62.

SUTCLIFFE, D. W., CARRICK, T. R., HERON, J., RIGG, E., TALLING, J. F., WOOF, C. & LUND, J. W. G. 1982. Long term and seasonal changes in the chemical composition of precipitation and surface-waters of lakes and tarns in English Lake District. *Freshwat. Biol.* 12, 451–506.

SWANSON, G. A. *et al.* 1974. Advantages in mathematically weighting waterfowl food habits data. *J. Wildlife Mgmt.* 38, 302–7.

TOWNSEND, C. R., HILDREW, A. G. & FRANCIS, J. 1983. Community structure in some southern English streams: the influence of physiochemical factors. *Freshwat. Biol.* 13, 521–44.

TYLER, S. J. 1970. Observations of the Grey Wagtail in the New Forest. *Hampshire Bird Rept.* 1969, 37–40.

TYLER, S. J. 1972. Breeding biology of the Grey Wagtail. *Bird Study* 19, 69–80.

TYLER, S. J. 1979. Mortality and movements of Grey Wagtails. *Ring. Migr.* 2, 122–31.

TYLER, S. J. & ORMEROD, S. J. 1985. Aspects of the breeding biology of Dippers (*Cinclus cinclus*) in the southern catchment of the River Wye, Wales. *Bird Study* 32, 164–9.

TYLER, S. J. & ORMEROD, S. J. 1986. Interactions between resident and migratory wagtails (*Motacilla*) spp. in Ethiopia—an ecological conundrum. *Scopus.* 10, 10–19.

ZIEMANN, H. 1975. On the influence of hydrogen ion concentration and the bicarbonate concentrations on the structure of and biocoenoses of mountain brooks. *Int. Rev. Ges. Hydrobiol.* 60, 523–55.

COLONIAL WATERBIRDS AS BIO-INDICATORS OF ENVIRONMENTAL CONTAMINATION IN THE GREAT LAKES

GLEN A. FOX[1] & D. V. WESELOH[2]

1   Canadian Wildlife Service, National Wildlife Research Centre,
     Environment Canada, Ottawa, Ontario, K1A 0H3, Canada
2   Canadian Wildlife Service, Ontario Region, Canada Centre for
     Inland Waters, Environment Canada, Box 5050, Burlington,
     Ontario, L7R 4A6, Canada

ABSTRACT

We have found the eggs of colonial waterbirds to be a convenient medium in which to monitor temporal and spatial trends in environmental contaminant levels in the Great Lakes. A monitoring programme, using Herring Gull (Larus argentatus) eggs, was established in 1973 to support the Canada-United States Agreement on Great Lakes Water Quality. This programme has allowed managers to assess the effects of remedial measures and has been responsible for the identification of dioxins and many other important microcontaminants within the Great Lakes ecosystem.

Since fish-eating birds and man share a common food resource, environmental factors affecting the welfare of populations of these birds have the potential for impact on the welfare of man. We have used these colonial birds as convenient model populations in which to study the impact of chronic exposure to complex mixtures of persistent lipophilic environmental contaminants. We have studied eggshell thinning, embryotoxicity, teratogenicity, genotoxicity, behavioural toxicity and demography in one or more species in the Great Lakes basin. We believe such manifestations of target organ toxicity as thyroid hyperplasia, hepatic porphyria, and mixed function oxidase induction show promise as health effects monitors for the Great Lakes ecosystem.

INTRODUCTION

The Great Lakes of North America represent 20 percent of the world's freshwater resources. The human population of the Great Lakes basin represents 1/6th of the combined population of the United States and Canada, the majority of whom depend on the lakes for their drinking water and waste disposal (Shear 1984). The Great Lakes supported commercial and sport fisheries with an approximate combined value of US$400 million as recently as 1980 (IJC Facts Sheets). The influx of wastes from municipal, industrial, and agricultural sources has adversely affected both the quality of the lakes and their fishery resources. It is estimated that 30,000 man-made chemicals are in use in the Great Lakes basin, and more than 1000 different industrially-produced chemicals have been measured in the Great Lakes ecosystem (Nriagu & Simmons 1984). Some of these chemicals are suspected of causing adverse health effects in fish-eating birds and other terminal members of the food chain. The bioaccumulation of contaminants, and associated adverse health effects in colonial fish-eating birds, have been of key importance in the identification of toxic levels of contaminants, and in monitoring the effectiveness of remedial measures taken to reduce this contamination.

Here we review the major findings of studies of these birds in the Great Lakes, as they relate to environmental contamination, and illustrate the value of related ecological, biochemical and physiological studies as surveillance tools.

TOXIC CONTAMINATION vs EUTROPHICATION

The problem of eutrophication was the focus of Great Lakes water quality research and remedial actions in the 1960s. However, the publication of Rachael Carson's *Silent Spring* in 1962 resulted in an increased public awareness of the potential biological hazards of pesticides to non-target organisms. The investigations of DDT contamination in the Lake Michigan food chain, and its impact on reproduction of Herring Gulls (*Larus argentatus*) (Hickey *et al.* 1966; Keith 1966; Ludwig & Tomoff 1966) opened a new chapter in the history of the Great Lakes, and initiated a shift in the research and remedial focus from nutrient enrichment to toxic contamination. Observations of thinning of Herring Gull eggshells in the Pigeon Island colony in eastern Lake Ontario (Edwards 1970) and of hatching failure and deformed chicks in colonies of Common Terns (*Sterna hirundo*) in Hamilton Harbour in 1970 (Gilbertson 1975) focused early Canadian investigations on toxic contamination in Lake Ontario.

EGGS AS A MONITORING MEDIUM

The high lipid content of the avian egg (7–10 percent) makes it a good medium in which to measure lipid-soluble environmental contaminants. Eggs are easy to collect, store, and process. Norstrom *et al.* (1978) found that DDE and PCBs were bioconcentrated in Herring Gull eggs 2.5×10^7 times the ambient concentration in Lake Ontario water; approximately 20 times more than in salmon tissues. A study initiated by Gilbertson in 1973 (Gilbertson 1974) resulted in the adoption of the Herring Gull egg as a monitoring medium for surveillance purposes by the International Joint Commission on Great Lakes Water Quality. The reasons for selecting the Herring Gull were:

1. Its diet in the Great Lakes consists primarily of fish.
2. Breeding adults are year-round residents in the Great Lakes, with comparatively little movement between lakes.
3. It nests colonially, so it is easy to collect eggs, census, and study.
4. It breeds in all of the lakes, and has a holarctic distribution allowing comparisons with coastal and European populations. Its biology has been extensively studied.

Two colonies were selected in each lake to detect geographical variation, and ten eggs have been collected from ten randomly selected clutches in each of these colonies each year.

Herring Gull eggs have been shown to be a useful medium in which to monitor both spatial and temporal variation in mercury and organohalogen contaminant levels (Mineau *et al.* 1984). The average population half-lives for the various contaminants in the various lakes have been calculated for the period 1974–79 and range from 10 years for PCBs in western L. Erie to 1.4 years for DDT in eastern

L. Ontario and L. Superior. The levels of most contaminants have declined markedly from 1974 to 1979. Recently, these declines seem to have bottomed out and some residues have increased (Mineau *et al.* 1984). This information has allowed managers to assess remedial measures taken to reduce contamination.

Extensive and ultra-sensitive qualitative analysis of the lipid extracts of these eggs has revealed lower chlorinated benzenes, chlorinated styrenes, polyaromatic hydrocarbons, polychlorinated terphenyls, polychlorinated dibenzofurans and dibenzodioxins including TCDD. In this way, in addition to serving as a monitor of distribution and abundance, the gull eggs serve as a medium for the detection of new contaminants in the Great Lakes food chain.

Norstrom *et al.* (1986) determined the energetic requirements and body constituents of Great Lakes Herring Gulls and have produced a bioenergetics-based computer model of the chemobiodynamics of organochlorine pollutants in Herring Gulls (Clark *et al.* 1987). This model will allow the prediction of residue trends in eggs in response to a variety of biological and remedial scenarios.

FISH-EATING BIRDS AS HEALTH EFFECTS INDICATORS

As mentioned in the previous section, colonial fish-eating birds bioconcentrate lipophilic pollutants. This, coupled with their longevity, makes them convenient organisms at risk in which to study the chronic toxicity of lipophilic contaminants in a free-living terminal member of the Great Lakes food chain.

Eggshell thinning
Severe eggshell thinning was associated with the population declines and reproductive failures observed in Double-crested Cormorants (*Phalacrocorax auritus*) in the Great Lakes (Postupalsky 1978). Declines in numbers of breeding cormorants in Lake Michigan were first noted in the early 1950s, and the last nesting was reported in 1962 (Anderson & Hamerstrom 1967). By the early 1970s this species had ceased to breed on Lakes Superior and Michigan, and in the Ontario waters of Lake Ontario, and had suffered an overall decline within the Great Lakes basin of approximately 80 percent (Postupalsky 1978). Studies of the Lake Huron population in 1972 suggested that only 8 of 331 eggs had shells thick enough to survive to hatching (Weseloh *et al.* 1983). Eggshells were 30 percent thinner than normal and 79 percent of the eggs were broken or disappeared within eight days of laying. Since the late 1970s eggshell thickness has increased in response to markedly declining DDE levels (Weseloh *et al.* 1980). This has been accompanied by an expansion of the breeding population which has been increasing rapidly and experiencing normal reproductive success (Scharf & Shugart 1981; Ludwig 1985; Price & Weseloh 1986).

The population of Black-crowned Night Herons (*Nycticorax nycticorax*) nesting on Pigeon Island declined by 80 percent during the 1960s. Price's study (1976) of this colony in the mid-1970s revealed that eggshells were 12–17 percent thinner than normal and that productivity was well below that suggested by Henny (1972) to be necessary to maintain the population.

Demographic considerations
Our observations suggest that the current annual growth rate of cormorant breeding populations in the Great Lakes is approximately 50 percent and that Herring Gull numbers in Lake Ontario colonies are currently equal to or exceed those recorded prior to the period in which they experienced reproductive failure.

This suggests that breeding cormorant and Herring Gull populations can recover rapidly once contaminant concentrations in the food chain fall below toxic levels.

An abnormally high incidence of supernormal clutches (resulting from female-female pairing) was observed in Herring Gull nests in Lakes Ontario (Fox *et al.* unpub.) and Michigan (Shugart 1980) in the late 1970s. In Lake Ontario, supernormal clutches were most prevalent in 1977, declining rapidly over the next four years. Since Herring Gulls usually do not breed until they are at least four years of age, the period during which female-female pairing was observed would correspond with the period in which cohorts hatching in the late 1960s and early 1970s would be expected to be recruiting into the colonies. Fry & Toone (1981) presented histological and anatomical evidence that environmentally relevant concentrations of DDT and its estrogenic isomers induce feminization of male embryos when injected into gull eggs. Fry examined 17 formalin-preserved near-term embryos and newly hatched chicks collected from Lake Ontario colonies in 1975 and 1976. Five (71 percent) of the seven males were significantly feminized and five of the ten females had abnormally enlarged oviducts. Since DDE and related residues in eggs collected in 1975/76 were one-half those found in eggs collected in 1971, it is possible that the majority of male embryos were feminized during the period of peak DDT contamination in Lakes Ontario and Michigan. If the majority of males in these numerically weak cohorts were feminized and incapable of reproducing, then the operational sex ratio in these colonies in the late 1970s was very likely seriously skewed towards females.

Embryotoxicity and behavioural toxicity

Studies of Herring Gull reproduction in Lake Michigan in the mid-1960s suggested that environmental contaminants influence hatching success via intrinsic (embryotoxic) and extrinsic (adult behavioural) mechanisms (Keith 1966). Similarly, studies of Herring Gull colonies in the eastern basin of Lake Ontario in the early 1970s suggested that reproductive success was five to ten percent of normal and that this was primarily due to embryonic death and egg disappearance (Gilbertson 1974; Gilbertson & Hale 1974). Artificial incubation of eggs collected in Lake Ontario colonies and colonies from outside the Great Lakes, clearly demonstrated that an embryotoxic factor(s) was present in the Lake Ontario eggs (Gilbertson & Fox 1977 and 1983). Subcutaneous edema, enlarged liver, impaired growth and congenital malformations were present in hatchlings from the Lake Ontario eggs. Egg exchanges between nests in Lake Ontario colonies and relatively uncontaminated colonies resulted in differential hatching rates and implicated both intrinsic and extrinsic factors. 'Clean' adults were unable to hatch 'dirty' eggs and 'dirty' adults were unable to hatch 'clean' eggs (Peakall *et al.* 1980). Detailed comparisons of incubation behaviour of Lake Ontario gulls with that of a successful coastal colony, using telemetered eggs, revealed that the Lake Ontario gulls applied less heat and were less attentive (Fox *et al.* 1978). The increased absences of adults from the Lake Ontario nests were thought to account for the increased egg disappearances observed. The total organochlorine content of eggs from Lake Ontario nests was positively correlated with the total time the eggs were unattended.

When eggs from an unsuccessful colony of Forster's Terns (*Sterna forsteri*) in Green Bay, Lake Michigan, and a successful inland colony were artificially incubated, the hatching success of eggs from the Green Bay colony was 52 percent of that of eggs from the inland colony (Hoffman *et al.* 1987). Egg exchanges indicated that both intrinsic and extrinsic factors were contributing (Kubiak *et al.* 1987). The mean minimum incubation period of 'dirty' eggs was 8.25 days longer than that of 'clean' eggs, and many eggs in 'dirty' nests were abandoned. The residue content of eggs from the Green Bay colony was markedly higher than those from the inland colony. Embryos from eggs collected from the Green Bay colony weighed less, had an increased liver to body weight ratio and shorter femurs than those from the inland colony. Several were malformed (Hoffman *et al.* 1987).

Genotoxicity

Sister chromatid exchange (SCE) rates were determined in seven-day embryos of Herring Gulls collected in 1981 from five colonies in the Great Lakes and a 'clean' Atlantic coast colony (Ellenton & McPherson 1983). No significant differences could be detected in the number of SCE/chromosome in embryos from these colonies. Extracts of eggs from the same nests did not induce point mutations in the Salmonella/mammalian microsome assay (Ames Test) or contaminant-related variation in the number of chromosome aberrations in Chinese hamster ovary cells (Ellenton *et al.* 1983). To our knowledge this is the only study in which the genotoxic potential of bioaccumulated contaminants in local food chains of the Great Lakes has been examined.

Teratogenicity

We have established a registry of congenital anomalies in fish-eating colonial birds as a biological monitor for teratogens in the food chains of the Great Lakes (Fox 1982). Congenital malformations have been observed in chicks of Herring Gulls, Ring-billed Gulls (*Larus delawarensis*), Common Terns, Caspian Terns (*Hydroprogne caspia*), Forster's Terns, Black-crowned Night Herons, and Double-crested Cormorants in one or more of the lakes between 1971 and 1985 (Gilbertson 1975; Gilbertson *et al.* 1976; Kubiak *et al.* 1987). They occurred most frequently and in the most species in Lake Ontario during the early 1970s. The species-specific prevalence in Lake Ontario increased 25 to 100 times that encountered by banders and researchers working in colonies located outside the Great Lakes (Fox 1982; Gilbertson & Fox 1983). Recently the prevalence of deformities in cormorants in Lake Michigan was markedly elevated and became the subject of considerable concern (Hill & Hoffman 1984; Weseloh *et al.* 1985). The prevalence of gross congenital anomalies in colonial fish-eating birds, particularly terns and cormorants, is a sensitive surveillance tool for detecting biologically significant concentrations of teratogens in Great Lakes food chains.

Target organ toxicity

Adult Herring Gulls nesting in colonies on the Great Lakes, like the introduced Pacific Salmon, suffer from goitre (Moccia *et al.* 1986). The severity of the goitre in salmon and gulls is similar and consistent with a forage fish-borne etiological agent. Spatial and temporal variation in the severity of the goiter in gulls varies with their contaminant burden.

Hepatic aryl hydrocarbon hydroxylase (AHH) levels in 25-day Herring Gull embryos from five Great Lakes colonies in 1981 were significantly correlated with the concentration of 2,3,7,8-tetrachlorodibenzo-p-dioxin (TCDD), but not DDE or PCBs, present in eggs from these colonies (Ellenton *et al.* 1985). Hoffman *et al.* (1987) found elevated AHH levels in hatchling Forster's Terns from Green Bay, Lake Michigan, and in Common Tern and Black-crowned Night Heron embryos from Green Bay and Saginaw Bay (Lake Huron). The activities of other mixed function oxidases were assayed in livers of artifically incubated Herring Gull embryos collected from a variety of sites within the Great Lakes in 1982 (Boersma *et al.* 1986). Activities varied spatially but there was no clear association with any specific chemical. Mixed function oxidase induction is an adaptive response to exposure to xenobiotics (man-made chemicals) and is not chemical-specific.

We have measured the concentrations of highly carboxylated porphyrins (HCPs) in the livers of adult Herring Gulls collected on colonies situated throughout the Great Lakes and compared them to those in livers of gulls from the Atlantic Coast (Kennedy *et al.* unpub.). Median levels of HCPs in the livers of Great Lakes gulls were 2 to 38 times higher than the coastal median. The spatial pattern reflected the degree of polyhalogenated aromatic hydrocarbon contamination of the local food chain; the highest elevation occurred in gulls from lower Green Bay, Saginaw Bay, and Lake Ontario. Porphyria represents a toxicant-induced derangement of heme biosynthesis which could serve as a sensitive and specific biochemical endpoint for monitoring levels of a specific suite of environmental contaminants. The occurrence of hepatic porphyria in local populations of Great Lakes Herring Gulls is an indication that concentrations of some contaminants in local food chains are currently sufficient to produce a toxic biochemical response in an organism dependent upon this food chain.

CONCLUSION

In his discussion of the value and strategy underlying ecological monitoring, Gray (1980) suggested that such monitoring should be based on a few species, and that ecological endpoints relevant to the population should be studied in conjunction with a suite of biochemical and physiological techniques. The physiological and biochemical approaches predict effects on populations. Ecological monitoring tests whether these predictions are correct, and provides a measure of the hazard to the population under study.

Our integrated studies of colonial fish-eating birds in the Great Lakes are currently based on such a strategy and have taught us much about the potential impact of chronic exposure of bird populations to complex mixtures of persistent environmental contaminants. The value of this programme as a general surveillance tool is recognized by the International Joint Commission on the Great Lakes, which has incorporated several aspects into its annual monitoring programme under the Canada-United States Agreement on Great Lakes Water Quality.

Like Hill and Hoffman (1984) we have found birds to be 'invaluable models for environmental toxicology'. Since fish-eating birds and man share a common food resource, environmental factors affecting the welfare of populations of these birds have potential for impact on the welfare of man.

REFERENCES

ANDERSON, D. W. & HAMERSTROM, F. 1967. The recent status of Wisconsin Cormorants. *Passenger Pigeon* 29, 3–15.

BOERSMA, D. C., ELLENTON, J. A. & YAGMINAS, A. 1986. Investigation of the hepatic mixed-function oxidase system in Herring Gull embryos in relation to environmental contaminants. *Environ. Toxicol. Chem.* 5, 309–18.

CLARK, T. P., NORSTROM, R. J., FOX, G. A. & WON, H. T. 1987. Dynamics of organochlorines in Herring Gulls (*Larus argentatus*): II A two compartment model and data for ten compounds. *Environ. Toxicol. Chem.* 6, 547–59.

EDWARDS, M. 1970. 43. Uninhabited island in Lake Ontario. *Audubon Field Notes* 24, 767–8.

ELLENTON, J. A., BROWNLEE, L. J. & HOLLEBONE, B. R. 1985. Aryl hydrocarbon hydroxylase levels in the herring gull embryos from different locations on the Great Lakes. *Environ. Toxicol. Chem.* **4**, 615–22.

ELLENTON, J. A. & McPHERSON, M. F. 1983. Mutagenicity studies on herring gulls from different locations on the Great Lakes. I. Sister chromatid exchange rates in herring gull embryos. *J. Toxicol. Environ. Health,* **12**, 317–24.

ELLENTON, J. A., McPHERSON, M. F. & MAUS, K. L. 1983. Mutagenicity studies on herring gulls from different colonies on the Great Lakes. II. Mutagenic evaluation of extracts of herring gull eggs in a battery of in vitro mammalian and microbial tests. *J. Toxicol. Environ. Health* **12**, 325–36.

FOX, G. A. 1982. Congenital anomalies in colonial fish-eating birds: A monitor for environmental teratogens. *Am. Public Health Assoc. Meeting,* Montreal. November 17, 1982.

FOX, G. A., GILMAN, A. P., PEAKALL, D. B. & ANDERKA, F. W. 1978. Behavioral abnormalities of nesting Lake Ontario herring gulls. *J. Wildl. Manage.* **42**, 477–83.

FRY, D. M. & TOONE, C. K. 1981. DDT-induced feminization of gull embryos. *Science* **213**, 922–4.

GILBERTSON, M. 1974. Pollutants in breeding herring gulls in the lower Great Lakes. *Can. Field-Naturalist* **86**, 273–80.

GILBERTSON, M. 1975. A Great Lakes tragedy. *Nature Canada* **4**, 22–25.

GILBERTSON, M. & FOX, G. A. 1977. Pollutant-associated embryonic mortality of Great Lakes herring gulls. *Environ. Pollut.* **12**, 211–16.

GILBERTSON, M. & FOX, G. A. 1983. Chick edema disease and hepatic porphyria in Lake Ontario Herring Gull embryos in the early 1970s. Pp. 341–356 *In:* Tucker, R. E., Young, A. L. & Gray, A. P. (eds.) *Human and environmental risks of chlorinated dioxins and related compounds.* Plenum Press, New York.

GILBERTSON, M. & HALE, R. 1974. Early embryonic mortality in a herring gull colony in Lake Ontario. *Can. Field-Naturalist* **88**, 354–58.

GILBERTSON, M., MORRIS, R. D. & HUNTER, R. A. 1976. Abnormal chicks and PCB residue levels in eggs of colonial birds in the lower Great Lakes (1971–73). *Auk* **93**, 434–42.

GRAY, J. S. 1980. Why do ecological monitoring? *Marine Pollution Bull.* **11**, 62–5.

HENNY, C. J. 1972. An analysis of the population dynamics of selected avian species, with special reference to changes during the modern pesticide era. *Wildlife Res. Rpt. 1*, U.S. Fish and Wildl. Serv., Bur. Sport Fish. Wildl. 99 pp.

HICKEY, J. J., KEITH, J. A. & COON, F. B. 1966. An exploration of pesticides in a Lake Michigan ecosystem. *J. Appl. Ecol.* **3** (Suppl), 141–54.

HILL, E. F. & HOFFMAN, D. J. 1984. Avian models for toxicity testing. *J. Am. Coll. Toxicol.* **3**, 357–76.

HOFFMAN, D. J., RATTNER, B. A., SILEO, L., DOCHERTY, D. & KUBIAK, T. J. 1987. Embryotoxicity, teratogenicity, and aryl hydrocarbon hydroxylase activity in Forster's Terns on Green Bay, Lake Michigan. *Environ. Res.* **42**, 176–84.

KEITH, J. A. 1966. Reproduction in a population of herring gulls (*Larus argentatus*) contaminated by DDT. *J. Appl. Ecol.* **3** (Suppl), 57–70.

KUBIAK, T. J., HARRIS, H. J., SMITH, L. M., STALLING, D. L., SCHWARTZ, T. R., TRICK, J. A., SILEO, L., DOCHERTY, D. E. & ERDMAN, T. C. 1987. Microcontaminants and reproductive impairment of the Forster's Tern on Green Bay, Lake Michigan—1983. *Arch. Environ. Contam. Toxicol. (in press).*

LUDWIG, J. P. 1985. Decline, resurgence and population dynamics of Michigan and Great Lakes Double-crested Cormorants. *Jack-pine Warbler* **62**, 91–102.

LUDWIG, J. P. & TOMOFF, C. S. 1966. Reproductive success and insecticide residue levels in Lake Michigan herring gulls. *Jack-pine Warbler* **44**, 77–85.

MINEAU, P., FOX, G. A., NORSTROM, R. J., WESELOH, D. V., HALLETT, D. J. & ELLENTON, J. A. 1984. Using the herring gull to monitor levels and effects of organochlorine contamination in the Canadian Great Lakes. Pp. 426–452 *In:* Nriagu, J. O. & Simmons, M. S. (eds.) *Toxic contaminants in the Great Lakes.* J. Wiley and Sons, New York.

MOCCIA, R. D., FOX, G. A. & BRITTON, A. 1986. A quantitative assessment of thyroid histopathology of herring gulls (*Larus argentatus*) from the Great Lakes and a hypothesis on the causal role of environmental contaminants. *J. Wildl. Diseases* **22**, 60–70.

NORSTROM, R. J., CLARK, T. P., KEARNEY, J. P. & GILMAN, A. P. 1986. Herring gull energy requirements and body constituents in the Great Lakes. *Ardea* **74**, 1–23.

NORSTROM, R. J., HALLETT, D. J. & SONSTEGARD, R. A. 1978. Coho salmon (*Oncorhynchus kisutch*) and herring gulls (*Larus argentatus*) as indicators of organochlorine contamination in Lake Ontario. *J. Fish. Res. Board Can.* **35**, 1401–09.

NRIAGU, J. O. & SIMMONS, M. S. 1984. Preface, pp. ix-x *In:* Nriagu, J. O. & Simmons, M. S. (eds.) *Toxic Contaminants in the Great Lakes.* J. Wiley and Sons, New York.

PEAKALL, D. B., FOX, G. A., GILMAN, A. P., HALLETT, D. J. & NORSTROM, R. J. 1980. The herring gull as a monitor of Great Lakes contamination. *In:* Afghan, B. K. & MacKay, D. (eds.) *Hydrocarbons and halogenated hydrocarbons in the aquatic environment.* 337–44. Plenum Press, New York.

POSTUPALSKY, S. 1978. Toxic chemicals and cormorant populations in the Great Lakes. *Wildlife Toxicology Division, C.W.S. Manuscript Report* **49**, 25 pp.

PRICE, I. 1976. Black-crowned night herons on Pigeon Island, Lake Ontario. *In: Proc. Fish-eating Birds of the Great Lakes and Environmental Contaminants:* 248–74, Ottawa, 1976.

PRICE, I. M. & WESELOH, D. V. 1986. Increased numbers and productivity of Double-crested Cormorants, *Phalacrocorax auritus,* on Lake Ontario. *Can. Field-Nat.* **100**, 474–82.

SCHARF, W. C. & SHUGART, G. W. 1981. Recent increases in Double-crested Cormorants in the United States Great Lakes. *American Birds* **35**, 910–11.

SHEAR, H. 1984. Contaminants research and surveillance—a biological approach. Pp. 31–51 *In:* Nriagu, J. O. & Simmons, M. S. (eds.) *Toxic contaminants in the Great Lakes.* J. Wiley and Sons, New York.

SHUGART, G. W. 1980. Frequency and distribution of polygyny in Great Lakes herring gulls in 1978. *Condor* **82**, 426–29.

WESELOH, D. V., MINEAU, P., TEEPLE, S. M. MCKEATING, G. B. & POSTUPALSKY, S. 1980. Improvement of quality of life parameters of Double-crested cormorants in Canadian waters of the Great Lakes. *Pacific Seabird Group Bull.* **7**, 56.

WESELOH, D. V., STRUGER, J. & KUBIAK, T. J. 1985. The occurrence of congenital anomalies in Double-crested Cormorants and Herring Gulls in the Great Lakes; 1983–84. *Abstracts of the 28th Conf. on Great Lakes Research,* Milwaukee, Wisconsin. P. 66.

WESELOH, D. V., TEEPLE, S. M. & GILBERTSON, M. 1983. Double-crested cormorants of the Great Lakes: Egg-laying parameters, reproductive failure, and contaminant residues in eggs, Lake Huron 1972–1973. *Can. J. Zool.* **61**, 427–36.

SEABIRDS AS MONITORS OF THE MARINE ENVIRONMENT

ROBERT W. FURNESS

Applied Ornithology Unit, Department of Zoology, University of Glasgow, Glasgow G12 8QQ, Scotland

ABSTRACT

Seabirds are large, conspicuous, easily studied members of the upper trophic levels of marine ecosystems. As such they can fulfil a valuable monitoring role to complement studies at other levels of the ecosystem. Although their value in providing indices of fish stock dynamics or behaviour has yet to be assessed in detail, several studies of seabird ecology have found that seabird diets, breeding numbers or breeding success can be used to obtain information on fish stocks, or on the behaviour of fisheries.

Sampling eggs or tissues of seabirds can allow monitoring of levels of organochlorines and heavy metals in marine environments, and analysis of feathers can provide a tool for retrospective monitoring of heavy metal levels in marine ecosystems over the past 150 years. Some limitations of monitoring using seabirds are discussed.

Seabirds can also be used to examine levels of oil and plastic pollution, and may be of use in studies of radionuclides discharged into the sea. A growing awareness of global pollution problems, and concern for human health and wildlife, provides a strong incentive for the development of carefully planned pollutant monitoring programmes, in which seabirds can provide information unobtainable from other sources.

INTRODUCTION

The world's seas and oceans are used as sinks for many of man's waste products and for substances lost or discharged by accident. The enormous volume of water into which these wastes are discharged results in rapid dilution so that oceans have often been considered a cheap and safe site for disposal. In general, marine pollution problems are most often detected in small seas with little water exchange (e.g. the Mediterranean, Baltic and Irish Seas), and in estuaries or coastal areas close to industrial or urban sources of pollution.

Many marine organisms are capable of accumulating substances in their tissues to concentrations many orders of magnitude greater than those found in seawater; consequently, assumptions that pollutants are harmlessly diluted are not always valid. For example, seaweeds and marine invertebrates may concentrate some metals by factors of 10,000 to 100,000 times the levels found in seawater (Bryan 1984). Further increases in concentration can occur as a result of biomagnification, with animals higher up the food chain accumulating higher concentrations than those found in their prey. Although this is not necessarily always the case, top predators can be exposed to very high levels of pollutants. Certainly they contain much higher levels than those present in seawater. Thus seabirds may provide a tool for monitoring pollutant levels in marine ecosystems and can provide information on pollutant accumulation within food chains.

Since seabirds are large, conspicuous, easily studied organisms they can also be used to provide an indication of changes that take place in lower trophic levels. Hence they may provide indications of changes in fish stocks that complement results from conventional surveys by fishery research vessels or from analysis of fishery catch data.

In this review I shall consider the uses of seabirds to monitor changes in fish stocks and fisheries, and to monitor levels of pollution due to organochlorines, heavy metals, radionuclides, oil and plastics.

FISH STOCKS

The idea that seabird diets or breeding may provide a useful indication of the state of fish stocks has only recently led to studies aimed directly at testing this possibility. At present it is not known how useful an approach this might be, but several observations suggest that it is worthy of consideration.

South African Anchovies (*Engraulis capensis*) occur in closed (concentrated) or open (dispersed) shoals. Only closed shoals are commercially exploitable. While Jackass Penguins (*Spheniscus demersus*) prey mainly on open shoals, Cape Cormorants (*Phalacrocorax capensis*) prey primarily on closed shoals. Comparison of the diets of these two seabirds at South African colonies might provide information on the behaviour of local stocks. In addition, since these seabirds appear to feed on all age classes of Anchovy, the sizes of fish taken could provide information on the rates of recruitment of juvenile fish. Since predation by seabirds occurs earlier in the year than commercial catches are made, analysis of seabird diets might be used to predict the prospects for the fishery (Hockey *et al.* 1983).

Crawford & Shelton (1978) showed that the guano harvests at certain seabird islands off South Africa and Namibia correlated well with measured pelagic fish stock sizes, indicating that the breeding numbers or breeding success of seabirds was strongly influenced by fish stock size (*Figure 1*). Because seabirds tend to be long-lived and have a low production of recruits, their population size cannot track changes in fish stock size closely, but it is possible that breeding numbers of some species do, since birds may elect not to breed in years when food is short, or may move elsewhere. The latter strategy is rare in seabirds, which are generally highly philopatric, but does occur in some terns and Stercorariids. Monaghan & Zonfrillo (1986) found a correlation of about 0.8 between the number of terns breeding at colonies in the Clyde Sea area and the catch-per-unit-effort of Herring (*Clupea harengus*) two years later in the Clyde Herring fishery. As Herring recruit into the commercial fishery predominantly as two-year-olds, this suggests that tern breeding numbers are determined by larval Herring abundance.

Hislop & Harris (1985) demonstrated that the average annual proportions of Herring and Sprats (*Sprattus sprattus*) in the food loads of Puffins (*Fratercula arctica*) brought to chicks at the Isle of May, east Scotland, correlated with estimates for the same year of larval Herring abundance and Sprat total biomass in the North Sea, obtained by fishery research surveys. They concluded that dietary data from seabirds might not be a reliable method for estimating strengths of recruiting year classes of Sprats and Herring, but they suggested that seabird diets might be of value as indicators of trends in fish abundance.

The proportion of Sandeels (*Ammodytes marinus*) in food samples obtained

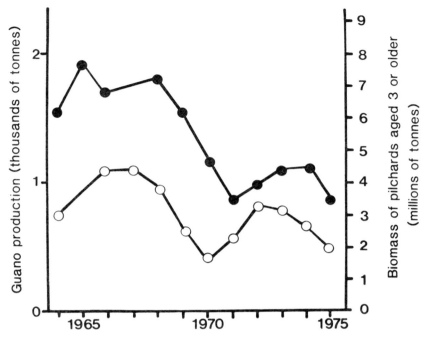

Figure 1:   Relationship between guano production (solid dots) on Ichaboe Island, and biomass of South African Pilchards (*Sardinops ocellata*) aged three years or older (open circles). (*From:* Crawford & Shelton 1978.)

from Fulmars (*Fulmarus glacialis*) and Great Skuas (*Catharacta skua*) in samples collected in May to July each year between 1975 and 1985 at Shetland colonies shows a general reduction since 1980 which correlates with a decline in Sandeel recruitment in recent seasons (Dr R. Bailey, DAFS, Furness unpubl.; Hudson 1986). These correlations are perhaps not surprising since Herring, Sprats and Sandeels are all fish with a high caloric density, and so are preferred prey of many seabirds feeding chicks. It is less likely that meaningful correlations will exist for fish that are not the preferred diet of the seabird, and seabirds that feed on a varied diet and often switch between prey species may not be good indicators of the fortunes of a fish stock since reduced consumption of a prey species may reflect increased availability of an alternative food rather than a reduced stock of the fish species in question. Gannets (*Sula bassana* and *S. capensis*) have been perceived to be useful seabirds for studies of prey availability since they tend to feed in a relatively non-selective way on a wide variety of food species (Nelson 1978). However, this very generalized feeding behaviour can make it more difficult to relate changes in diet composition to the changes in fish stock abundances. Nevertheless, Gannet diets have been claimed to give insights into the dynamics of prey stocks (Montevecchi 1986; Duffy *et al.* in press).

While seabird diets and breeding numbers may both be useful in providing information on food availability, other aspects of breeding biology probably merit consideration. Breeding failure of Puffins at Rost in Norway has been related to much reduced Herring stock size off west Norway, although Puffin numbers have not shown detectable changes in response to this food shortage (Lid 1981; Barrett & Vader 1984). Philopatry of breeding adults and their high life expectancy makes Puffin numbers at breeding colonies insensitive to changes in food stocks. One might expect chick growth rates to reflect food availability, but our studies of seabirds in Shetland suggest that this may not be the case until food is very scarce. Many seabird species spend only a small part of the day in foraging, and when food becomes less readily available they may only need to increase the time spent foraging in order to keep chick growth close to the maximum physiological rates. However, adult activity budgets may be particularly susceptible to influence of food availability, so might, together with diet, provide a greater insight into changes in fish stocks than a study of diet alone.

In regions where commercial fisheries are absent, seabirds may be the major source of information about some fish stocks: for example, in the high Arctic many details of Arctic Cod (*Boreogadus saida*) biology can be elucidated from alcid stomach samples (Bradstreet 1986; Bradstreet & Brown 1985).

FISHERIES

Some activities of fisheries can be difficult to monitor. For example, the whitefish and Norway Lobster (*Nephrops norvegicus*) fisheries around the British Isles discard large amounts of fish that have been caught but are too small to be marketable or are of species of little commercial value. Scavenging seabirds feed on these discarded fish and consume the majority of the discards (Furness *et al.*1987). Discarding practices vary among boats, fishing methods, regions, hauls, seasons, years, nationalities, catch sizes, weather conditions, demand for fish, and times of day. Little is known about the effects of these factors on the total amounts of fish discarded or on the proportions of different species and fish sizes discarded. Hudson (1986) showed that identification and measurement of otoliths from pellets regurgitated by Great Black-backed Gulls (*Larus marinus*) in Shetland, gave a close agreement between the distributions of sizes and species of Gadoids consumed by these gulls, and the sizes and species of Gadoids discarded by whitefish boats around Shetland (*Figure 2*). Great Black-backed Gull diet could be used to indicate changes in proportions of Haddock (*Melanogrammus aeglefinus*) and Whiting (*Merlangius merlangus*) in the discarded component of catches and to monitor the size distributions of the discards. Such applications would, however, need to consider a number of potential pitfalls. Smaller seabirds are unable to swallow large discards (Furness *et al.* 1987) and so Great Skuas, for example, select smaller fish than the average size currently discarded (*ca* 28 to 29 cm in length). There is also evidence that scavenging seabirds compete for preferred foods and so changes in Great Black-backed Gull diet could occur as a result of changes in numbers of other seabird species. Nevertheless, with a knowledge of such potential problems, gull diets (as determined by pellet analysis) could provide a considerable amount of information on the composition of whole-fish discards from fishing vessels.

ORGANOCHLORINES

Problems of organochlorine pollution are well known and have been widely studied. Organochlorine levels in seabirds are normally measured in lipid extracted from eggs, or from samples of liver, muscle or body fat taken from adults. Many analyses have been performed on birds found dead or even found

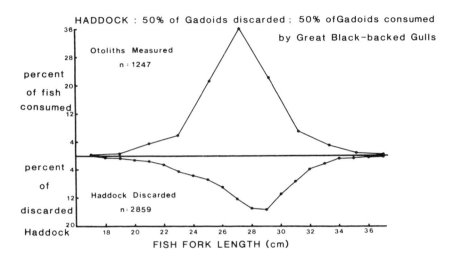

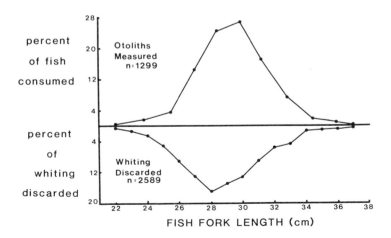

Figure 2: Fork lengths of Gadoid fish consumed by Great Black-backed Gulls in Shetland (derived from mesurements of regurgitated otoliths) compared with fork lengths of a measured sample of discard fish on fishing vessels around Shetland in 1985.

dying in convulsions. Not surprisingly, concentrations in the liver of such birds tend to be extremely high, since body fat reserves have been used up. However, the total body burden may be quite small since mobilization of fat reserves removes the main store of organochlorines and causes the high liver levels. Nearly half of the determinations of organochlorines in 250 seabirds listed in Bourne (1976) were samples from dead or dying individuals, and in many cases the organochlorine levels tabulated include mixtures of healthy and starved birds, with no indication of total body burdens. Such analyses tell us little about organochlorine pollution of the environment, and can give a misleading impression of variation within a population.

The distribution of organochlorines between organs varies greatly from bird to bird and this information could be of use in assessing the pollution condition of the bird. However, at present we do not know enough about the reasons for observed distribution patterns, except that in healthy seabirds most of the residues are in fat reserves. High levels in the liver and other organs tend to imply poor condition.

Robinson *et al.* (1967) showed that organochlorine levels in young seabirds reach a dynamic equilibrium within a short period of exposure; within the first year of life in Shags (*Phalacrocorax aristotelis*) and Kittiwakes (*Rissa tridactyla*) in east Britain. One of their main foods, sandeels, showed a pronounced seasonal cycle in organochlorine levels, suggesting that the residence time of organochlorines in their tissues is relatively short. That study, and that of Tanabe *et al.* (1984) showed that organochlorine levels were higher at higher trophic levels, and the latter study showed that the more lipophilic and less metabolizable organochlorines tended to represent a higher proportion of the total in animals at higher trophic levels. This indicates that much of the organochlorine burden is broken down and lost, but that this is a selective process. Seabirds therefore provide a slightly different measure of organochlorine pollutants than would samples of seawater or plankton. They have the advantage of concentrating the pollutants into more easily measured amounts and they average out short-term and small-scale geographic variation. They may therefore provide a better general measure of pollution levels for an area of sea or ocean.

Seabird eggs can provide an index of organochlorine levels and also avoid the need to kill healthy birds, but levels in eggs may reflect either levels in the diet during egg formation, levels in stored fat deposits of the adult female, or a combination of these two. Thus levels in eggs do not always correlate with levels in the birds laying them, although they usually do. Mineau (1982) found that organochlorine levels increased with laying sequence in Herring Gulls (*Larus argentatus*). This was probably due to an increased use of fat reserves by the female as successive eggs were formed. Body fat will contain more organochlorine residues than lipid derived directly from food. It may be a common phenomenon in seabird clutches, but the difference between first, second and third-laid eggs reported by Mineau was small compared to differences found between birds or between populations, so will not seriously affect the value of eggs as indicators of organochlorine levels in seabird populations, and hence in marine ecosystems. (See also Gilbertson *et al.*, this volume.)

Monitoring of organochlorine levels has shown changes over time which can be attributed to changes in the use of these substances. Shags were chosen by Coulson *et al.* (1972) as a good indicator species because the organochlorine levels were known to be high enough to allow changes to be measured; the birds normally remain within 60km of the natal locality so that local pollution levels can be monitored; the diet was known; it had already been shown that after six months of age organochlorine levels were independent of age in that species; and egg levels correlated with adult levels. Dieldrin and DDE levels were monitored in

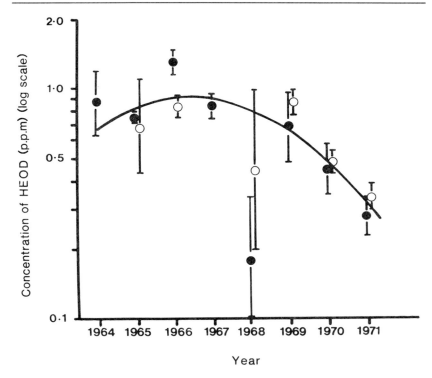

Figure 3: Concentrations of dieldrin in Shag eggs (geometric means) from the Farne Islands (solid dots) and the Isle of May (open circles) with 95% confidence intervals. The line represents the best fit quadratic relationship. (*From:* Coulson *et al.* 1972.)

samples of 9 to 69 eggs each year from 1964 to 1971 (Coulson *et al.* 1972) and showed that restrictions in the use of aldrin and dieldrin in the mid to late 1960s were reflected by reductions in levels of dieldrin in the Shag eggs (*Figure 3*). DDE levels also fell after reaching a peak in 1967–68, possibly also as a consequence of reduced use of this insecticide. However, Fimreite *et al.* (1977) found no detectable decrease in DDE levels in Herring Gull eggs over a period of three years after the ban on use of DDT in Norway in 1970, but found marked variation in levels between localities.

Voluntary restrictions on the use of PCBs in situations where environmental contamination could result came into effect around 1971, and levels of PCBs in North Atlantic seawater were found to decline almost immediately (Harvey *et al.* 1974). Levels in marine organisms remained high. Levels in Great Skuas and their eggs collected in Scotland and Iceland between 1969 and 1983 suggest that reduced use of DDT and dieldrin has resulted in reductions in these pollutants in the marine food chain. DDE and dieldrin levels in Great Skua eggs show a decline, as do levels in adult muscle tissues. However, results for PCBs are less clear-cut. Analyses of eggs suggest a decline in PCB levels between 1974 and 1983 while analyses of adult muscle tissues suggest that PCB levels had continued to increase from 1971 to 1980 (Muirhead, Bogan & Furness, unpubl.).

Golden Eagles (*Aquila chrysaetos*) on Rhum, Inner Hebrides, are also top marine predators, feeding on Fulmars, Manx Shearwaters (*Puffinus puffinus*) and gulls to a considerable extent. They also show signs of decreasing levels of DDE, but increases in PCBs. DDE levels (ppm wet weight) in eggs from Rhum Golden Eagles averaged 3.06 in five eggs in the 1960s, 2.3 and 2.7 in 1975, but only 1.4, 1.7 and 2.1 in eggs collected in 1984 and 1985. In contrast, PCB levels (ppm in lipid) were 3.0 in 1971, 12.4 and 13.4 in 1975 and 239, 248 and 294 ppm in 1984 and 1985. These data suggest that despite a knowledge of the toxic nature of PCBs, and some restrictions of use and evidence of local decreases in PCB levels in some areas, levels of PCBs in marine food chains have continued to increase on the east side of the Atlantic.

HEAVY METALS

Our knowledge of heavy metals in marine ecosystems is very limited. Estimates of the global inputs of metals into the oceans suggest that anthropogenic input is 18 times greater than natural input for lead, 9 times greater than natural input for cadmium, and somewhere in between these two values for mercury (Bryan 1984). However, the annual input of mercury into the oceans is several orders of magnitude less than the total amount already present and so it is not clear whether anthropogenic input will result in more than local pollution. These three metals probably provide the greatest hazard to marine ecosystems, and through these to man.

Analytical techniques are still improving, but have become adequate for accurate measurements of heavy metal concentrations in seawater, ice or snow samples only in the last six or seven years. This makes it almost impossible to assess long-term trends in metal concentrations. Analyses of cores of ice from the Antarctic or Greenland could, in theory, be used to measure global contamination by airborne routes, but attempts to detect changes have been hampered by the exceedingly low levels of metals in such samples and by contamination between collection and analysis. The most recent review of this subject concluded that there are no reliable data for heavy metals in ancient Antarctic ice and that data from Greenland may also be inaccurate due to contamination problems (Wolff & Peel 1985). Seabird samples provide an alternative method of assessing changes in metal levels with time, since bioaccumulation and biomagnification result in metal concentrations in seabird tissues that are three to six orders of magnitude higher than those found in water samples. For example, levels of mercury in Great Skua livers or feathers are generally in the range 1–10 ppm (μg g^{-1}) while levels in seawater are in the range 0.00001–0.00003 ppm.

Although feathers are predominantly composed of keratin, many elements enter feathers from the blood during feather growth. This is particularly the case with metals, many of which bind strongly to sulphur atoms in sulphur amino acids that are especially abundant in keratins. Metal levels in feathers are determined by levels in the blood at the time of feather growth, although surface contamination can cause changes after feather growth (Goede & de Bruin 1984). Feather washing can remove most surface contamination while having little effect on levels of heavy metals bound to feather proteins during growth. Thus feathers may be used to measure metal levels in seabirds providing the pattern of feather replacement is taken into account (Furness *et al.* 1986). Feathers have particularly been used to measure mercury levels and, since mercury bonding to feather proteins is strong, stored feathers (i.e. from museum skins) may be used to determine historical levels (Appelquist *et al.* 1984).

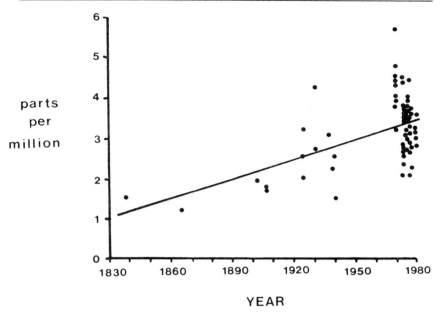

YEAR

Figure 4:   Concentrations of mercury (ppm dry weight) in the sixth primary of Guillemots from the Baltic Sea collected between 1830 and 1980. (*From:* Appelquist *et al.* 1985.)

Measurement by Instrumental Neutron Activation Analysis of levels of total mercury (inorganic plus organic) in feathers from museum specimens has shown that mercury levels in Guillemots (*Uria aalge*) and Black Guillemots (*Cepphus grylle*) have increased over the last 150 years in the Baltic (*Figure 4*) and probably also to a smaller extent in the North Atlantic (Appelquist *et al.* 1985). One problem with using museum specimens to monitor mercury levels is that mercuric chloride was often used as a preservative by taxidermists, so that museum skins may be heavily contaminated by inorganic mercury. Since the mercury in birds is usually thought to be almost all organic (methyl) mercury, it should be possible to discriminate between these two categories by analysing levels of methyl mercury in the feathers, but this has yet to be examined critically.

Feather analysis has great potential in studies of mercury in marine ecosystems since feathers are readily available without having to kill birds, and museums hold long time-series of many species.

RADIONUCLIDES

Discharge of radionuclides into the Irish Sea from Sellafield (formerly Windscale) Nuclear Reprocessing Plant have led to concern about the health hazards that these might present. There has been a large decline in numbers of Black-headed Gulls (*Larus ridibundus*) and terns nesting on the Cumbrian coast, and a suggestion that this might be due to radionuclide pollution. While this seems improbable, studies of the seabirds are being undertaken to investigate the possible relationship with radionuclide discharges. It may also be possible to examine the extent to which radionuclides accumulate through the food chain by examining their presence in seabirds.

OIL

The conspicuous threat that oil presents to seabirds has resulted in a considerable literature on this subject. Oiled seabirds coming ashore are often our first indication of an oil spill. Beached bird surveys (regular counts of dead seabirds on coastlines and the recording of numbers contaminated by oil) provide a valuable monitor of the oiling of seabirds at sea and also of natural mortality incidents. The use of these data in monitoring problems of oil pollution was thoroughly reviewed by Bourne (1976), while problems of monitoring oil pollution and its effects were also reviewed by Holmes (1984), Stowe & Underwood (1984), U.S. National Research Council (1984), Leighton *et al.* (1985), and Boersma (1986).

PLASTICS

The world's seas and oceans are widely contaminated with plastic flotsam and jetsam. Since plastic is not readily broken down, and the production of plastics is increasing worldwide, levels of contamination are likely to increase. Plastic fragments may be ingested by fish, seabirds or marine mammals, and their effects on the digestive system or physiology are unknown. Plastics can be categorized into two groups. User-plastics are fragments of items such as polystyrene cups, plastic toys or torn pieces of synthetic netting. The other group, plastic pellets, comprises the raw material from which user products are moulded. Plastic particles, which are largely the raw plastic pellets but contain a small quantity of eroded fragments from consumer items, are present at average densities of 1000 to 4000 per square kilometre on the surface of the North Atlantic, South Atlantic and Pacific Oceans and are probably now distributed over the other oceans and seas as well (Morris 1980).

Plastic particles have been found in the gizzard or proventriculus of many species of seabirds from Alaska to the Antarctic. Seabirds probably mistake plastic particles for zooplankton or fish eggs, but it is also possible that some derive from the stomachs of prey animals. PCBs are adsorbed on to the surface of plastic, and so ingestion by seabirds may increase their uptake of PCBs. Plastics cause ulceration of the stomach of seabirds (Bourne 1976), but the most likely damage caused by ingesting plastic is the reduction in functional volume of the gizzard leading to a reduction in digestive capacity (Connors & Smith 1982). Connors and Smith reported a negative correlation between the number of plastic particles in the gizzard of Grey Phalaropes (*Phalaropus fulicarius*) and their body mass. This correlation failed to reach statistical significance, partly because only a very small number of birds had been examined, but it suggested the need for further research into the occurrence and effects of plastic in seabirds.

Charadriiform and Sphenisciform seabirds (such as gulls and penguins) generally have few plastic particles in the gizzard, and this appears to be due to their habit of regularly regurgitating pellets of indigestible matter. Gulls and skuas generally regurgitate at least one pellet per day, and these occasionally contain plastic particles. Procellariiform seabirds generally have the most plastic in the gizzard, although there is great variation between individual birds, with even some individuals of what are generally the most contaminated species containing no particles (Furness 1985a, 1985b). The extent to which procellariiformes can eject gizzard contents is unknown. Gizzard and proventriculus anatomy differ from that of Charadriiformes, and the constriction at the entrance to the gizzard may make regurgitation of gizzard contents difficult. Procellariiformes do regurgitate food to their chicks, but this appears to derive from stores in the proventriculus rather than from the gizzard. Albatrosses can eject pellets of squid beaks but there is no record of shearwaters or petrels doing this. A plastic telemetry transmitter fed to a Laysan Albatross (*Diomedea immutabilis*) remained in the stomach for over 40 days (Pettit *et al.* 1981) and squid beaks fed to a Shy Albatross (*D. cauta*) remained in the stomach for at least six weeks (B. L. Furness 1983). The state of erosion of particles in Short-tailed Shearwater (*Puffinus tenuirostris*) gizzards suggested that these may have a residence time of about 15 months (Day 1980), though this estimate needs verification by direct testing. Plastic particles may be worn down in size until they can pass through the intestine, but examination of the distribution of sizes of particles in different species does not strongly support this idea. Although in most cases larger seabirds select larger particles, they also contain a variety of smaller particles, with no evidence of a cut-off point as small particles are lost.

Both northern and southern hemisphere procellariiformes are heavily contaminated with plastic. Differences between species can probably be attributed to different feeding behaviours. When removed from a dead bird, the gizzard can be inflated to about four times its relaxed volume, but this may not be possible *in vivo*. The volume of plastic may represent a large part of the space available for food in the most contaminated birds, so that a reduction in digestive ability is likely. Within a seabird species, body mass is closely related to body size, so that individual variation due to size should be taken into account before considering effects of ingested plastic. Multiple regressions relating mass to the best measures of body size and the quantity of plastic in the gizzard suggest that plastic contamination may reduce body mass (presumably by causing a loss of stored energy reserves), but that the effect is rather difficult to demonstrate statistically (Furness 1985a, 1985b).

DISCUSSION

Seabird population declines, or mortality incidents, by their conspicuous nature, may signal environmental problems that are otherwise undetected, and in this way seabirds may be a valuable marine 'canary'.

Pollutants

As a number of fish stocks throughout the world have been declared unsafe for human consumption due to their high mercury content, there is a need for a better understanding of the dynamics of mercury, and other toxic metals, in marine environments. Seabirds seem to provide the best opportunity to determine historical changes in metal levels and to investigate geographical patterns in metal distributions.

Most studies where concentrations of organochlorines or heavy metals have been measured in seabirds have been short-term, and not aimed at environmental monitoring. Consequently, inferences about long-term changes in levels of pollutants are difficult to make because they involve comparing data from small sample sizes collected in different ways and analysed using different laboratory techniques. Seabirds can provide valuable information on trends in pollutant levels, but in order to make best use of seabirds as indicators a planned long-term monitoring approach is required to complement studies into the harmful effects that pollutants may have. Such long-term monitoring studies are required urgently.

The ubiquitous nature of plastic particle pollution of oceans, and increasing use of plastics, means that there is an urgent need for experimental studies to determine the residence time and physiological effects of ingested plastic in seabirds. Monitoring levels of plastic contamination of seabirds, particularly Procellariiformes, would be valuable, but since there is no obvious way of doing this without killing birds, it would be better to concentrate on studies to determine whether or not plastic pollution is a serious problem to seabirds or surface-feeding fish. Meanwhile, the opportunity should be taken to examine the gizzard contents of Procellariiform seabirds that may be available for study as a result of beached bird collections, fishing net mortality or scientific collecting. Some method of determining numbers of plastic particles in live seabird gizzards needs to be developed before seabirds can be used to monitor this form of pollution.

Fish stocks

There is a need for studies aimed at evaluating the use of seabirds as monitors of fish stocks. We can predict that seabirds would be most useful when the fish stock of interest is the preferred prey of the seabird; when the seabird can consume a variety of age-classes of the fish; when the seabird diet is relatively narrow in range of prey species taken; and, perhaps, when the seabird has little spare time available that could act as a buffer against reduced food availability by allowing increased foraging effort. This would suggest that terns might be particularly suitable for monitoring of fish such as Sandeels, or Puffins for monitoring young Herring, Sprats or Sandeels. More general feeders, such as gulls or skuas, may be less suitable by comparison, but these ideas remain to be tested. Since pelagic schooling fish are among the most difficult for fisheries biologists to study, and these are the main prey species that might be amenable to study through sampling seabird breeding and diets, there is reason to hope that a positive and fruitful interaction between fisheries and seabird biologists might develop through common interests in pelagic fish stocks.

ACKNOWLEDGEMENTS

This paper has benefited greatly from my discussions with Dr Sandra Muirhead, Dr Anne Hudson, Dr Roger Bailey and Dr John Hislop and members of the Biology and Psychology Departments at Memorial University, Newfoundland. I am grateful for financial support from the Natural Environment Research Council and for a visiting scholarship from Newfoundland Institute for Cold Ocean Science, where this paper was conceived. I thank Dr David Peakall and an anonymous reviewer for helpful comments.

REFERENCES

APPELQUIST, H., ASBIRK, S. & DRABAEK, I. 1984. Mercury monitoring: mercury stability in bird feathers. *Mar. Pollut. Bull.* **15**, 22–4.

APPELQUIST, H., DRABAEK, I. & ASBIRK, S. 1985. Variation in mercury content of guillemot feathers over 150 years. *Mar. Pollut. Bull.* **16**, 244–8.

BARRETT, R. T. & VADER, W. 1984. The status and conservation of breeding seabirds in Norway. Pp. 323–34 *In: ICBP Technical Publication No. 2: Conservation of the World's Seabirds.* Croxall, J. P., Evans, P. G. H. & Schreiber, R. W. (eds.) ICBP, Cambridge.

BOERSMA, P. D. 1986. Ingestion of petroleum by seabirds can serve as a monitor of water quality. *Science* **231**, 373–6.

BOURNE, W. R. P. 1976. 'Seabirds and pollution' *In: Marine Pollution* Vol. 6, Johnston, R. (ed.), Academic Press, London.

BRADSTREET, M. S. W. 1986. *Pacific Seabird Group Newsletter.*

BRADSTREET, M. S. W. & BROWN, R. G. 1985. Feeding ecology of the Atlantic Alcidae. Pp. 264–318 *In: The Atlantic Alcidae.* Nettleship, D. N. & Birkhead, T. R. (eds.) Academic Press, London.

BRYAN, G. W. 1984. 'Pollution due to heavy metals and their compounds' *In: Marine Ecology* Vol. 5, Kinne, O. (ed.), John Wiley, London.

CONNORS, P. G. & SMITH, K. G. 1982. Oceanic plastic particle pollution: suspected effect on fat deposition in Red Phalaropes. *Mar. Pollut. Bull.* **13**, 18–20.

COULSON, J. C., DEANS, I. R., POTTS, G. R., ROBINSON, J. & CRABTREE, A. N. 1972. Changes in organochlorine contamination of the marine environment of eastern Britain monitored by Shag eggs. *Nature* **236**, 454–6.

CRAWFORD, R. J. M. & SHELTON, P. A. 1978. Pelagic fish and seabird inter-relationships off the coasts of South West and South Africa. *Biol. Conserv.* **14**, 85–109.

DAY, R. H. 1980. *The occurrence and characteristics of plastic pollution in Alaska's marine birds.* Thesis, University of Alaska.

DUFFY, D. C., WILSON, R. P., BERRUTI, A. & BRONI, S. C. (in press). Temporal patterns of recruitment of Cape Anchovy monitoring through seabird diets. *J. Exp. Mar. Biol. Ecol.*

FIMREITE, N., BJERK, J. E., KVESETH, N. & BRUN, E. 1977. DDE and PCBs in eggs of Norwegian seabirds. *Astarte* **10**, 15–20.

FURNESS, B. L. 1983. Plastic particles in three procellariiform seabirds from the Benguela current, South Africa. *Mar. Pollut. Bull.* **14**, 307–8.

FURNESS, R. W. 1985a. Plastic particle pollution: accumulation by Procellariiform seabirds at Scottish colonies. *Mar. Pollut. Bull.* **16**, 103–6.

FURNESS, R. W. 1985b. Ingestion of plastic particles by seabirds at Gough Island, South Atlantic Ocean. *Environ. Pollut.* **38**, 261–72.

FURNESS, R. W., MUIRHEAD, S. J. & WOODBURN, M. 1986. Using bird feathers to measure mercury in the environment: relationships between mercury content and moult. *Mar. Pollut. Bull.* **17**, 27–30.

FURNESS, R. W., HUDSON, A. V. & ENSOR, K. 1987. Interactions between scavenging seabirds and commercial fisheries around the British Isles. *In: Interspecific Interactions of Birds and other Marine Vertebrates.* Burger, J. (ed.) Columbia University Press.

GOEDE, A. A. & DE BRUIN, M. 1984. The use of bird feather parts as a monitor for metal pollution. *Environ. Pollut. B.* **8**, 281–98.

HARVEY, G. R., STEINHAUER, W. G. & MIKLAS, H. P. 1974. Decline of PCB concentrations in North Atlantic surface water. *Nature* **252**, 387–8.

HISLOP, J. R. G. & HARRIS, M. P. 1985. Recent changes in the food of young Puffins *Fratercula arctica* on the Isle of May in relation to fish stocks. *Ibis* **127**, 234–9.

HOCKEY, P. A. R., COOPER, J. & DUFFY, D. C. 1983. The roles of coastal birds in the functioning of marine ecosystems in Southern Africa. *S. Afr. J. Sci.* **79**, 130–4.

HOLMES, W. N. 1984. Petroleum pollutants in the marine environment and their possible effects on seabirds. *Rev. Environ. Toxicol.* **1**, 251–317.

HUDSON, A. V. 1986. The biology of seabirds utilising fishery waste in Shetland. Ph.D. thesis, University of Glasgow.

LEIGHTON, F. A., BUTLER, R. G. & PEAKALL, D. B. 1985. Oil and arctic marine birds: an assessment of risk. *In: Petroleum effects in the arctic environment.* Engelhardt, F. R. (ed.) Elsevier, London.

LID, G. 1981. Reproduction of the puffin on Rost in the Lofoten Islands in 1964–1980. *Cinclus* **4**, 30–39.

MINEAU, P. 1982. Levels of major organochlorine contaminants in sequentially-laid Herring Gull eggs. *Chemosphere* **11**, 679–85.

MONAGHAN, P. & ZONFRILLO, B. 1986. Population dynamics of seabirds in the Firth of Clyde. *Proc. Royal Soc. Edinburgh* **90**, 363–375.

MONTEVECCHI, W. A. 1986. *Pacific Seabird Group Newsletter.*

MORRIS, R. J. 1980. Plastic debris in the surface of the South Atlantic. *Mar. Pollut. Bull.* **11**, 164–6.

NELSON, J. B. 1978. *The Sulidae: Gannets and Boobies.* Oxford University Press, Oxford.

PETTIT, T. N., GRANT, G. S. & WHITTOW, G. C. 1981. Ingestion of plastics by Laysan Albatross. *Auk* **98**, 839–41.

ROBINSON, J., RICHARDSON, A., CRABTREE, A. N., COULSON, J. C. & POTTS, G. R. 1967. Organochlorine residues in marine organisms. *Nature* **214**, 1307–11.

STOWE, T. J. & UNDERWOOD, L. A. 1984. Oil spillages affecting seabirds in the United Kingdom, 1966–1983. *Mar. Pollut. Bull.* **15**, 147–52.

TANABE, S., TANAKA, H. & TATSUKAWA, R. 1984. Polychlorobiphenyls, DDT, and Hexachlorocyclohexane isomers in the Western North Pacific ecosystem. *Arch. Environ. Contam. Toxicol.* **13**, 731–8.

U.S. NATIONAL RESEARCH COUNCIL 1985. *Oil in the sea. Inputs, fates and effects.* National Academy Press, Washington, D.C.

WOLFF, E. W. & PEEL, D. A. 1985. The record of global pollution in polar snow and ice. *Nature* **313**, 535–40.

SEABIRDS AS INDICATORS OF MARINE POLLUTION

M. Gilbertson[1], J. E. Elliott[2] & D. B. Peakall[2]

1 *Chemical Hazards Division, Department of Fisheries & Oceans,*
200 Kent Street, Ottawa, Ontario[1]
2 *Canadian Wildlife Service, National Wildlife Research Centre,*
Ottawa, K1A 0H3

ABSTRACT

There is a continuing need to monitor levels of xenobiotic (man-made) pollutants in the marine environment. This paper explores the use of seabirds as indicators of spatial and temporal trends in levels of organochlorine chemicals in the North Atlantic. Data from seabird monitoring projects carried out by authorities in a number of countries during the past 20 years are analysed. Based on a statistical comparison with other marine monitor species (fish and seals), the seabird egg is shown to be an efficient, conservative tool for monitoring organochlorine levels. A statistical analysis of sampling design demonstrates the value of pooled samples for increasing monitoring efficiency for some chemicals. A review of published data shows that three seabird species have been widely used and have proved valuable for integrating chemical levels in the pelagic marine environment. These are: the Atlantic Puffin (*Fratercula arctica*), the Guillemot or Common Murre (*Uria aalge*) and the Leach's Storm-petrel (*Oceanodroma leucorhoa*).

THE NEED FOR AN INTERNATIONAL SCHEME TO MONITOR THE NORTH ATLANTIC

The North Atlantic receives large quantities of chemical wastes from a variety of sources. These include discharges from manufacturing and waste dump-sites, use, transport accidents, ocean dumping and incineration. These releases of chemicals reach the North Atlantic through direct discharge into coastal areas and by indirect translocation in river, estuarine and atmospheric fluxes. These fluxes may cross international boundaries, and subsequent redistribution of chemicals by ocean currents may cause transboundary pollution and affect the utilization of marine resources. Thus chemicals have become a sovereignty issue. Treaties and agreements, such as the London Dumping Convention and the Declaration of the Stockholm Conference, have set the international framework for administration of direct and indirect chemical releases to the sea. Individual countries have set up the legal mechanisms to control marine pollution. There is, however, no international system for monitoring the effectiveness of these national and international instruments. Thus, though a country may believe that it and its neighbours are complying with the laws and agreements, the quality of the ocean environment could be deteriorating without anyone knowing.

The United Nations Environment Program (1985), through the Ad Hoc Working Group of Experts on the Protection of the Marine Environment against Pollution from Land-Based Sources, advocated the establishment of international joint programmes for monitoring sources and levels of pollutants to assess the need for pollution prevention measures and the effectiveness of any protection measures introduced.

The International Maritime Organization (1983) established a Task Team to study the long-term strategies and objectives of the London Dumping Convention to the year 2000. The report describes the technically feasible mitigative measures to effectively manage the use of marine resources so as to mitigate short-range damage leading to long-range degradation, and recommended monitoring the health of the oceans on a continuing worldwide basis.

There is a need for a scheme to monitor the North Atlantic as a large system. This paper explores the reliability of seabirds as long-term monitors of marine pollution and examines the feasibility of an international scheme. The paper considers only long-term trend monitoring of levels (not effects) of organochlorines. The principles, however, should be applicable to selection of indicators of other pollutants such as trace metals and polynuclear aromatic hydrocarbons. Other organisms such as Grey Seals (*Halichoerus grypus*) (Addison *et al.* 1984) and Cod (*Gadus morhua*) (Scott *et al.* 1981) have been used as indicators of marine pollution and their value as monitor species will be compared with that of seabirds.

REVIEW OF CRITERIA FOR SELECTING MONITOR SPECIES

For the purposes of this study, seabirds are defined as bird species whose habits enable them to earn at least part of their living in, or on, salt water (Fisher & Lockley 1954).

Various authors have set out criteria for selecting organisms as monitors of pollutants (Moore 1966; Butler *et al.* 1971; Phillips 1980). Others have listed criteria for selecting seabirds as monitors of organochlorine pollution (Coulson *et al.* 1972; Gilbertson 1974a; Peakall *et al.* 1980). These various criteria have been grouped under the following headings:
  (a) Tendency to accumulate high levels.
  (b) Migratory habits, range and distribution.
  (c) Ease of sampling and handling.
  (d) Biology and physiology.

Tendency to accumulate high levels
Moore (1966) noted that monitor species should be those that, in a pilot survey, exhibit quite high levels of the pollutant. He noted that those that contain very high residues would be likely to suffer toxicological effects if the levels even marginally increased, and that this might affect sampling of the population. Butler *et al.* (1971) considered the ability of a monitor species to accumulate pollutants without being killed by the existing levels of pollutant to be the primary selection factor. Similarly, Coulson *et al.* (1972), in explaining their selection of the Shag (*Phalacrocorax aristotelis*) as a suitable marine monitor species, stated that concentrations in the indicator should be sufficiently high to allow changes to be readily detected.

The organism should be sufficiently long-lived that the cumulative build-up of residues in the environment can be determined (Moore 1966) and so that more than one year class can be sampled (Butler *et al.* 1971).

Migratory habits, range and distribution
Moore (1966) noted the importance of knowing the range of the indicator species and that species with extensive ranges may give a reliable guide to changes in contamination of a large area. Coulson *et al.* (1972) stated that the movement of the organism should be restricted to the area under study. Butler *et al.* (1971) said that not only were the residence time and migratory habits of some marine birds reasonably well known, but that they also regarded them as excellent integrators because they constantly move over large areas. They also noted that the selected species should have a broad distribution both ecologically and geographically so that direct comparisons can be made between locations.

Ease of sampling and handling
Monitor species should be relatively abundant and easy to collect, and each sampling unit should be large enough for individual chemical analysis. Rare or local species, and those with prolonged sexual immaturity or low fecundity, are unsuitable as monitor organisms for conservation reasons (Moore 1966). Marine bird species are taxonomically well known (Butler *et al.* 1971) and their eggs are adaptable to handling and transfer between localities (Peakall *et al.* 1980) and for controlled laboratory experimentation (Gilbertson 1983). Many species are colonial and thus can be easily sampled (Gilbertson 1974a).

Biology and physiology
There should be a sufficient knowledge of the biology of the monitor species to be able to determine the age of the organism (Moore 1966) so that any association of age and pollutant concentration can be determined (Coulson *et al.* 1972). In addition, the sensitive life stages and the non-anthropogenic factors that affect the species (Butler *et al.* 1971) should be recognized. The trophic position of the species at different locations must be established, together with the seasonal fluctuations and kinetics of the pollutants in the food web (Butler *et al.* 1971). Contamination at the breeding colony may cause seasonal variation in residue levels in the monitor species (Gilbertson 1974b).

The rates of uptake and excretion of a pollutant in an organism determine the degree of time integration of ambient pollutant levels exhibited by that organism (Phillips 1980). Thus, variations in lipid metabolism (deFreitas & Norstrom 1974) and mixed function oxidase activity (Walker & Knight 1981) should be determined for various species at different locations (Butler *et al.* 1971). To understand the various aspects of the pharmacokinetics of chemicals in seabirds, the Canadian Wildlife Service has prepared a bioenergetic-based model of Great Lakes Herring Gulls (*Larus argentatus*) (Clark *et al.* 1987).

Summary of criteria
Many species of fish, marine mammal and seabird meet most of the criteria reviewed. Seabirds seem to be particularly good integrators (Boersma 1986) of chemicals in large oceanic systems. Their eggs are easily sampled and because re-laying is likely and only a small percentage of eggs result in adults, the conservation objections are minimized. In addition, egg laying is a fixed seasonal event in the annual physiological cycle and thus less influenced by seasonal variations. Some seabird species, however, may range over extremely large areas of the North and South Atlantic during the course of a year. Selection of these species as monitors might pose problems of interpretation since the birds would

have been exposed to widely differing pollution situations and it would be unclear as to what was actually being integrated (see **Migratory habits, range and distribution,** above).

CANDIDATE SPECIES

Fisher & Lockley (1954) have listed the presence and distribution of seabirds in the North Atlantic. The twenty-three species that breed in the east and west temperate Atlantic and/or in the Arctic are shown in *Table 1*. Birds are exposed to persistent chemicals mainly through their food. Thus the species listed in *Table 1* have been arranged by food location (pelagic or coastal) and by food kind (planktivore or piscivore). For many of these twenty-three species, the migratory habits, range and distribution are, by now, fairly well established from banding data and shipboard sightings.

For the purposes of selecting a planktonic pelagic integrator species, only the Leach's Storm-petrel and Kittiwake (*Rissa tridactyla*) are candidates. The Fulmar (*Fulmarus glacialis*) is a pelagic omnivore. There are five species of auks that are pelagic piscivores: the Razorbill (*Alca torda*), Guillemot or Common Murre, Black Guillemot (*Cepphus grylle*), Brunnich's Guillemot or Thick-billed Murre (*Uria lomvia*), and Atlantic Puffin.

Table 1: Candidate seabirds for monitoring organochlorine chemicals in the North Atlantic (*After:* Fisher & Lockley, 1954).

	Temperate West Atlantic	Arctic	Temperate East Atlantic
Pelagic planktivore			
Leach's Storm-petrel (*Oceanodroma leucorhoa*)	+	−	+
Pelagic piscivore			
Razorbill (*Alca torda*)	+	+	+
Common Guillemot (Murre) (*Uria aalge*)	+	+	+
Brunnich's Guillemot (*Uria lomvia*)	+	+	+
Black Guillemot (*Cepphus grylle*)	+	+	+
Atlantic Puffin (*Fratercula arctica*)	+	+	+
Pelagic planktivore/piscivore			
Northern Fulmar (*Fulmarus glacialis*)	+	+	+
Pelagic/coastal/piscivore			
Northern Gannet (*Sula bassanus*)	+	−	+
Coastal planktivore			
Black-legged Kittiwake (*Rissa tridactyla*)	+	+	+
Coastal piscivore			
Great Cormorant (*Phalacrocorax carbo*)	+	+	+
Double-crested Cormorant (*Phalacrocorax auritus*)	+		
Herring Gull (*Larus argentatus*)	+	+	+
Great Black-backed Gull (*Larus marinus*)	+	+	+
Glaucous Gull (*Larus hyperboreus*)	+	+	+
Arctic Skua (Parasitic Jaeger) (*Stercorarius parasiticus*)	+	+	+
Long-tailed Skua (Jaeger) (*Stercorarius longicaudus*)	+	+	+
Gull-billed Tern (*Gelochelidon nilotica*)	+	−	+
Caspian Tern (*Hydroprogne caspia*)	+	−	+
Common Tern (*Sterna hirundo*)	+	+	+
Arctic Tern (*Sterna paradisaea*)	+	+	+
Little Tern (*Sterna albifrons*)	+	−	+
Sandwich Tern (*Thalasseus sandvicensis*)	+	−	+
Black Tern (*Chlidonias nigra*)	+	−	+

SELECTED EXAMPLES OF GEOGRAPHIC AND
TEMPORAL TREND DATA USING SEABIRD EGGS

A search of the literature shows that very few monitoring programmes have been designed to determine geographic and temporal variation in chemical contamination using seabirds or their eggs. Most residue data are for samples that seem to have been collected adventitiously (Gilbertson & Reynolds 1974; Peakall 1975; Bourne 1976; Ohlendorf et al. 1978, 1982; NERC 1983).

Geographic trends
Dyck & Kraul (1984) compiled published data (*Table* 2) for levels of organochlorine chemicals in samples of Common Guillemot (Murre) eggs from the Northern Hemisphere. The data show high levels of DDE in the Baltic and off the coast of California at the end of the 1960s. Levels in the rest of coastal Europe and in coastal Canada were about an order of magnitude lower. Similarly, high levels of PCBs were found in the Baltic Sea and off the coast of California. However, high levels were also found in eggs sampled from the Irish sea and the east and southwest coasts of England.

Ohlendorf & Harrison (1986) examined the differences in heavy metal, selenium and organochlorine residues in the eggs of three species of seabirds in the central Pacific. These workers found a southeast-to-northwest trend toward higher concentrations of mercury. DDE concentrations were higher in the southeastern sites and consistently higher in shearwaters.

Nisbet & Reynolds (1984) used Common Tern eggs to determine the geographic variation in levels of various organochlorine compounds in coastal Massachusetts. The results (*Figure 1*) show elevated levels of DDE and PCB at colonies outside Boston Harbour and New Bedford. Levels at the colonies on Cape Cod were lower than on the mainland. The authors then related the levels found at the colonies to the use of these compounds in the watersheds.

Table 2: Levels of DDE and PCB in Common Guillemot (Murre) eggs, Northern Hemisphere, 1968–1976, expressed in μg/g on a lipid basis. (*After:* Dyck & Kraul, 1984.)

Location	Year	DDE	PCBs
Baltic Sea			
Stora Karlso	1968–69	590	225
Graesholmen	1971–76	450	480
British Isles			
East coast	up to 1974	9.8	36–56
Southwest	up to 1974	12–24	61–70
Irish sea	up to 1974	21–29	130–220
Western Eire	up to 1974	8.3	39
Scotland	up to 1974	6.3	16
Shetland	up to 1974	6.5	14
Faeroes	up to 1974	6.5	15
Norway			
Southern	1972	3.2	9.1
Northern	1972	4.7–6.7	13–20
Canada			
Gulf of St. Lawrence	1971	12	13
California			
Farallon Islands	1968	300	170

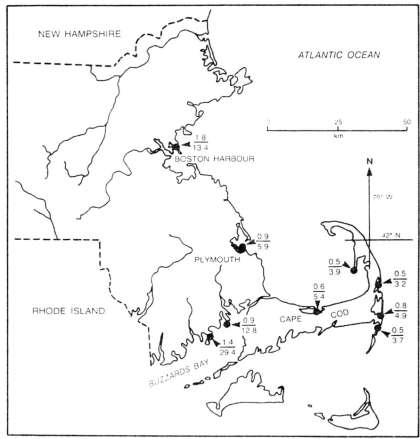

Figure 1:   DDE/PCB ratios in Common Tern eggs from eastern Massachusetts, 1973/74.
(*After:* Nisbet & Reynolds 1984.)

Temporal trends

During the 1960s and early 1970s, Shags' eggs were analysed to determine the
levels of dieldrin and DDE in coastal areas of the North Sea (Coulson *et al.* 1972).
Samples were collected from the Farne Islands off the Northumberland coast and
from the Isle of May in the Firth of Forth, Scotland. The results showed the
increase in levels of dieldrin between 1964 and 1966 and the subsequent decrease
as the use of aldrin and dieldrin declined. The levels of DDE similarly increased
in the mid-1960s but started to decline around 1968.

The decline in the levels of DDE and PCB in the southern Baltic Sea was
documented by Dyck & Kraul (1984) using Common Guillemot eggs sampled
between 1971 and 1976. The levels are reported in *Table 3*. Similarly, a longer
series of time trend data for eggs collected between 1968 and 1984 from Baltic Sea
Guillemot colonies showed that DDE peaked in 1969 at over $600\mu g/g$ and that
PCB peaked in 1973 at over $400\mu g/g$ on a lipid basis (Olsson & Reutergardh 1986).
They felt that Guillemot eggs were, 'a perfect biological material for trend studies
on persistent chemicals'.

Table 3:   Concentration of DDE and PCB (in µg/g lipid) in eggs of Common Guillemots sampled from Graesholmen, southern Baltic Sea, 1971–1976. (*After:* Dyck & Kraul, 1984.)

Year	No. of eggs	DDE		PCBs	
		$\bar{x}$ S.D.		$\bar{x}$ S.D.	
1971	9	548 ± 113		523 ± 143	
1972	12	586 ± 166		580 ± 154	
1973	9	409 ± 67		424 ± 72	
1974	12	399 ± 87		486 ± 106	
1975	8	358 ± 91		429 ± 73	
1976	10	393 ± 68		408 ± 67	

Similar long-term declines in organochlorine levels were noted by Nisbet & Reynolds (1984) for the Common Tern colony at Bird Island, in Buzzards Bay, Massachusetts, between 1971 and 1981. The data for DDE, dieldrin, hexachlorobenzene (HCB) and PCB in fresh or partly incubated eggs are shown in *Table 4*.

By re-analysing eggs stored in the Canadian Wildlife Service specimen bank (Elliott 1985), it was possible to show changes in chemical residues from 1969 to 1984 in Northern Gannets from Bonaventure Island, Québec, using standard analytical methodology. Levels of DDE declined more quickly (Elliott *et al.* in prep.) than other compounds (*Table 5*). PCBs, HCB and dieldrin also declined significantly ($p < 0.05$) but at a slower rate. Oxychlordane, a metabolite of the pesticide chlordane, declined very slowly over the study period, probably reflecting the fact that this chemical was used during the 1970s in North America as a replacement for DDT.

The final example concerns the seabird monitoring programme on the east coast of Canada that was started in 1968. Eggs of three species of seabirds, Double-crested Cormorant, Atlantic Puffin and Leach's Storm-petrel, have been sampled every four years from the three areas of the east coast, the St. Lawrence River, the Bay of Fundy and insular Newfoundland. The results of the analyses for DDE and PCB are shown in *Figure 2*. Results to 1976 were reported in Pearce *et al.* (1979). There has been a steady decline in the levels of these organochlorine compounds during the past sixteen years at the coastal locations. The results of the analysis of eggs of Double-crested Cormorants from the St. Lawrence river indicates that the declines in levels of PCB and DDE have not continued during the 1980s.

Table 4:   Organochlorine residues (µg/g, wet weight) in Common Tern eggs from Bird Island, Massachusetts, 1971–81. (*After:* Nisbet & Reynolds, 1984.)

Year	Number of Eggs	DDE	Dieldrin	HCB	PCBs
1971	9	1.02	0.12	0.028	15.4
1972	5	0.95	0.08	0.014	15.8
1973	5	0.90	0.09	0.016	12.8
1975	11	0.73	0.067	0.020	20.2
1976	8	0.35	0.014	—	21.9
1977	11	0.31	0.046	0.009	10.2
1978	11	0.66	0.052	0.017	8.9
1980	8	0.25	0.037	0.009	6.8
1981	12	0.20	0.044	0.009	9.5
Spearman rank correlation coefficient with year		−0.90	−0.73	−0.88	−0.67

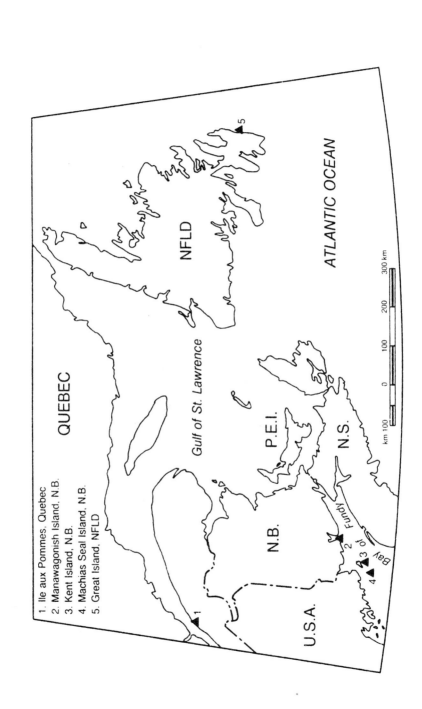

1. Ile aux Pommes. Quebec
2. Manawagonish Island. N.B.
3. Kent Island, N.B.
4. Machias Seal Island. N.B.
5. Great Island, NFLD

QUEBEC

NFLD

Gulf of St. Lawrence

P.E.I.

N.S.

N.B.

Bay of Fundy

U.S.A.

ATLANTIC OCEAN

km 100   0   100   200   300 km

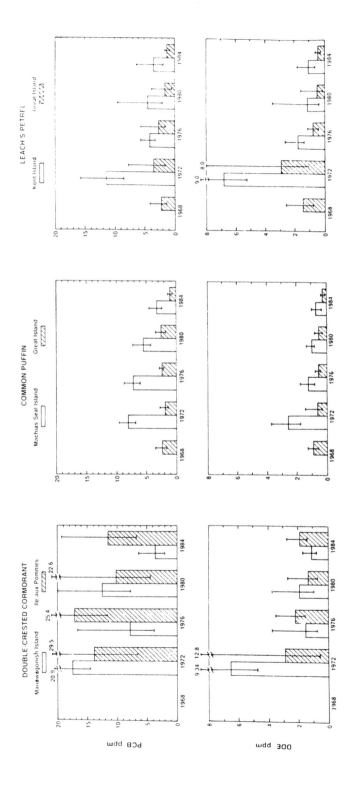

Figure 2: Trends in PCB and DDE concentrations (ppm, wet weight) in eggs of eastern Canadian seabirds.

Table 5:   Organochlorine residues (geometric mean, $\mu g/g$, wet weight) in Gannet eggs from Bonaventure Island, Quebec, 1969–1984: N = 6 for each year. (After: Elliott et al., in prep.)

Year	DDE	Dieldrin	HCB	Oxychlordane	PCBs
1969	18.5	0.641	0.075	0.093	23.9
1973	11.1	0.381	0.046	0.090	18.8
1974	7.96	0.330	0.057	0.095	17.7
1976	4.35	0.324	0.063	0.097	15.4
1984	1.12	0.148	0.025	0.070	9.54
Average annual percentage decrease in residue level	19%	9.4%	6%	2%	6%

These selected examples show the scientific value of consistently sampling and analysing seabird eggs for organochlorine chemicals. The results presented here have been concerned mainly with DDE and PCB. However, the geographic variation and temporal trends of a large number of other organochlorine compounds have also been demonstrated.

COMPARISONS WITH OTHER MARINE SPECIES

For a species to be a useful indicator of spatial and temporal trends of levels of pollutants, the within-collection variation in levels must be small enough for changes to be readily detected. In any monitoring programme, there is a balance between the increased reliability of the estimate gained by increasing the sample size, and increased analytical costs. A detailed analysis of the statistical sampling design for seabirds based on data from the CWS National Registry of Toxic Chemicals Residues is given in Appendix 1.

Basically, within-colony variation in the levels of pollutants is expressed by a coefficient of variation (CV) which is the standard deviation of the sample divided by the sample mean. Coefficients of variation and geometric means for four contaminants in Puffin eggs from Great Island, Newfoundland, and Machias Seal Island, New Brunswick, and Leach's Storm-petrel eggs from Great Island, Newfoundland, and Kent Island, New Brunswick are shown in Table 6. During the past fifteen years or so, levels in eggs of these species have declined significantly. Generally, the coefficients of variation, particularly for the offshore colony at Great Island, Newfoundland, have also declined. Thus, Table 6 contains values for the earliest and most recent years in which samples were taken. The table also shows that, despite the small sample size, the coefficients of variation are relatively small, suggesting that even if a small increase or decrease in any contaminant occurred it would be detected with a modest sample size. In other words, even this preliminary analysis indicates a favourable signal-to-noise ratio.

These coefficients of variation can be compared to those for DDE and PCB found in other marine organisms (Table 7). In seals, despite much higher residue levels and a somewhat larger sample size, Addison et al. (1984) found CV values roughly twice those found in seabirds: CV values in fish are much higher, even when the sample size is much larger than the seabird data presented in Table 6.

The choice of organism for a monitoring programme depends on many factors, but from the viewpoint of the number of samples needed to obtain statistical reliability, seabird eggs are superior to marine mammals or fish. A number of seabirds have wide distribution in the northern Atlantic (Table 1) and the eggs of

Table 6: Coefficients of variation and geometric means (μg/g, wet weight) for four organochlorine compounds in eggs (N = 5) of Puffin and Leach's Petrel, Atlantic Provinces, Canada.

| | Common (Atlantic) Puffin | | | | Leach's Petrel | | | |
| | Great Island Newfoundland | | Machias Seal Island Bay of Fundy | | Great Island Newfoundland | | Kent Island Bay of Fundy | |
	1968	1984	1972	1984	1968	1984	1972	1984
DDE								
Coefficient of Variation	18%	19%	29.4%	23.8%	50%	27.6%	17.2%	38.9%
Geometric Mean	0.90	0.30	2.57	0.74	1.46	0.40	6.81	1.05
Dieldrin								
Coefficient of Variation	19.4%	14.6%	18.6%	32.2%	42.3%	17.2%	14.8%	30.5%
Geometric Mean	0.05	0.041	0.09	0.05	0.05	0.05	0.05	0.04
HCB								
Coefficient of Variation	39.6%	24.4%	42.6%	26.6%	37.7%	20.1%	45.1%	30.1%
Geometric Mean	0.08	0.09	0.06	0.07	0.06	0.06	0.03	0.04
PCBs								
Coefficient of Variation	34.4%	11.6%	11%	20.2%	50.9%	24.3%	21.2%	36.4%
Geometric Mean	2.33	0.99	7.20	3.20	2.28	1.16	11.1	3.44

Table 7: Coefficients of variation (mean in brackets, μg/g wet weight) for PCBs and DDE residues in marine vertebrates other than seabirds.

Species	Site	Year	Sex	Age	Tissue	N	PCBs	DDE	Referred
							Coefficient of Variation		
Grey Seal (*Halichoerus grypus*)	Sable Island, Nova Scotia	1982	Female	Adult	Blubber	8	37% (15.7)	32% (2.5)	Addison *et al.* 1984
Grey Seal (*H. grypus*)	Sable Island, Nova Scotia	1982	N/A	Immature	Blubber	8	70% (5.0)	40% (1.5)	Addison *et al.* 1984
Herring (*Clupea harengus*)	Nova Scotia	1972	N/A	4 years	Muscle	29	108% (0.25)	492% (0.059)	Zitko *et al.* 1974
Herring (*C. harengus*)	Gulf of St. Lawrence	1972	N/A	N/A	Muscle	26	98% (0.44)	506% (0.085)	Zitko *et al.* 1974
Cod (*Gadus morhua*)	Norway	1982	N/A	N/A	Liver	18	56.8% (0.454)	78.7% (0.703)	Skaare *et al.* 1985
Flounder (*Platichthys flesus*)	Norway	1982	N/A	N/A	Liver	10	63.3% (0.030)	116% (0.057)	Skaare *et al.* 1985
Cod (*G. morhua*)	Terence Bay Nova Scotia	1980	N/A	2–9 years	Liver	100	52.5% (1.71)	53.6% (0.28)	Uthe (pers. comm.)
Cod (*G. morhua*)	Terence Bay Nova Scotia	1980	N/A	5 years	Liver	38	48.9% (1.81)	49.7% (0.28%)	Uthe (pers. comm.)

selected species could be used as a basis for an international monitoring pro-gramme. The statistical design of such a programme is discussed in Appendix 1. International co-ordination and co-operation would be necessary, and in addition a well-designed quality assurance programme for the analytical work would be essential. Nevertheless, analysis of seabird eggs may well be the most cost-effec-tive way of monitoring the levels of stable lipophilic compounds in marine systems.

CONCLUSIONS

1. International organizations are agreed that there is a need for an oceanic monitor of trends of organochlorine levels that is both cheap and reliable, because organochlorine chemicals reach the oceans by a variety of routes including direct discharge from coastal areas and ocean dumping and indirect translocation by river, estuarine and atmospheric fluxes.
2. Seabird eggs have been effectively used to monitor trends in levels of organochlorine levels during the past twenty years.
3. Based on a review of the published data, three species have proved valuable for integrating levels of organochlorine pollutants in the pelagic marine environ-ment. These are: the Atlantic Puffin, the Common Guillemot or Murre and the Leach's Storm-petrel.
4. An international pilot project using seabird eggs as spatial and temporal trend monitors of organochlorine compounds could provide valuable information on the health of the North Atlantic.

ACKNOWLEDGEMENTS

We are indebted to John Struger and Brian Collins for the use of their statistical approaches to sampling design, to Dr Jack Uthe for permission to use his unpublished data on cod, to Keith Marshall who suggested the need for compari-son of the various levels in seabird eggs with those in other existing marine monitors, to Dr Harry Ohlendorf for his review of the manuscript and to Brenda Black who typed the manuscript.

APPENDIX 1

STATISTICAL SAMPLING DESIGN FOR SEABIRD EGG COLLECTION

For seabirds to be useful indicators of spatial and temporal trends in levels of marine pollutants, the within-colony variation in levels must be small. The reliability of the estimate increases as the sample size increases. However, to minimize analytical costs, an estimate of the number of affordable analyses compared with the reliability of the estimate of the variation must be made.

Data have been used from the files of the National Registry of Toxic Chemical Residues of the Canadian Wildlife Service to estimate within-colony variation for the East Coast Monitoring Program for the following four chemical contaminants: DDE, Dieldrin, HCB and PCB. These estimates are then used to design a sampling strategy that should prove to be both statistically valid and cost effective. The statistical approach used below is from Struger & Collins (in prep.).

Sokal & Rohlf (1969 p. 247) have devised the following formula to estimate sample size required to detect, with a certain level of confidence, a change in a certain parameter:

$$N \geqslant 2\left(\frac{\sigma}{\delta}\right)^2\{t\alpha[v] + t_2(1\text{-P})[v]\}^2$$

where, N = number of samples
σ = true standard deviation δ = smallest true difference desired to detect
v = degrees of freedom α = significance level
P = desired probability that a difference found will be significant
$t\alpha[v]$ and $t_2(1\text{-P})[v]$ = values from a two tailed t-table with v degrees of freedom and corresponding to probabilities of α and $2(1\text{-P})$, respectively.

Using, for example, the coefficients of variation for 1984 Great Island Puffins, we can estimate the sample size needed to detect a 20 percent change with 80 percent certainty for the four contaminants (*Table A1*).

By sampling 10 eggs each year, a 20 percent change in PCB could be detected with 80 percent confidence at the 95 percent probability level. This level of change would not be detected for the other compounds. One method of decreasing the variance without increasing analytical costs is by pooling. Programme managers can decide the degree of confidence, the probability levels and the desired sensitivity in designing monitoring programmes.

The total variance (S^2tot.) in pooled samples is derived from the natural variance (s^2egg) in the sample of eggs and from the analytical variance (S^2anal.). This can be described by the following equation:

$$S^2\text{tot.} = \frac{S^2\text{egg}}{mn} + \frac{S^2\text{anal.}}{m} \tag{3}$$

where m is the number of mixtures and
n is the number of eggs per mixture.

This equation can now be used to formulate various pooling designs to see whether the number of Puffin eggs needed to detect a 20 percent change in the level of HCB, can be reduced (*Table A1*) from 34.

In order to estimate the analytical variance, we need data for the precision of the laboratory in analyzing replicates of a homogenized sample. There are no precise estimates of analytical variance for organochlorine in Great Island Puffins. However, the analytical variance for organochlorine compounds in Lake Huron Herring Gulls has been estimated for a sample prepared for quality assurance purposes (*Table A2*). Thus, assuming that the analytical variance is a function of the analyst, the matrix (eggs), the methodology and the level of

Table A1: Sample size estimates to be 80 percent confident of detecting a 20 percent change in residue levels at 0.05 level of significance for Atlantic Puffins, Great Island, 1984.

	Chemical			
	DDE	*Dieldrin*	*HCB*	*PCB*
CV	19%	14.6%	24.4%	11.6%
N	21	13	34	8

Table A2:   Quality assurance results based on analyses of a pool of Lake Huron Herring Gull eggs (Reference Sample CWS–8001) over a five year period by a contract laboratory (Ontario Research Foundation).

	Chemical (μg/g, wet weight)			
	DDE	Dieldrin	HCB	PCBs
N	91	77	91	91
Mean	4.70	0.28	0.77	25.0
SD	0.49	0.33	0.17	3.82
CV	10.4%	11.9%	22.6%	15.3%

contamination, it is probably valid to use the estimate of the analytical variance derived from the Lake Huron Herring Gull samples.

We can calculate the components of total variance as follows:

$$S^2\text{anal.} = \left(\frac{CV}{100}\right)^2 \times X^2$$

$$S^2\text{egg} = \left(\frac{CV}{100}\right)^2 \times X^2 - (S^2\text{anal.})$$

Comparing the data in Table 6 with those in Table A2, we can see that for some chemicals in seabird eggs (e.g. dieldrin and PCBs in Great Island Puffins), the between-egg variance is relatively small once the analytical variance is taken into account. For these chemicals, we cannot reduce variance significantly by pooling eggs for analysis. Reduction in variance would come only from increasing the number of analyses. However, in other cases, such as for DDE in Kent Island Storm-petrels, the between-egg variance is much greater than the analytical variance and pooling should reduce total variance significantly.

To estimate total variance, we will use the geometric mean for DDE in Kent Island Storm-petrels (1.05 μg/g), the CV for this location (38.9%) and the CV for DDE in the Lake Huron Herring Gull reference pool (10.4%).

$$\text{Thus, } S^2\text{anal.} = \left(\frac{CV}{100}\right)^2 \times X^2$$

$$= \left(\frac{10.4}{100}\right)^2 \times (1.05)^2$$

$$= 0.012$$

$$\text{and, } S^2\text{egg} = \left[\left(\frac{CV}{100}\right)^2 \times X^2\right] = (S^2\text{anal.})$$

$$= \left[\left(\frac{38.9}{100}\right)^2 \times 1.05^2\right] - 0.012$$

$$= 0.155$$

We can now use these values to substitute in equation (3) using the m = 10, and n = 1.

$$S^2\text{tot} = \frac{S^2\text{egg}}{mn} + \frac{S^2\text{anal.}}{m}$$

$$= \frac{0.155}{(10)(1)} + \frac{0.012}{10}$$

$$= 0.017$$

Table A3:   Comparison of Relative Efficiency of various pooling designs for monitoring DDE levels in storm-petrels from Kent Island, New Brunswick.

Number of Mixtures (m)	Number of eggs per mixture (n)	Relative Efficiency
10	1	100%
10	3	283%
8	3	213%
7	4	214%
6	5	242%
5	5	198%
5	1	40%

Consider an alternate sampling design of 10 mixtures of 3 eggs per mixture:

$$S^2 = \frac{0.155}{(10)(3)} + \frac{0.012}{10}$$

$$= 0.006$$

How does this theoretical reduction in variance translate into capacity to detect a certain level of change with a given sample size? We can compare sample designs by computing the relative efficiency (R.E.) of one design to the other, by placing the design to be tested in the denominator.

$$R.E. = \frac{S_1^2}{S_2^2} \times 100$$

$$= \frac{0.017}{0.006} \times 100 = 283\%$$

Thus by sampling 30 eggs and combining them into 10 mixtures with 3 eggs per mixture there is a 183 percent improvement in efficiency. *Table A3* reports the relative efficiencies of various pooling designs. There is, of course, an upper limit to N because sampling should not impact on the population.

We have shown, therefore, that pooled samples can increase the effectiveness of monitoring without an increase in analytical costs. However, this approach is not applicable to all situations and depends on the relative sources of variance in the measurement.

FOOTNOTE

1. M. Gilbertson—Present address: Commercial Chemicals Branch, Environment Canada, Ottawa, Canada K1A 0H3.

REFERENCES

ADDISON, R. F., BRODIE, P. F. & ZINCK, M. E. 1984. DDT has declined more than PCBs in eastern Canadian seals during the 1970s. *Environ. Sci. Technol.* **18**, 935–7.

BOERSMA, P. D. 1986. Ingestion of petroleum by seabirds can serve as a monitor of water quality. *Science.* **231**, 373–6.

BOURNE, W. R. P. 1976. Seabirds and pollution. *In:* Johnston, R. (ed.). *Marine pollution.* Academic Press. London.

BUTLER, P. A., ANDRÉN, L., BONDE, G. J., JERNELOV, A. & REISH, D. J. 1971. Monitoring organisms. *In:* FAO Technical conference on marine pollution and its effects on living resources and fishing, Rome, 1970. Report on the seminar on methods of detection, measurement and monitoring pollutants in the marine environment, pp. 101–112. FAO Fisheries Reports No. 99, Suppl. 1.

CLARK, T. P., NORSTROM, R.J., FOX, G. A. & WON, H. T. (1987). Dynamics of organochlorines in Herring Gulls (*Larus argentatus*) II, A two compartment model and data for ten compounds. *Environ. Toxicol. Chem.* **6**, 547–59.

COULSON, J. C., DEANS, I. R., POTTS, G. R., ROBINSON, J. & CRABTREE, A. N. 1972. Changes in organochlorine contamination of the marine environment of eastern Britain monitored by shag eggs. *Nature.* **236**, 454–6.

deFREITAS, A. S. & NORSTROM, R. J. 1974. Turnover and metabolism of polychlorinated biphenyls in relation to their chemical structure and the movement of lipids in the pigeon. *Canad. J. Physiol. Pharmacol.* **52**, 1080–94.

DYCK, J. & KRAUL, I. 1984. Environmental pollutants and shell thinning in eggs of the guillemot *Uria aalge* from the Baltic Sea and the Faeroes, and a possible relation between shell thickness and sea water salinity. *Dansk Orn. Foren. Tidsskr.* **78**, 1–14.

ELLIOTT, J. E. 1985. Specimen banking in support of monitoring for toxic contaminants in Canadian wildlife. *In:* Wise, S. A. & Zeisler, R. (eds.). International review of environmental specimen banking. National Bureau of Standards, Special Publication No. 706. Washington.

FISHER, J. & LOCKLEY, R. M. 1954. *Seabirds*. Collins, London. 320 pp.

GILBERTSON, M. 1974a. Pollutants in breeding herring gulls in the lower Great Lakes. *Canadian Field-Naturalist.* **88**, 273–80.

GILBERTSON, M. 1974b. Seasonal changes in organochlorine compounds and mercury in common terns in Hamilton Harbour, Ontario. *Bull. Environ. Contamin. Toxicol.* **12**, 726–32.

GILBERTSON, M. 1983. Etiology of chick edema disease in herring gulls in the lower Great Lakes. *Chemosphere* **12**, 357–70.

GILBERTSON, M. & REYNOLDS, L. 1974. DDE and PCB in Canadian birds, 1969–1972. *Canadian Wildlife Service, Occasional Paper, No. 19.* Ottawa.

INTERNATIONAL MARITIME ORGANIZATION. 1983. Report of the Task Team 2000 on the long range strategy for the convention. London Dumping Convention 8/4.

MOORE, N. W. 1966. A pesticide monitoring system with special reference to the selection of indicator species. *J. of Appl. Ecol.* **3** (Suppl.): 261–9.

NERC (NATURAL ENVIRONMENT RESEARCH COUNCIL). 1983. Contaminants in marine top predators. Publication Series C. No. 23, 31 pp.

NISBET, I. C. T. & REYNOLDS, L. M. 1984. Organochlorine residues in common terns and associated estuarine organisms, Massachusetts, U.S.A., 1971–81. *Mar. Environ. Res.* **11**, 33–66.

OHLENDORF, H. M., BARTONEK, J. C., DIVOKY, C. J., KLAAS, E. E. & KRYNITSKY, A. J. 1982. Organochlorine residues in eggs of Alaskan seabirds. *U.S. Fish and Wildlife Service. Special Scientific Report—Wildlife No. 245.* Washington, D.C.

OHLENDORF, H. M., RISEBROUGH, R. W. & VERMEER, K. 1978. Exposure of marine birds to environmental pollutants. *U.S. Fish and Wildlife Service. Wildlife Research Report No. 9.* Washington, D.C.

OHLENDORF, H. M. & HARRISON, C. S. 1986. Mercury, selenium, cadmium and organochlorines in eggs of three Hawaiian seabird species. *Environ. Pollut.* (Ser. B.) **11**, 169–91.

OLSSON, M. & REUTERGARDH, L. 1986. DDT and PCB pollution trends in the Swedish aquatic environment. *Ambio* **15**, 103–9.

PEAKALL, D. B. 1975. PCBs and their environmental effects. *Crit. Rev. Environ. Control.* **5**, 469–508.

PEAKALL, D. B., FOX, G. A., GILMAN, A. P., HALLETT, D. J. & NORSTROM, R. J. 1980. Reproductive success of herring gulls as an indicator of Great Lakes water quality. *In:* Afghan, B. K., MacKay, D. (eds.). *Hydrocarbons and halogenated hydrocarbons in the aquatic environment.* Plenum Press. New York and London. Pp. 337–344.

PEARCE, P. A., PEAKALL, D. B. & REYNOLDS, L. M. 1979. Shell thinning and residues of organochlorine and mercury in seabird eggs, Eastern Canada, 1970–76. *Pesticide Monitoring J.* **13**, 61–8.

PHILLIPS, D. J. H. 1980. *Quantitative aquatic biological indicators: their use to monitor trace metal and organochlorine pollution.* Applied Science Publishers Ltd. London. 488 pp.

Scott, D. P., Uthe, J. F. & Chou, C. L. 1981. Further considerations of time trend determinations of contaminant levels in Canadian cod. International Council for the Exploration of the Sea. C.M. 1981/E:47.

Skaare, J. U., Sternesen, J., Kveseth, N., & Polder, A. 1985. Time trends of organochlorine chemical residues in seven sedentary marine fish species from a Norwegian Fjord during the period 1972–82. *Arch. Environ. Contamin. Toxicol.* **14**, 33–41.

Sokal, R. R. & Rohlf, F. J. 1969. *Biometry.* W. H. Freeman and Co. San Francisco. 776 pp.

United Nations Environment Program. 1985. Protection of the marine environment against pollution from land-based sources. UNEP Working Group 120/3 (Part IV): Environment Policy and Law. Elsevier Science Publishers B.V. North Holland.

Walker, C. H. & Knight, G. C. 1981. The hepatic microsomal enzymes of seabirds and their interaction with liposoluble pollutants. *Aquatic Toxicol.* **1**, 343–54.

Zitko, V., Choi, P. M. K., Wildish, D. J., Monaghan, C. F. & Lister, N. A. 1974. Distribution of PCB and *p,p'*-DDT residues in Atlantic herring (*Clupea harengus larengus*) and yellow perch (*Perca flavescens*) in eastern Canada—1972. *Pesticide Monitoring J.* **8**, 105–9.

FOREST BIRDS AS BIOLOGICAL INDICATORS OF THE PROGRESSION OF MAPLE DIEBACK IN QUÉBEC

JEAN-LUC DESGRANGES

Canadian Wildlife Service, P.O. Box 10100, Sainte-Foy, Québec, Canada, G1V 4H5

ABSTRACT

Recent surveys have shown that nearly 85 percent of maple stands in Québec exhibit advanced signs of dieback. Undoubtedly, any changes the forest is subjected to will have considerable repercussions on birds. This paper attempts to list the probable effects of maple dieback on bird communities. These effects should depend on the stage of dieback and the feeding niches of the bird species involved. Six species of bird are proposed as biological indicators of the progression of dieback in Québec's hardwood forests. Examination of the data collected to date through three bird population monitoring programmes (using volunteers) tends to confirm the anticipated repercussions of dieback on the bio-indicator species.

INTRODUCTION

In Québec, few environmental problems have given rise to as much emotion as maple dieback. For forest specialists, the dieback phenomenon is a clear sign of breakdown—in what has to date been a 'fairly' stable ecosystem—due to atmospheric pollution generated over many years by industrial society (Bernier & Brazeau 1986a; Dessureault 1986).

Recent surveys have shown that nearly 85 percent of Québec maple stands exhibit advanced signs of dieback (Roy *et al.* 1985). According to the UPA (Union des Producteurs Agricoles) 60 percent of tapped maples are already affected by the disease. Some foresters actually predict that within the next twenty years or so most hardwood species will lose their crown foliage in a large proportion of the deciduous forests in the south of the province. The opening in the canopy should encourage the growth of herbaceous and shrub species in the understory (Gagnon *et al.* 1986). The weakened trees will also lose some of their resistance to insects, which will speed up dieback by consuming additional foliage and leaving the trees more vulnerable to pathogenic fungi and rotting (Kulman 1971; Manion 1981; Smith 1981). In general, a healthy forest is more resistant to insect attack than a forest affected by dieback. This is partly due to the fact that environmental stress factors upset the chemical defence mechanism of the leaves (Rhoades 1983).

Undoubtedly, the role played by insectivorous birds is also very important. Over the summer, birds catch thousands of insects to feed their young and themselves. In many cases, considerable predation pressure exerted by birds on phytophagous insects helps to protect the forest from serious infestation damage (Holmes *et al*. 1979a; Price *et al*. 1980). It is highly likely that a number of bird species will no longer find the vegetative cover they need to hide from predators and will gradually leave stands defoliated by dieback. Once the birds are gone, insect populations might be less effectively controlled and could grow to epidemic levels and spread to healthy maple stands. This would lead to considerable economic losses: hardwoods make up more than 20 percent of the total wood volume of Canadian forests (Bonner 1982) and the maple syrup industry alone contributes nearly $30 million to the Québec economy (UPA communication).

Maple dieback: a complex phenomenon
For researchers studying the problem of maple dieback, the phenomenon appears to be complex, not yet fully understood, and probably related to various aspects of the way the forest operates as a biological system. A number of tree and ecosystem functional processes are disrupted: photosynthesis is reduced, causing declines in growth and energy reserves; defence mechanisms are weakened, leaving the forest less resistant to infestations of phytophagous insects; and root systems become deficient, meaning that uptake of nutrients from the soil is reduced and nutrient shortages develop (Dessureault 1985, 1986; Bernier & Brazeau 1986a, 1986b).

When symptoms become apparent, dieback has already reached an advanced stage. Initially, for some time, the foliage of the overstory will often be abnormally erect and unusually dark green in colour. Other symptoms that may occur include small-sized leaves with a waxy appearance that turn bright red prematurely. Then major damage appears. In summer, the overstory is bare of foliage. Formation of tufts of foliage is also a characteristic symptom. Desiccation advances gradually from the tips of the branches to the interior of the crown, and the tree finally dies. Bark peels away abnormally, first from large branches and then from the trunk. In some cases, the wind eventually blows the trees over, thus contributing to entanglement of the underbrush (Bernier & Brazeau 1986a).

Thousands of forest birds under threat
Some 25 species of bird nest each summer in the Sugar Maple-Yellow Birch forest domain (*Acer saccharum—Betula lutea; sensu* Grandtner 1966). While the abundance of each species varies considerably, the number of breeding birds per hectare of maple forest in summer is estimated at approximately ten (DesGranges 1980; Erskine 1984). Since hardwood stands cover an area of 2.4 million hectares in Québec (Service de l'inventaire forestier du Québec, *in litt.*), it can be seen that more than 20 million forest birds are directly threatened by dieback in the province's deciduous forests.

Table 1 provides a list of the main insectivorous bird species found in maple stands. It also shows the birds' stratigraphic feeding niches—the manner and location in which they acquire their share of the food resources present within the forest environment.

Undoubtedly, changes to the forest could have considerable repercussions for birds. Several studies have concluded that birds are 'sensitive' to both stand physiognomy (e.g. DesGranges 1980) and the species composition of plant associations (e.g. Holmes & Robinson 1981). *Table 2* attempts to list the probable effects of maple dieback on bird communities. These effects should depend on the stage of dieback and the feeding niches of the bird species involved.

At the onset of dieback, the sparser crown foliage should encourage development of the shrub stratum and possibly produce an increase in the number of

Table 1: Statigraphic feeding niches of main bird species found in maple stands (from Holmes and Sturges (1975), Holmes *et al.* (1979b) and DesGranges (1980)).

Level	Gleaning[a]	Probing[b]	Boring[c]	Flushing[d]	Snatching[e]	Flycatching[f]
Canopy	Red-eyed Vireo (*Vireo olivaceus*) Scarlet Tanager (*Piranga olivacea*) Rose-breasted Grosbeak (*Pheucticus ludovicianus*)			American Redstart (*Setophaga ruticilla*)	Great Crested Flycatcher (*Myiarchus crinitus*) Least Flycatcher (*Empidonax minimus*)	Eastern Wood Pewee (*Contopus virens*)
Trunk		White-breasted Nuthatch† (*Sitta carolinensis*)	Pileated Woodpecker† (*Dryocopus pileatus*) Yellow-billed Sapsucker (*Sphyrapicus varius*)			
Shrubs	Wood Thrush (*Hylocichla mustelina*) Hermit Thrush (*Catharus guttatus*) Black-throated Blue Warbler (*Dendroica caerulescens*) Canada Warbler (*Wilsonia canadensis*)					
Ground	Veery (*Catharus fuscescens*) Ovenbird (*Seiurus aurocapillus*)	White-throated Sparrow (*Zonotrichia albicollis*)	Yellow-shafted Flicker (*Colaptes auratus*)			

Notes: a Gleaning: bird is perched and non-flying prey is visible.
b Probing: bird is perched and prey is hidden.
c Boring: bird is perched and catches prey by boring into its hiding place
† Year-round resident of Québec hardwood forests.

d Flushing: perched bird flushes out prey and catches it.
e Snatching: bird in flight catches non-flying prey.
f Flycatching: bird and prey are in flight.

Table 2: Anticipated effects of maple dieback on forest bird communities.

Symptoms*	Overstory species	Trunk species	Shrub species	Ground species	Number of species	Number of birds
Reduction of twig growth producing tufts of foliage.	Facilitates gleaning.				+	+
Reduction of leaf size and curling of leaves in top of crown producing open overstory.	Facilitates flycatching and snatching but leaves less foliage for gleaners to explore.		Progressive opening of the stand leads to shrub growth and indirectly encourages	Progressive opening of the stand dries the soil and hampers ground probers.	+	+
Mortality of twigs and small branches in overstory.			shrub species that feed in the shrub stratum. Replacement of light-intolerant hardwood seedlings by shrubs produces changes in the species composition of the bird community.		?	–
Frequent appearance of adventitious twigs on trunk and main branches.		Hampers feeding of trunk gleaners			Nil	?
Invasion of large roots by honey mushroom (Armillariella mellea).				?	?	?
Bark detaches from branches and trunk and eventually peels off in strips.	These species gradually disappear.	Encourages probers and borers.			–	–
Tree is completely desiccated.	Elimination.	Encourages borers and probers.			–	–
Tree falls to the ground.	Elimination.	Elimination.	Increases underbrush 'entanglement' and encourages shrub and ground species.		–	–
Short-term effects	+	0	+	0	+	–
Middle-term effects	–	+	++	+	–	– –
Long-term effects	– –	– –	+++	+	– –	– –

Note: *From Bernier & Brazeau (1986a).

species and birds feeding in the underbrush. Species that feed in flight may also benefit from the situation when hunting becomes easier in a more open stand (fewer obstacles and more-visible prey). Gleaners will suffer in terms of the quantity of foliage to be searched, but may save time and energy in exploring more leaves per unit of time since the leaves are shorter and grouped in tufts (see Robinson & Holmes 1984).

After several years, the presence of greater numbers of dead trees with bark peeling off in strips should attract more woodpeckers and nuthatches, birds that probe large branches and trunks in search of boring insects. Eventually, most trees will dry out and fall to the ground, causing the majority of overstory and trunk species to leave. As the stand becomes increasingly open, shrub growth will be encouraged at the expense of light-intolerant hardwood seedlings. At this point, the bird community will undergo a radical change: overstory and trunk species will be almost completely eliminated and gradually replaced by shrub and ground species. At present, we do not know how plant succession will proceed from then on.

METHODS

Most bird species have a varied diet. However, over the course of evolution each has developed a particular morphology which makes it especially well adapted to catching certain prey in specific habitats. Thus, competition with other species in the vicinity is limited. While they may occasionally hunt other prey in unfamiliar habitats, the organisms that make up the basis of their diet are no longer present. Birds might not be able to meet their own energy requirements, much less those of their young. The number of young per brood, and the density of breeding pairs, could drop in areas where this happens, and some bird populations might become locally extinct. The birds' vulnerability to environmental changes makes them good biological indicators.

To monitor the progression of dieback in Québec's hardwood forests, good use can be made of ornithological data collected each year by hundreds of amateur birdwatchers in the province. Québec currently has three volunteer data collection programmes: the Breeding Bird Atlas, the Breeding Bird Survey (BBS), and the Christmas Bird Count (CBC). The Atlas provides information on the geographical ranges of birds, and could reveal 'anomalies' in the distribution of certain deciduous forest species. These anomalies could be related to the severity of dieback in the forests of a given region. The Breeding Bird Survey yields information on both the ranges and relative abundance of birds. Since counts are taken each year at the same locations, changes in the make-up of bird communities could be used to monitor the progression of dieback, and even calculate its rate of advance within the province. The Christmas Bird Count is of considerably less use since it is conducted in the winter, generally around major cities (and thus at a fair distance from the large forests). None the less, it can provide data on year-to-year fluctuations among winter residents of an area, and may contribute to the monitoring of trunk birds, some of which are common winter residents and ones that are easy to observe at this time of year.

For each of these 'monitoring tools', *Table 3* suggests species that could make excellent biological indicators. The birds are easy to identify by both their appearance and their calls. Since several of them are members of the core group of typical maple-stand species, they should react sharply to changes that occur in stands suffering from dieback. The study of these birds should economically yield a wide range of data on the extent of damage and the progression of the disease

Table 3: Suggested bio-indicator species and possible uses of the three major North American bird monitoring programmes for following the progression of dieback in Québec hardwood forests.

	Gleaners	Probers	Flycatchers
Canopy	Red-eyed Vireo[1,2] (*Vireo olivaceus*)		Eastern Wood Pewee[1,2] (*Contopus virens*)
Trunk		White-breasted Nuthatch[1,2,3] (*Sitta carolinensis*)	
Shrubs	Wood Thrush[1,2] (*Hylocichla mustelina*)		
Ground	Ovenbird[1,2] (*Seiurus aurocapillus*)	White-throated Sparrow[1,2] (*Zonotrichia albicollis*)	

Notes: 1. Breeding Bird Atlas (ATLAS).
          2. Breed Bird Survey (BBS).
          3. Christmas Bird Count (CBS).

while providing very good arguments to convince the public in general and Government in particular of the need to act quickly to counter the harmful effects of air pollution.

RESULTS

To assess the value of the selected species as biological indicators, an examination has been made of the data collected to date through the three bird population monitoring programmes mentioned above. *Table 4* shows the anticipated repercussions of dieback on these species as the disease progresses. Recent trends exhibited by the populations of these species breeding in southeastern Québec (Eastern Townships, Bois-Francs, and Beauce) are also presented. At the outset, mention should be made of the remarkable consistency of the demographic trends detected through the three monitoring tools. This is very likely indicative of the value, if not the speed, of these tools for showing up population fluctuations. These variations in bird populations may have been caused by diverse factors, including weather events, changes in food abundance, mortality during the winter, and other events that may or may not be connected with maple dieback (see Holmes *et al.* 1986). However, agreement between these recent trends and the anticipated repercussions of maple dieback is remarkable. In two species out of six—the White-breasted Nuthatch (*Sitta carolinensis*) and the White-throated Sparrow (*Zonotrichia albicollis*)—their relative abundance appears to have increased. The first species could have benefited from the larger number of dead branches and trees in the maple forests, while the latter could have been encouraged by increased shrub growth where openings in stand cover have let in more light. The Red-eyed Vireo (*Vireo olivaceus*), Eastern Wood Pewee (*Contopus virens*), Wood Thrush (*Hylocichla mustelina*), and Ovenbird (*Seiurus aurocapillus*) are showing signs of population decline in the forest regions most seriously affected by dieback. These maple forest specialists might be leaving maple stands where progressive openings in the canopy coincide with a diminishing presence of maple in the forest strata.

When we compare these demographic trends with the sequence of repercussions anticipated in response to changes in the stands, we are prone to conclude that the majority of maple stands affected by dieback contain moribund trees and are probably on their way to a stage where most trees will be completely

Table 4: Anticipated repercussions of chronic maple dieback for species suggested as biological indicators.

	Formation of tufts of foliage and reduction of leaf size in overstory	Mortality of twigs in overstory; peeling of bark on branches and trunk	Trees completely desiccated; some fallen. Tangled undergrowth	Recent population trends in southeastern Quebec.*		
				ATLAS	BBS	CBC
Canopy gleaner	Red-eye Vireo (*Vireo olivaceus*)	↑(?)	Stable	→	−17%	−21%	N/A
Canopy flycatcher	Eastern Wood Pewee (*Contopus virens*)	↑(?)	Stable	→	−15%	−75%	N/A
Trunk forager	White-breasted Nuthatch (*Sitta carolinensis*)	↑(?)	←	↑	Stable	+91%	+31%
Shrub gleaner	Wood Thrush (*Hylocichla mustelina*)	Stable	↓(?)	→	Stable	−50%	N/A
Ground gleaner	Ovenbird (*Seiurus aurocapillus*)	Stable	→	→	−7%	Stable	N/A
Ground prober	White-throated sparrow (*Zonotrichia albicollis*)	Stable	←	←	Stable	+300%	N/A

*Three different approaches were used to determine trends:

ATLAS: $[(a–b) \div b] \times 100$ where 'a' = % occurrence of the species in 47 affected $10 \times 10km$ grid units and 'b' = % occurrence in 45 unaffected units.

BBS: $[(c–d) \div d] \times 100$ where 'c' = % occurrence of the species at 190 stops located close to an affected maple stand and 'd' = % occurrence at 190 unaffected stops.

CBC: $[(e–f) \div f] \times 100$ where 'e' = Average number of individuals per group of observers at three localities since 1980 and 'f' = average number of individuals per group of observers between 1974–79. Birds at feeders were excluded from calculations. Data for Granby, Lennoxville and Georgeville found in Christmas Bird Count annual reports. *American Birds*, vols. 29 to 39.

desiccated. This is exactly the situation that prevails in southeastern Québec, an area that has been particularly hard hit by maple dieback (Gagnon *et al.* 1986).

CONCLUSION

The Canadian Wildlife Service is concerned about the possible effects of dieback in deciduous forests on forest birds and the insects they eat. In Québec, a multidisciplinary team of researchers from both levels of Government and the university sector has just begun an ecosystem study to gain a better understanding of the role played by birds in the ecological dynamics of maple stands.

ACKNOWLEDGEMENTS

Extensive discussion with my colleague entomologist Yves Mauffette helped me to develop this research project. I would also like to thank Gilles Gagnon of the Québec Department of Energy and Resources for his assistance in setting up the study, and Gaétan Fillion for processing some of the data. Yves Aubry and André Cyr provided raw data from the Québec Breeding Birds Atlas and the Québec Breeding Bird Survey respectively. Anthony W. Diamond and Richard T. Holmes made constructive comments on an earlier draft of the manuscript.

REFERENCES

BERNIER, B. & BRAZEAU, M. 1986a. Le dépérissement de l'érablière au Québec: rôle de la pollution atmosphérique. *Journée d'information sur l'acériculture au Québec. Cahier de conférences.* Conseil des productions végétales du Québec. Ministère de l'Agriculture, des Pêcheries et de l'Alimentation du Québec. Mai. Pp. 105–17.

BERNIER, B. & BRAZEAU, M. 1986b. *Un patrimoine en détresse.* Ministère de l'Énergie et des Ressources du Québec.

BONNOR, G. M. 1982. *Canada's forest inventory—1981.* Canadian Forestry Service, Ottawa.

DESGRANGES, J.-L. 1980. Des communautés aviennes du Parc national de la Mauricie, Québec. Service canadien de la faune. *Publications hors-série* N° 41. 32 pp.

DESSUREAULT, M. 1985. Le dépérissement des arbres; nature, causes et mécanismes. *Phytoprotection* 66, 71–81.

DESSUREAULT, M. 1986. Le dépérissement des forêts: un problème international. *Journée d'information sur l'acériculture au Québec. Cahier de conférences.* Conseil des productions végétales du Québec. Ministère de l'Agriculture, des Pêcheries et de l'Alimentation du Québec. Mai. Pp. 11–19.

ERSKINE, A. J. 1984. Répertoire préliminaire des études de dénombrement des oiseaux du Canada par parcelles-échantillons, 5e partie. Service canadien de la faune. *Cahiers de biologie* 144. 35 pp.

GAGNON, G., ROY, G. GRAVEL, C. & GAGNÉ, J. 1986. État des recherches sur le dépérissement au Ministère de l'Énergie et des Ressources. *Journée d'information sur l'acériculture au Québec. Cahier de conférences.* Conseil des productions végétales du Québec. Ministère de l'Agriculture, des Pêcheries et de l'Alimentation du Québec. Mai. Pp. 47–85.

GRANDTNER, M. M. 1966. *La végétation forestière du Québec méridional.* Presse Univ. Laval, Québec. 216 pp.

HOLMES, R. T. & STURGES, F. W. 1975. Bird community dynamics and energetics in a northern hardwoods ecosystem. *J. Anim. Ecol.* 44, 175–200.

HOLMES, R. T., SCHULTZ, J. C. & NOTHNAGLE, P. 1979a. Bird predation on forest insects: an exclosure experiment. *Science* 206, 462–3.

HOLMES, R. T., BONNEY, R. E., JR. & PACALA, S. W. 1979b. Guild structure of the Hubbard Brook bird community: a multivariate approach. *Ecology* **60**, 512–20.

HOLMES, R. T. & ROBINSON, S. K. 1981. The species preferences of foraging insectivorous birds in a northern hardwood forest. *Oecologia* **48**, 31–5.

HOLMES, R. T., SHERRY, T. W. & STURGES, F. W. 1986. Bird community dynamics in a temperate deciduous forest: Long-term trends at Hubbard Brook. *Ecol. Monogr.* **56**, 201–20.

KULMAN, H. M. 1971. Effects of insect defoliation on growth and mortality of trees. *Ann. Rev. Entom.* **16**, 289–324.

MANION, P. D. 1981. *Tree disease concepts.* Prentice-Hall. N.J.

PRICE, P. W., BOUTON, C. E., GROSS, P., MCPHERON, B. A., THOMPSON, J. N. & WEIS, A. E. 1980. Interactions among three trophic levels: influence of plants on interactions between insect herbivores and natural enemies. *Ann. Rev. Ecol. Syst.* **11**, 41–65.

RHOADES, D. R. 1983. Herbivore population dynamics and plant chemistry. *In:* Denno, R. F. & McCLURE, M. S. (EDS.). *Variable plants and herbivores in natural and managed systems.* Academic Press, N.Y. Pp. 155–220.

ROBINSON, S. & HOLMES, R. T. 1984. Effects of plant species and foliage structure on the foraging behaviour of forest birds. *Auk* **101**, 672–84.

ROY, G., ROBITAILLE, L. & GAGNON, G. 1985. Études des principaux facteurs du dépérissement des érablières au Québec. *Phytoprotection* **66**, 91–99.

SMITH, W. H. 1981. *Air pollution and forests.* Springer-Verlag. N.Y.

ICBP Technical Publication No. 6, 1987

BIRDS AS INDICATORS OF FOREST STAND CONDITION IN BOREAL FORESTS OF EASTERN CANADA

DANIEL A. WELSH

Canadian Wildlife Service, Ontario Region, 1725 Woodward Drive, Ottawa, Ontario, Canada.

ABSTRACT

The use of birds as bio-indicators to enhance forest management is discussed. Woodpeckers are shown to increase with increases in decay which reduces wood fibre volume production. It is also shown that some warbler species increase in density with insect defoliators. In both of these examples, results of regular bird monitoring could be used to effectively improve silvicultural management. Increased environmental awareness among professional foresters means that they are likely to accept novel approaches to problem solving. Finally, examples of successful large-scale volunteer-based projects are provided, and it is suggested that volunteer networks could be used in intensively managed forests to assist in effective silviculture.

INTRODUCTION

In recent years there has been an enormous increase in activity in the field of ornithology and in environmental awareness in general. As our knowledge of birds expands, it is exciting to consider ways in which birds can be used as bio-indicators of occurrences in other components of the ecosystem. This paper examines the question of whether there is potential to use our knowledge of forest birds to improve or simplify forest management. I have chosen examples from the eastern Canadian boreal forest because the data were readily available to me, but the ideas are likely to be transferable to other forests.

FOREST MANAGEMENT AND BIRDS

Two common problems that must be dealt with by the forest manager are when to harvest the forest, and how to detect serious insect outbreaks quickly and accurately. Birds could be used to help solve those problems efficiently.

When to cut
We are all familiar with the principles of forest succession, but from the forester's perspective succession means that there is an optimal time to harvest. This is particularly true with clear-cut silvicultural practices where maximum extraction

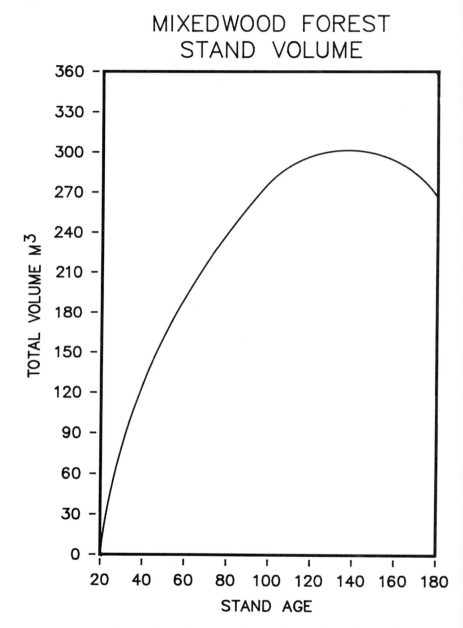

Figure 1:   Changes in the volume of merchantable wood in a mixed coniferous deciduous forest with increasing forest stand age. Based on standard yield tables for the boreal forest of Ontario. Volume is in m³ per ha.

of fibre volume is the goal. The change in volume of usable fibre with stand age can be seen in the generalized pattern shown in *Figure 1*. Volume increases as the stand grows to maturity because the losses to all sources are less than gains from growth. During senescence, rot, disease, insect depredations and other losses take proportionately more of the annual production, and at some point the volume of wood begins to decrease. Once losses exceed gains there is less and less to harvest each year.

Foresters have developed yield tables to tell them when they can expect maximum output from a stand. Use of the tables requires measurement of age, tree density and site quality for each stand. The tables provide mean values based on the average of many stands and are not specific to the forest stand being measured.

Several of the woodpeckers that excavate their own cavities regularly locate their nests in trees or portions of trees that have been damaged by decay. As well as increases in potential nest sites as the forest stand becomes overmature, the birds' food supply also increases. There are strong correlations between the number of bark-boring insects and the age and health of the forest stand.

If changes in number or species composition of the bird community could be used to forecast an increase in decay then the forester would have early warning that it was time to cut, without intensive forestry surveys. To investigate this possibility we examined the relationship between stand age and the number of Downy Woodpeckers (*Picoides pubescens*), Hairy Woodpeckers (*Picoides villosus*) and Yellow-bellied Sapsuckers (*Sphyrapicus varius*) in mature boreal mixed coniferous and deciduous forests as shown in *Figure 2*. The number of all three species increased as the stands matured, reaching a peak and then declining. The data were from stands that reach maximum volume at about 140–150 years of age, but are close to peak at 100 years. In those forests White Spruce (*Picea glauca*) is long-lived, but several other species including Balsam Fir (*Abies balsamea*), Trembling Aspen (*Populus tremuloides*) and White Birch (*Betula papyrifera*) have a shorter life span of about 100 years. The drop in woodpecker numbers at 220 years coincides with the time when most of the first generation of short-lived trees has died out and been replaced by new ones so there were few dead and dying trees.

If regular bird censuses were made in such stands, a decision to harvest could be made at the point at which woodpecker density exceeded a certain level, say 10 prs/km^2 in this example. The exact numbers would have to be determined from more extensive studies, and would be different for different types of stands such as pure coniferous, deciduous, and mixed. The important point is that the birds could give a stand-specific diagnosis that would be difficult and expensive to obtain otherwise.

Defoliating insects

The relationship between forest birds and their prey has long been a subject of study, particularly in relation to the question of the role of birds in the regulation of insect pests. Kendeigh (1947) first documented the extremely high densities that Bay-breasted Warblers (*Dendroica castanea*) and Cape May Warblers (*Dendroica tigrina*) can reach during a Spruce Budworm outbreak. Regardless of the impact that they have on their prey there is no doubt that the 'budworm warblers' show dramatic numerical responses to increases in insect numbers. In addition to Bay-breasted Warblers and Cape May Warblers, the Tennessee Warbler (*Vermivora perigrina*) is also included in the group of 'budworm warblers'. Each of these species can show great increases in reproductive output by increasing clutch size as well as increasing density through immigration.

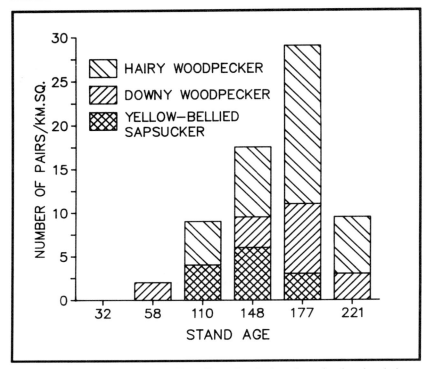

Figure 2:   Changes in the number of breeding pairs of selected woodpeckers in relation to
forest stand age in Ontario boreal forest. Bird numbers are averages of one or more plots,
each surveyed for five years. The stand age is the age at the third survey year.

In 1978, Spruce Budworm populations were so dense that they killed many
Balsam Fir and totally defoliated the White Spruce in forests in northeastern
Ontario. Bird densities of more than 2000 prs/km^2 were recorded, of which more
than 50 percent were Spruce Budworm specialists (Welsh & Fillman 1980). Since
our major interest was in understanding bird population dynamics in relation to
forest succession, we decided to relocate study sites. After consultation with
foresters we moved to an area near Manitouwadge in north-central Ontario. The
area chosen was reported to have among the lowest Spruce Budworm densities in
the province, with only one local hotspot or epicentre.

In 1979, on 18 plots selected to represent a successional sequence from 1 year
to 220 years of age, the budworm specialists represented 8.7 percent of the total
number of birds. One of the selected plots was a 'five-year-old selective cut' from
which all spruce and fir greater than 20m in height had been removed, but on
which there was extensive remaining conifer advance growth up to 15m in height
occurring in patches. In the first year there were 366 prs/km^2 of all species on that
plot and the only budworm specialist was the Tennessee Warbler with a density of
53 prs/km^2. We assumed that was a normal density for the species without
budworm. The following year there were 216 prs/km^2 of budworm specialists
alone on the plot of which 95 percent were Tennessee Warblers. We immediately
began an intensive budworm density sampling programme and found there were

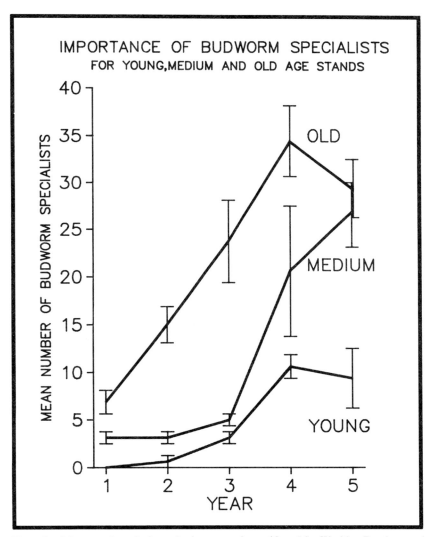

Figure 3:   Mean number of primary budworm predators (Cape May Warbler, Bay-breasted Warbler, Tennessee Warbler) expressed in pairs/10ha with standard deviation bars in relation to a Spruce Budworm outbreak. Budworm numbers changed from low to epidemic levels during the five-year period. The data are from surveys in four old stands over 100 years of age, four medium stands aged 20 to 35 years, and three young stands from 5 to 15 years of age.

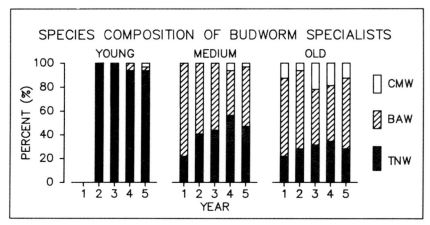

Figure 4: Relative proportion of three principal budworm specialists in different stand age
groups during five years of budworm outbreak. Stand grouping as in *Figure 3.*

high to incipient outbreak levels in all suitable budworm habitat in the area.
Although we could have known of the insect outbreak with intensive sampling,
the bird response indicated its occurrence before there were clear signs of
defoliation.

The potential for increase by Spruce Budworm is dependent in part on the age
and health of the stand, and is particularly highly correlated with foliage volume
of White Spruce and Balsam Fir. If the relative species composition of foliage-
gleaning bird species changes directly with changes in insect abundance then bird
censuses could be used to forecast potential problems.

The changes in the contribution that three budworm specialists made to the
total number of breeding birds during an outbreak period is shown in *Figure 3* for
three different stand age-groups in the study area. Several representative stands
were grouped for each age class to provide a general indication of the pattern of
change.

If one were going to try to use those changes to advise forest managers of a
major increase in budworm density it would be advisable to use budworm
specialists as a group because individual species respond differently in different
ages of stand. *Figure 4* shows the relative proportion of the three species in stands
of different successional stages. Tennessee Warblers would not be a good
indicator on the older plots or Cape May Warblers on the younger ones.

To simplify decision-making using bio-indicators it is preferable to have a single
number rather than multiple species or detailed community analyses. In *Table 1*,
I have used the ratio of budworm-specialist warblers to other warblers over the
course of the rapid-increase phases of the outbreak as an example of the
appropriate form for an indicator. As numbers of other warblers also increase, the
ratio is conservative and simply monitoring numbers of individuals of each species
might be more effective. For different classes of stand ages one could pick an
index level above which some management response would be necessary. For
example a ratio above 0.10 in mid-seral stands could call for cutting, spraying or
some other activity.

Table 1:   Index of outbreak severity. Values of the ratio of three species of 'spruce budworm warblers' to other warblers from three stand age groups at different budworm density. Ranges for individual stand values are in parentheses.

Stand age	Level of Spruce Budworm outbreak				
	Endemic[1]	Increasing	Incipient	Epidemic	Decline
Young	0	0.01	0.11	0.39	?
(< 15 yrs)		(0–0.04)	(0.05–0.21)	(0.12–0.85)	
Mid-seral	0	0.11	0.36	1.05	?
(15–40 yrs)	0–0.02	(0–0.23)	(0.20–0.59)	(0.60–1.89)	
Old	0	0.26	0.61	1.80	?
(50–220 yrs)	0–0.05	(0.11–0.30)	(0.36–1.02)	(1.06–3.88)	

Note: 1. The endemic level data are taken from Erskine (1977), Martin (1960), and Sanders (1970).

BIO-MONITORING IMPLEMENTATION

Once a bio-indicator is developed, the next major step is to determine how to make use of it in practice. Three basic criteria would have to be met in order to implement a system using birds as forest-stand condition indicators. First, birds would have to tell us something more effectively than other means, either because the procedure was more cost-effective or because the birds integrate information more quickly, or better. We have reviewed two examples of how birds could be used. Secondly, non-ornithologists such as foresters and land managers would have to be willing to accept the value of birds as bio-indicators. Thirdly, people who could gather the information on bird species composition and density effectively would have to be available. I will briefly discuss these three requirements and then give examples of how such a bio-monitoring system might work.

Effectiveness
There are several methods of determining when a forest is experiencing an increase in decay rates or when it is infested with defoliators, so it is unlikely that birds would ever be the sole indicator for either of these conditions. In many instances though it would be much more cost-effective to monitor woodpeckers than to measure changes in growth rate and the incidence of various fungi. In the case of defoliating insects, regular survey by experienced field experts is both time-consuming and expensive, yet regular counts of warblers might be conducted as recreation by amateur ornithologists in many circumstances.

Environmental awareness
Historically there was a strong tie between forestry and wildlife because those who worked in the woods were 'close to nature' and had a basic understanding of the interrelatedness of the various components of the forest ecosystem. Gradually, with the development of highly mechanized mass-production forest harvesting, much of that traditional empathy and knowledge was lost and forestry became almost exclusively oriented towards short-term production. There has been a gradual but steady re-awakening of environmental awareness in the forest industry and throughout society recently during the 'ecological revolution', which is often dated as starting with the publication of *Silent Spring* (Carson 1962). Today's professional forester has studied basic ecology and wildlife and is aware of the concepts of multiple use of the land. The prestigious International Union of

Forestry Research Organizations (IUFRO), which holds International Congresses every four years, regularly has a major section on wildlife. I believe that the professional forestry community is ready to accept practical suggestions on using birds as bio-indicators.

Practitioners

Forest birds are often difficult to locate by sight alone, and they are often discovered and identified by song. Although not particularly easy, it is now quite possible with quality field-guides and records of bird songs to teach novices quickly to identify forest birds accurately. If a knowledge of birds was important, foresters could learn to identify them.

Bird-watching is now a major recreational pastime and rather than training novices it might be more cost-effective to make use of volunteers. Successes in using bird-watching volunteers to gather certain kinds of data have already been enormous. The Common Bird Census (CBS) in Britain and the Breeding Bird Census (BBC) in North America annually provide data on bird numbers in a broad selection of habitats. The Breeding Bird Survey (BBS) (Robbins 1979) provides trend data on bird populations (Robbins *et al.* 1986) and has been successfully used to show the effect of changing land-use patterns. Most countries of Europe have volunteer-based census projects, some of which have been in place for a long time.

More recently we have seen the advent of atlases of bird distribution prepared from information gathered by volunteers (Udvardy 1981). Increasingly such information is being used to indicate changes in the environment. For example, Schifferli (1985), using atlas data, provided a fascinating analysis of bird distribution in Switzerland in relation to habitat variables. The 'atlasing' movement is now so active that we have local, regional, national and continental activities, and in several cases groups are making plans to revise their first atlas, thus providing detailed information on distributional changes over time.

The scale of the potential contribution of volunteers can be seen in the Ontario Atlas, which completed its fifth and final year of field work in 1985. In that project 1300 volunteers contributed over 120,000 hours of field survey time. It seems likely that an effective system could be developed using volunteer census efforts to provide information for forest management. Although the volunteers are centred in developed areas removed from forest harvesting, it is likely that logistical problems could be overcome if nothing else hindered that approach. Many people took holidays to travel to remote forested areas to record birds for the Ontario Atlas, when travel assistance was provided.

To implement a system one might establish a volunteer network in representative forest habitats in parks and conservation areas where it would be possible to rely on regular visitors with appropriate skills. Alternatively, a selection of sites across the province or state could be assigned to co-operating naturalist clubs. Exact procedures for implementation would depend on specific definition of goals.

CONCLUSIONS

The major point that I wish to make is that we do have the potential to use forest birds as a practical early warning system to improve silviculture. The potential use of woodpeckers to forecast decreased wood volume production, and of 'spruce budworm warblers' to indicate an outbreak of a major conifer defoliator, are provided as examples of how birds might be used as bio-indicators. The forestry community seems likely to accept such ideas as a result of increased environmental awareness. Although persons without prior experience could be trained, the huge resource of volunteer bird watchers might well be made use of to assist effectively in forest management schemes.

REFERENCES

CARSON, R. L. 1962. *Silent Spring,* Houghton Mifflin Co., Boston.

KENDEIGH, S. C. 1947. Bird population studies in the coniferous forest biome during a spruce budworm outbreak. *Ont. Dept. Lands and Forests Biol. Bull No. 1.* 100 pp.

ROBBINS, C. S. 1979. *Instructions for conducting breeding bird survey routes.* Migratory Bird and Habitat Research Laboratory. U.S. Fish and Wildl. Serv. Laurel Md.

ROBBINS, C. S., BYSTRAK, D. & GEISSLER, P. H. 1986. *The breeding bird survey: its first fifteen years, 1965–1979.* U.S. Dept. of Int., Fish and Wildlife Serv., Resource Publication 157. Washington, D.C. 196 pp.

SCHIFFERLI, L. 1985. Factors influencing the breeding distribution of some bird species in Southern Switzerland: a preliminary analysis. Pp. 313–19 *In: Bird Census and Atlas Studies.* Taylor, K., Fuller, R. J. & Lack, P. C. (eds.) B.T.O., Tring.

UDVARDY M. D. F. 1981. An overview of grid-based atlas works in ornithology. *Studies in Avian Biology No. 6.* 103–9.

WELSH, D. A. & FILLMAN, D. R. 1980. The impact of forest cutting on boreal bird populations. *Am. Birds* **34**, 84–94.

SAVE THE BIRDS

Save the Birds is the most comprehensive book ever written about the conservation of birds and their habitats. But its ultimate message goes even further: by saving the birds we will be saving ourselves. *Save the Birds* is the result of a four-year collaboration between ICBP and the specialist environmental and conservation publisher ProNatur in Germany.

From each book sold, a contribution is made to ICBP's special Save the Birds fund for the support of conservation programmes worldwide.

Save the Birds takes a bird's-eye view of the earth's great ecosystems and the threats facing them today—illustrating these problems and their possible remedies through case studies of rare and endangered bird species. The book's 384 lavishly illustrated pages feature:
- a highly readable text by Dr A. W. Diamond (co-editor of *The Value of Birds*) in association with many other experts worldwide
- more than 600 colour illustrations including photographs, maps, diagrams and 55 specially commissioned artwork portraits of threatened birds
- a special 32-page 'national chapter' exclusive to each country of publication and prepared in that country by recognized experts on national conservation issues

Save the Birds has already been published in five countries. At least four more national editions will be published in 1988.

Save the Birds is available through good bookshops everywhere. Details of national editions' publishers and prices are given below.

National publisher	National authors	Price
Ravensburger Buchverlag,	Horst Stern	DM58,—
Ravensburg, West Germany	Gerhard Thielcke	
Uitgeverij M+P,	HRH Prince Claus	DFL74,50
Weert, Netherlands	Karel H. Voous	
Cambridge University Press,	Sir David Attenborough	£17.50 (until
Cambridge, England	Ian Prestt	31.12.87)
Verlag Sauerlaender,	Leni Robert	SFR54,—
Aarau, Switzerland	Christoph Imboden	
Streiffert & Co,	Sven G. Nilsson	SKR320,—
Stockholm, Sweden	Staffan Ulfstrand	

Save the Birds